Ze

ZEN Imagery Exercises

Meridian Exercises
for Wholesome Living

Shizuto Masunaga
with Stephen Brown

Japan Publications, Inc.

Published by JAPAN PUBLICATIONS, INC., Tokyo and New York

Distributors:
UNITED STATES: *Kodansha International/USA, Ltd., through Harper & Row,
Publishers, Inc., 10 East 53rd Street, New York, New York˙10022.* SOUTH AMERICA:
Harper & Row, Publishers, Inc., International Department. CANADA: *Fitzhenry &
Whiteside Ltd., 195 Allstate Parkway, Markham, Ontario, L3R 4T8.* MEXICO AND
CENTRAL AMERICA: *HARLA S. A. de C. V., Apartado 30–546, Mexico 4, D. F.*
BRITISH ISLES: *International Book Distributors Ltd., 66 Wood Lane End, Hemel
Hempstead, Herts HP2 4RG.* EUROPEAN CONTINENT: *Fleetbooks, S. A., c/o Feffer
and Simons (Nederland) B. V., 61 Strijkviertel, 3454 PK De Meern, The Netherlands.*
AUSTRALIA AND NEW ZEALAND: *Bookwise International, 1 Jeanes Street, Beverley,
South Australia 5007.* THE FAR EAST AND JAPAN: *Japan Publications Trading Co., Ltd.,
1–2–1, Sarugaku-cho, Chiyoda-ku, Tokyo 101.*

First edition: May 1987

LCCC No. 86–80220
ISBN 0–87040–669–8

Printed in U.S.A.

Foreword

Shizuto Masunaga was a respected friend of mine as a fellow scholar, and as a shiatsu practitioner, he was my teacher. It is truly a pleasure to have the opportunity to write the foreword for the English edition of his most unique book *Zen Imagery Exercises*.

Mr. Masunaga was a man who zealously incorporated the meridians, which are the foundation of Oriental medicine, into the practice of shiatsu. This book goes into detail concerning the meridians, and you will no doubt get a better understanding of them as you read on. In his shiatsu Mr. Masunaga applied the principles of Oriental medicine, especially the concept of meridians, based on his insight that the ancient Chinese practices, Do-In and Ankyo, played a vital role in the development of these principles. This is how Mr. Masunaga came to develop meridian shiatsu (Zen Shiatsu) and establish the Iokai Shiatsu Center and became its leader. The reason for creating Zen Imagery Exercises can be found in the name he chose for his shiatsu center Iokai. (Io is pronounced ee-oh and means the king or master of medicine.) In one of the oldest Buddhist scriptures recording the teachings of Shakyamuni Buddha, there is mention of the master of medicine. According to Mr. Masunaga this scripture says, "The master of medicine knows the true nature of diseases. He knows how diseases come to be and he knows how to prevent them. He knows how to deal with illness and he is able to keep people from becoming ill." This is why Mr. Masunaga chose the name Iokai (Kai means group or association) for his school. Given this noble aspiration to become masters of medicine, Zen Shiatsu has been studied widely by many dedicated students and practitioners in Japan as well as overseas.

It goes without saying that Zen Shiatsu is a powerful method for curing people who happen to be suffering from disease. Yet at the same time Zen Shiatsu is also a way of keeping people from becoming ill. Zen Shiatsu is a way to assist the natural healing power which resides in everyone. People have the innate ability to cure themselves. Since this is the ideal, people have to be shown a way to treat the meridians and cure themselves without the aid of shiatsu practitioners. Mr. Masunaga did in fact explain in many of his books how to give yourself meridian shiatsu. But he knew there had to be a simpler and more approachable way to work on the meridians than giving yourself shiatsu. He was therefore compelled to devise a better way that would enable people to prevent ill health. This is what caused him to create his original meridian exercises. Through the practice of these meridian exercises, I myself have been able, not only to maintain my health, but to experience the profound truth of what Mr. Masunaga taught. The original meridian exercises are represented by the letters "A," "B," "C," "D," "E," and "F" in this book. Since these six exercises with simple alphabet images are the very minimum required to stretch all the meridians, Mr. Masunaga went on to devise ways in which people could work on their meridians in more specific ways and this was how Zen Imagery Exercises came into being.

Life by its very nature is uncertain, so naturally there is no guarantee that disease will never strike so long as a person practices Imagery Exercises. Sooner or later we all have to die. Nevertheless, those who read this book will learn that being "healthy" is not just a matter of being without illness. Dr. Rene Dubos, a world renowned bacteriologist, states in his famous book *Mirage of Health* that "It is just an illusion to think that we might become totally free of disease." This being the case, the most significant thing we can do is to try and experience "health" for ourselves and get a feel for it with our own body. It would be ideal if this pursuit could be fun and exciting. This book shows a way in which this can be done.

In Zen Imagery Exercises the importance of breathing is stressed from the beginning. Breathing is a very fundamental and crucial point in this system along with the application of the Yin-Yang principle of Chinese philosophy. The importance of breathing is also emphasized in yoga, which originated in India. If we place value on the accumulation of human experience, compared to the two centuries of Western medicine based on natural science, the approaches from India and China are based on more than two thousands years of experience. Therefore I encourage you to practice Imagery Exercises, paying attention to your breathing and holding the postures represented by the letters of the alphabet. However briefly, I recommend wholeheartedly that you put these exercises into practice and experience the wonderful feeling of relaxing and stretching. This wonderful feeling can be felt not only on an intellectual level but more deeply with your whole being by not using your mind to control your movements but instead letting your body assume postures according to mental images. Through this personal experience you will become aware that we all share a common bond. I have experienced this wonderful feeling to some extent already, and with great admiration for Mr. Masunaga's work, I invite you to try these exercises and experience this wonderful feeling for yourself.

YOSHINARU FUJIOKA M.D.

Preface

When I returned to Japan eight years ago to study shiatsu, "Shiatsu Ryoho (Shiatsu Therapy)" by Shizuto Masunaga was the first book I read on the subject. It was evident that his approach was solidly founded on the principles of Chinese medicine, and I decided then to study with Masunaga-Sensei. His shiatsu clinic and teaching facility, the Iokai Shiatsu Center, was open to everyone, Japanese and non-Japanese alike. Many of his Japanese students, however, came to Iokai after first getting their shiatsu license and were seeking to add another dimension to their shiatsu practice. I also decided to study at an approved shiatsu and acupuncture school before undertaking my study of shiatsu at Iokai. I never imagined that Masunaga-Sensei, then a robust man in his early fifties, would not be around to teach me after I got my license. The untimely death of this leading figure in the field of shiatsu by cancer in 1981 came as a shock to me as well as everyone involved in shiatsu and Oriental medicine.

Masunaga-Sensei's death did not deter me from going to the Iokai Shiatsu Center to study Zen Shiatsu after obtaining my license. The great importance of Masunaga-Sensei's work really struck me only after studying his approach in depth. It was clear that he had taken shiatsu, which even in Japan is sometimes confused with massage, and firmly established its position among the Oriental healing arts. Masunaga-Sensei was not only a gifted shiatsu practitioner but a widely read scholar and a bold theoretician. His unique ideas about the meridians and shiatsu, rather than being a product of empty theorizing, were the fruit of a long and successful clinical practice. His unconventional ideas were controversial especially in the fairly non-intellectual field of shiatsu, but he found broad support throughout Oriental medicine circles. His books were widely read and inspired many people within and without the healing profession.

The last work Masunaga-Sensei tackled before passing away was to create a system of meridian exercises. His study of the Chinese classics had lead him to the conclusion that exercise and manipulation were the key to the discovery of the meridians. He began to investigate ancient Chinese exercises for helath after realizing that, although shiatsu is a powerful healing method, it takes another level of personal participation to attain perfect health. Based on his knowledge and experience of these exercises as a means of working with the meridians, he formulated a new system of meridian exercises to complement shiatsu as the ideal method for health and well-being. Imagery Exercises were the logical next step to Zen Shiatsu, which had elevated shiatsu to a "way," or spiritual path. Imagery Exercises takes stretching exercises and heightens them to a practice engaging the whole self. The mind is reintegrated with the body as it relinquishes control and becomes one with the body to experience the primal awareness of life.

When I read the Japanese text of Imagery Exercises, I was convinced that this represented a culmination of Masunaga-Sensei's life work and that its translation would be of enduring value to laymen and health professionals alike. I had no idea that this would become a five year project, but it was a great learning experience and Masunaga-Sensei's perspective served as a valuable reference as I continued my studies in Oriental medicine. I never would have been able to complete this book had it not been for the encouragement and support of Mrs. Masunaga and the dedicated practitioners at Iokai Shiatsu Center, and I remain greatly indebted to them. I owe my greatest inspiration, however, to Masunaga-Sensei and his universal message of acceptance and healing. His message is simple and clear. We can all reconcile our mental and physical imbalances and find deeper meaning in our life. That we can seek such relief and profound insights simply through gentle stretching exercises may come as a surprise. But who could doubt the healing power released by letting go of our habitual mental and physical patterns from time to time and allowing our inner sensitivity to lead us back to our original state of wholeness. This inner awareness is the most powerful healing force available to us and it is always at our disposal if we would but give it a chance.

STEPHEN S. BROWN

Contents

12/Contents

Introduction

Health Comes from Joy in Life

Generally speaking it goes against the grain of life to put up with hardships or to endure undue pain and suffering. It stands to reason, therefore, that the approaches to health which fail to give people enjoyment or to keep their interest will not bring more fulfillment and joy in life. This being the case, new and fashionable approaches to improve health, which attract interest mostly by their superficial features, often lack the substance to sustain people's interest and people tend to grow tired of them. The problem with these new approaches is that special steps have to be taken to hold people's interest, or otherwise people become bored with the method as soon as they get used to it. Those things in life which are capable of bringing people real satisfaction, however, do not cause boredom regardless of how many times they are repeated. Instead of becoming accustomed to these things, people learn to savor the experience more each time because it always has something new to offer.

The primary goal of the exercises in this book, therefore, is to get people to enjoy themselves. Learning to experience movement on a deeper level as something satisfying and enjoyable in itself is a possiblity open to all people at every stage of development. The approach offered here especially lends itself to those who wish to see clear signs of progress in terms of increased agility and flexibility. Those who simply wish to improve their level of health will find a unique approach outlined in clear and simple language. Also those who are worried about their physical condition or personal habits as well as those searching for more meaning in life should find something of personal value in these pages.

Universal Principles

Most of the methods for health and beauty popularized today were developed by the personal experience of the originator and were subsequently systematized. The more unique, dramatic, and revolutionary a method is, and the more it proves effective, the more the personality of the teacher comes into play. It is not uncommon for a group of people to become strongly attracted to a certain method or system and become deeply involved in it. It is true that if people let themselves be carried by the strong wave of popular appeal or group spirit, they find it easier to work toward a desired goal. This is often the case in many religions and cults in which a charismatic leader holds the group together. In such groups rational criticism is almost nonexistent, and nonmembers can quickly sense the oppressive atmosphere where a person is obliged to "believe." It is not just the personal power of the leader which creates a cult of zealous believers. There also seems to be a certain resonance and empathy among the individuals in the group which can fuel fanaticism. Unshakable faith and total reliance on the conviction that the leader or the object of worship is all powerful is the force behind most religions. Such blind faith is as dangerous as it is powerful. It is obvious that such groups wield a great amount of power and influence over people. Unfortunately there is also a tendency among believers to lose sight of the fundamental strength lying within themselves.

Perhaps you picked up this book because you felt that you could not go along with methods which involve an element of "faith." Maybe this book is more fitting to your nonconformist and pragmatic ways. Otherwise, it would seem unlikely that you would choose to study this method which is neither well known nor simple. It is fortunate that you chose this book because approaches to health popularized through mass advertising are usually simplistic and cater only to general interest. They often claim astonishing effectiveness and emphasize superficial features to produce an aura of novelty and uniqueness. Such "health fads" do not seem natural or beneficial from a common sense standpoint. Given this understanding, I will explain the reason I created Imagery Exercises in the pages which follow.

The methods presented in this book are not based on a flat denial of other approaches to health and beauty. It is not my intention to present this method as the only way. Imagery Exercises are based on the understanding and acceptance that all other methods have their merits despite being based on different principles which seem incompatible from a superficial perspective. There is a fundamental problem with those who lack tolerance for other approaches and insist that their way is the only right way. Everyone knows that many different religions exist in the world and that some of these religions are constantly at odds with each other. Many religions insist that theirs is the only way to salvation and profess that all other religions are either superstitions or the work of the devil. If the vow of Bodhisattvas (in Mahayana Buddhism) to save all souls before receiving their own salvation is really true, there must be a special reason for the existence of so many different religions. Some people may think the world would be better off with just one religion, but religion can be compared to food which everyone has to eat in order to survive. There are countless ways in which food can be prepared, but before food can be consumed and utilized as energy by each individual, one must choose a certain type of cooking. It is folly to remain ignorant of this basic principle of diversity in life and not to accept other ways of doing things.

In this same sense, every approach to health has its merits. This is due, not to the outward form, but the underlying principles which are unwritten. You cannot hope to succeed by copying just outward appearances. The method which works the best for you can only be arrived at by acquiring an understanding of the underlying principles. The most fundamental and important thing is for you to gain an understanding of the universal principles which are the common thread in all approaches.

The Nature of Life

While it may be difficult to come up with a scientific definition for life or even to define it in philosophical terms, it is not very hard to list a few characteristics which are common to all forms of life. First of all, living things never exist until they are born, and when they die, they cease to exist. Nonorganic things, naturally, do not live or die. In physics there is the law of "conservation of mass" (indestructibility of matter) and this states that the existence of physical matter is permanent, although it may change form. Life, on the other hand, is always limited in time and space and does not exist until it is born. No two living things are ever exactly alike. Also life comes into being from other life, and its existence is totally dependent on the presence of other life.

Another characteristic of living things is that they comprise an integrated organic unit contained in an outer covering which separates their internal environment from their external environment. The other basic characteristics of life include self-preservation and self-reproduction. All these characteristics must be unique to life and must hold true for all forms of life, from the most primitive to the most advanced. Such basic principles governing life are universal to all living things and operate within human beings as well as the biosphere as a whole. It is essential that we give a deeper consideration to the basic conditions indispensable for life.

One of the most important principles of life is that, living things always exist as a whole and make up a complete unit rather than being an assembly of parts. It may be scientifically correct to say that a human being is composed of billions of cells, but man does not come into being by combining billions of cells into one organism. Instead, a single cell divides countless times and forms billions of cells to develop into a human being.

Many organisms, including human beings, survive as a member of a colony or community, and aside from their individual identities, such organisms constitute another larger organism or unit of life. Although every human being has an individual existence, we are all a member of society which we depend on for survival. Human beings live by sharing the work of sustaining the community at large. Communities also do not form just by individuals being assembled at random, but grow from a core group of individuals. Living things survive as a group by the mutual exchange of basic life energy (Ki) which requires a certain empathy that enables individuals to share sustenance from nature. Thus, while all living things exist as a whole and independent physical entity, every individual in the biological community survives only by maintaining an interdependent relationship as one member in a greater order of life.

Breaking something down into its component parts and coming to an understanding of the whole as a combination of these parts is the work of the conscious mind. Our rational mind singles out certain parts and separates them from the rest to study its relationship with other parts and to comprehend the whole picture. This method of conceptualization developed through the history of man along with his intellectual advancement and work specialization. This development made it easier to define the precise role of each individual in the community and this created a stronger identification with the individual "self." Particularly in the West, the advancement of science, which minutely differentiates component parts, has caused the "self" or "I" to become the basic frame of reference.

In the conceptual framework which has become dominant today, parts that are tangible and readily distinguishable are viewed as the basic building blocks of everything that exists, including life itself. Along with this perspective, a dichotomy of mind and body has been imposed on human beings. Thus the body has been subdivided to comprehend the phenomenon of life as anatomical structures or cells which compose various tissues. Health has come to be viewed in terms of the state of our physical components, whether it be our bones, muscles, nerves, or blood vessels.

This same conceptual framework is applied in exercise, and most people think that just strengthening individual parts improves the whole. While this may be true in a sense, in reality we are never really able to completely isolate a single part and move or affect only one part. No matter how we focus on one part with our conscious mind and try to concentrate on it, the part we choose to isolate only exists and functions in connection with the whole body. In this same sense, just the collection of parts does not produce a whole.

This is why it is impossible to manipulate the skeleton or any other physical structure to affect only particular muscles or organs. Such parts are only conceptions of our conscious mind. Focusing on one part seemingly allows us to place emphasis or to act on that part. The whole fades into the background when we focus on just one part, but the whole still exists. All that happens is that the whole becomes invisible to the conscious mind. Often a physical problem appears in one part of the body, and people get the impression that this is the only part that has a problem, but a problem actually exists in the body as a whole. When the body as a whole has some problem, a symptom appears as a consequence in one particular part. Usually, rather than that one particular part having the problem, the problem can be said to lie in the process of life in the whole body.

Problems become manifested in a single part by a mechanism of life to quickly bring attention to the imbalance in the whole. Our conscious mind is effective in distinguishing parts and defining their role as a means to understand the whole. Our mind can therefore be applied to create a higher order of integration. The problem arises when the part is overemphasized and isolated from the whole and an attempt is made to deal with just that part alone. Just as a person becomes more isolated from society by becoming self-centered, the more a single part or aspect is emphasized over others, the more it becomes cut off from the whole to become a disconnected physical object. Such an approach to exercise causes the movement, flow, and harmony of the whole to become lost, and the part moved is reduced to a separate physical object which does not move in concert with the whole.

In one sense sick people can be considered as those who have such disconnected parts, or otherwise as those individuals who isolate themselves within society and become alienated. The purpose of our conscious mind is not to create totally independent and separate entities. The individual parts which come to the attention of our conscious mind should ideally serve as a guide to become aware of overall imbalances and bringing separate parts back into harmony with the whole.

The Yin-Yang principle,* originating in ancient China, embraces this characteristic of life. There is a fundamental difference between the concept of Yin and Yang and that of dualism in the West. In Western philosophy, both monism and dualism were originally based on the observation of physical matter, and these concepts comprise

* The Yin-Yang principle is a fundamental concept in Chinese philosophy which assigns two opposite but complementary aspects to every phenomenon in nature. This universal principle of change is best exemplified by night and day which constantly change from one to the other in a daily cycle.

the foundation for all scientific approaches. While the Yin-Yang principle embraces the totality of life, science only analyzes the workings of life in a piecemeal fashion. In the Orient, the perspective from the standpoint of living things was used as the basic framework for viewing all phenomena.

Therefore, although science is far more skillful and exact in manipulating physical objects, when it comes to actually dealing with life, great differences inevitably arise in the application of the same method. One obvious example of this is the variety of ways in which Western medicine is applied in clinical settings. In Oriental medicine, personal insight is applied in an attempt to come to grips with the intangible and profound aspects of life which are beyond the scope of orthodox science. In short, the Oriental approach is more useful for coming to grips with the totality of life. This is one of the basic reasons Oriental approaches and philosophy holds such an appeal for people in Western countries.

Health Fads

Young children are true to their own essential nature, and when left to their own devices, they usually develop various abilities on their own by playing freely. Children tend to learn only those things which they feel are important in their own personal experience. The learning of young children is not based so much on their intellect as on the general attitudes and personal relationships which they grow up with. Learning for children is more an intuitive and natural process. Even when the intellect becomes dominant later in childhood, all learning tends to follow the pattern that was established early in life.

There is a Japanese saying that "the soul of child of three remains unchanged at a hundred." This proverb points out the truth of the way behavioral patterns instilled at a very young age become the foundation on which a person develops and the fact that one's essential nature remains unchanged throughout life. Be that as it may, one of the strongest drives in growing up and becoming an adult is toward conformity. One learns early in the process of socialization that it is safest to pattern one's behavior after that of one's peers. Thus a behavioral tendency in conflict with one's essential nature begins to take over as one becomes an adult. Moreover, in today's society, the greatest value is attached to logical and scientific explanations and approaches, and sometimes this takes precedence over individual sensibilities. People readily accept products and approaches which conform to general standards and have popular appeal, but they seldom consider what is good for themselves from their own personal standpoint.

For example, when jogging is mentioned as being good for one's health, many people quickly take to the streets jogging and others get jogging boards to jog at home. While there is nothing wrong with popular approaches to health, it would serve a person better to decide what is truly beneficial from a personal standpoint. It could be that when people frantically go after every health regimen that comes into vogue including diets and exercise programs, they are operating under the basic behavioral program to conform which was input into their mind at an early age.

Those things which are truly important for living do not seem to be the new gimmicks which appear one after another. The essential nature of life has remained unchanged for several billion years, and the basic rules of nature applying to human beings have remained in effect since man first developed on earth more than a million years ago. They say that the average life of man has been extended with the advent of science, but this does not mean that individual lifespans have been doubled. In the *Yellow Emperor's Classic of Internal Medicine*, the two thousand year old classic of Chinese medicine, it is written as follows:

> The Yellow Emperor asks, "The people in the olden days used to work actively to the age of one hundred. Is there something wrong with society today that most people seem to become decrepit in their fifties? Or are people doing things that sap their vitality?" To this the royal physician answers, "People's attitudes toward life have changed and they follow their own selfish ways forgetting the way of nature."

This dialogue still applies today. The important thing is to develop a wholesome attitude toward life which conforms with nature. The problem lies precisely in how we each perceive what it means for us to be alive. The central theme in Oriental medicine is harmony with nature which gives birth to and nurtures life.

The recent boom in health foods and various folk remedies in many ways seems to run counter to the advancement of medicine. This growing interest in alternative approaches to health is actually the result of a grass-roots movement reflecting a decrease of confidence in modern medicine. In increasing numbers people are coming to the conclusion that modern medicine alone cannot protect their lives and also that a disease may progress too far before they receive medical attention. More and more, people are coming to realize that they cannot depend completely on modern medicine and that ultimately they are responsible for their own health.

It is only natural that the mainstream of alternative approaches to health should originate from sources outside the realm of modern medicine. Oriental medicine or more recently acquired empirical knowledge about health and the human condition offer a refreshing new approach to complement Western medicine where it is found wanting. It is interesting, however, that the majority of the wide array of alternative approaches to health today attempt to explain their system and benefits in terms of modern medical knowledge. It is true that, since Western medicine is based on the scientific method, the factual knowledge regarding the workings of the body is more accurate than in Oriental medicine. No doubt people find modern medicine far easier to comprehend than the often obscure concepts and terminology of yoga, Buddhism, and Oriental medicine. On the other hand, there are those who find the mysticism of the East exotic and fascinating, and this could very well have a certain psychological effect. Even so, most disciplines from the Orient remain mysterious and hard to comprehend for the majority of Western people.

Oneness of Knowing and Doing

Among those who admit that there are shortcomings to Western medicine, there are those who contend that these shortfalls are largely due to problems in medical care systems and are not the fault of medical science. Basically, their assertion seems to be that knowledge and practice are essentially two different issues. Therefore they contend that, although the scientific method is faultless, there are many obstacles in translating the results into something useful and workable in a real life situation. The distinction between pure knowledge and what can be done in actual practice is particularly emphasized in the scientific approach. It is said that prejudice concerning the outcome of a scientific experiment can undermine objectivity and produce unreliable results which render the experiment useless. For this reason some people maintain that scientific research should be conducted purely for the sake of knowledge and that its application should be an entirely separate consideration.

In pure science research is conducted on narrowly defined subject matter that is taken out of its context, and this makes its value difficult to appreciate. In the applied sciences seemingly fragmented experimental results are pieced together to come up with amazingly effective applications. Therefore, what may at first seem like useless knowledge by itself cannot be considered worthless when viewed in light of the possibilities created by a vast accumulation of knowledge. In the scientific method it is essential that the truth of fragments of reality be verified since science is founded on reduction and analysis.

When life is at issue, however, no matter how correct or suitable something may be in part, if it is not beneficial to the whole organism, it cannot be right. For example, even if it were deemed necessary to operate on a patient, it would be pointless if he were to die as the result of the operation. Otherwise doctors could make statements like "The operation was a success but the patient died." A similar point can be made about immunizations. Although immunizations are undoubtedly effective in preventing disease, there are cases where people die as a result of being immunized.

In the realm of science or nonliving things, pure knowledge can often be very useful in itself. But for living things abstract knowledge serves very little purpose. For the individual organism those things unrelated to its survival are of little significance. For most living things knowing means the ability to perform a certain act. Knowing how to swim means that one can swim, just as knowing how to drive means that one is able to operate a motor vehicle. Similarly, regardless of how many methods for health a person knows, so long as he is not healthy, he has no more than an intellectual understanding, and his body has not benefitted from it. Knowledge concerning health is of no use until it is put into practice.

Learning with the Body

In the Orient, where the traditional approach was always based on the perspective of living things, a holistic knowledge engaging one's physical as well as mental faculties has been held to be of prime importance. Speculation and theoretical arguments were regarded as secondary to the ability to act. This is apparent in Oriental precepts such as "Actions come before words." It is true that this practical approach did not foster the development of pure science as in the West. Nevertheless, valuable empirical knowledge was accumulated in the Orient through the centuries concerning matters directly related to life.

It therefore follows that, in the Orient more value was traditionally placed on the unity of knowledge and action, where "to know is to act." In Zen Buddhism trying to understand things intellectually is discouraged by admonitions such as "Do nothing

—just sit" and "Enlightenment comes not through words." Such an approach may be fine for those who are willing to accept such discipline, but it does seem to be a little too much to ask of the average person in this day and age.

The traditional skills and crafts of Japan have been taught with the dictum of "learn with your body, not your head." Very few detailed manuals existed in the old days. People had no more than brief notes to go by and most skills were learned by working beside a master of the craft and practicing the same thing over and over. Today most people could not be bothered with such a tedious approach to learning, especially when convenient step by step manuals are available for almost everything. This type of casual approach, however, at times fails to convey the essence of the teaching. While the explanations of this book may not always seem so simple or straightforward, the essential points are stated repeatedly in order to convey some of the profound aspects of exercise and life.

The reason I mention the importance of learning with your body rather than your head is because this is the most vital point in exercises for health. Doing meridian exercises by the use of imagery makes learning with the body simple and enjoyable. Furthermore, Zen Imagery Exercises is based on Oriental medicine which has an age old tradition of healing and promoting health through holistic practices, and they even address the issue of one's spiritual well-being. Now, with this approach, you can develop an appreciation for the profound value of ancient mystical practices through your own experience.

The primary object of this book is to enable you, the reader, to discover something new each day through the regular practice of meridian exercises. Rather than allowing an exercise program to become a monotonous routine, you can arrive at a living understanding of why you really need and want to exercise. It will become clear through doing these exercises that the approach in this book is especially beneficial because, instead of making you conform to a certain standard, the focus is always on you as a unique individual and your special needs. Once you come to appreciate this approach for yourself, the value of this book will become obvious and its worth will grow with you for the rest of your life.

Chapter 1

Exercise and Body-Mind Integration

The Meaning of Health

It may be possible that there are methods available which can fulfill your wishes to relieve whatever symptoms you have and resolve all your problems. It would be a modern day dream if such a method could be outlined with attention given only to the relevant points. I am well aware that many people are reading this book to get at the main points. You may wonder why I address topics in a roundabout manner, but I have learned time and again through long years of experience that fulfilling a person's desires right away is not really the best thing for that person.

Most sick people do not care what happens later so long as they can find relief from their present suffering. What then happens, however, is that as soon as one symptom goes away, another problem arises to take its place. When this happens, the previous problem is all but forgotten. What is really important for sick people is not that each and every one of their symptoms be removed but that they be restored to a whole state. Health is similar to happiness in that when we have it, we are rarely aware of it. It is not until we lose it that we realize just how precious it is.

The World Health Organization (WHO) has defined health as "the state of optimal physical, mental, and social well-being, and not merely the absence of disease and infirmity." Health has also been called "a functional surplus of energy, which is a relative but measurable factor," or otherwise, "the ability to maintain harmony in timing and balance." Disease, on the other hand, is looked upon as a unfortunate nuisance that must be avoided. The capacity to remain free of disease seems to be inherent in the word "health." This may be because the word "health" comes from "heal." But "heal" also has something in common with "hale," which means robust and full of life. Both "heal" and "hale" are very close to whole or wholesome. Be that as it may, these words are most often understood as recovering from disease to become whole and strong.

This was the reason it was necessary for the WHO to educate the public that "Health is not merely the absence of disease." Rene Dubos, the author of *Mirage of Health*, stated that "Life without stress and pressure is just an illusion; it is the destiny of man to grow through toil and strife." This being the case, in the West the predominant view of health is that a person must strengthen his defenses against disease and death by building up his body and conserving strength (Fig. 1). This concept seems to be the foundation on which all modern health systems are based.

Long ago the philosopher Lao Tsu said "Man attains health by returning to nature." Also in this regard it is stated as follows in the beginning of the *Yellow Emperor's Classic of Internal Medicine*: "The wise men of old followed the law of Yin and

Fig. 1   Western Concept of Health (Dualistic)

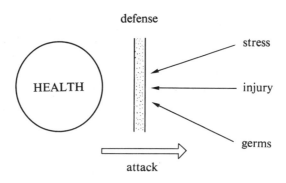

Yang, ordered their life in harmony with seasonal cycles, practiced moderation in eating and drinking, and were careful not to overwork. This is the way to keep the mind and body in harmony and live a long and full life."

The word for health in Chinese and Japanese is composed of two characters. The first character (健: Ken) denotes a human being and something which stands straight and upright. The second character (康: Ko) means to be at ease or relaxed after dispensing with all extraneous things. It is written as follows in the beginning of the *I-Ching*, the Chinese classic of divination: "The way of heaven is uprightness." Also there is a traditional Oriental ideal of an "upright body and a mind at ease." Thus the second character also refers to composure and peace of mind. These two characters together imply standing straight and tall while being relaxed and at ease.

Ease here has nothing to do with laziness or self-indulgence. In this respect, it is stated as follows in the *Yellow Emperor's Classic of Internal Medicine:* "People these days are constantly drinking and overindulging and they often have sex while drunk. Their lust knows no limits and they are forever bent on satisfying their passions. In this way they exhaust their life essence. They take no heed of natural rhythms and cycles, but instead are constantly seeking thrills and never really relax. People like this become weak and feeble in less than fifty years because their life is lacking in order and discipline."

Thus the attitude toward maintaining health more than two thousand years ago in China was based on an understanding of the need to live with some moderation and in harmony with natural cycles. There is nothing complicated about this. It is interesting to note that even two thousand years ago some people were lamenting that "people these days lead disorderly lives and do not live much past fifty." Since unhealthy lifestyles also existed a few thousand years ago, there is no reason for us to be overly pessimistic about recent trends.

Exercise for Health

Exercise and athletics have existed since the time of the ancient Greeks, who were among the earliest people to take an active interest in physical education, and they strove to develop the beauty and strength of the human physique. In more recent history, physical education has been encouraged by the government as a means of keeping the nation strong and fit. Medical research on physical education applying scientific knowledge about anatomy and physiology has been promoted as national projects especially in European countries like Germany, Sweden, and Denmark.

In Japan the role of exercise in keeping the nation strong was recognized prior to World War II and this was promoted in the form of "radio exercises," which are a regimented form of calisthenics done along with a daily radio program. Actually this type of exercise was temporarily banned after the war as a remnant of a militaristic government. Sports and athletics have become extremely popular in Japan since the war and great interest has been shown in exercise as a complement to competitive sports.

The word "sports" originated from "disport" which means to take off from work for leisure and recreation. Sports, therefore, includes not only those activities which require physical exertion, but also less physically demanding activities like fishing and target shooting. Nevertheless, sports can be loosely defined as activity primarily involving physical exercise. It can be distinguished from other pastimes where the activity is primarily mental.

Since the industrial revolution, work has come to be viewed principally in terms of efficiency and productivity. The need for free time to engage in enjoyable activity has increased with the growing trend toward occupational specialization. This development of society is one reason for the popularity of sports. However, once the main motivation in sports becomes competition, to set a record, or to prove one's superiority, it becomes biased in favor of specialized training which develops only specific skills and excludes nonexperts. Today professional athletes are looked up to models of physical fitness for everybody.

In contrast to sports, calisthenics and exercises are a series or pattern of specific movements for strengthening or developing parts of the body. Ideally exercises yield greater strength, balanced development, and improved health. A great deal of attention in medicine and physical education today is directed toward sports. However, sports medicine is mostly concerned with measurable quantities and physical problems resulting from sports. So far, research into exercises for well-rounded physical development and the improvement of health has been given little attention. Although the popularity of exercises purely for health and pleasure have grown along with the public's disenchantment with modern medicine, many such exercise systems are lacking in a sound theoretical foundation. This is because most of these exercises are formulated from personal experience and their merits are explained in scientific terms with what little knowledge is available.

Most athletes have a good physique and undeniably they have better than average endurance and are more capable of performing strenuous exercises. In the old days such physical prowess may have been useful for work, but since machines perform the majority of heavy work for us today, very few jobs remain where such strength is actually useful. It is also a fact that, as a result of mechanization, the physical condition of the average person has declined. Since the loss of physical strength in this manner is in some respects related to the loss of health, this has lead to the trend of taking up various sports to improve one's physical condition.

Even though this is a good development, some people go overboard and on occasion even end up losing their life by exercising beyond their capacity. For a novice, there always lies some danger of overexertion with sports. Therefore interest has grown in exercise programs where each individual can practice according to his own ability to improve his physical condition. It is questionable, however, to assume that increasing one's physical strength and stamina alone will provide health and longevity. Physical strength means the ability to perform a given amount of physical work, and although greater strength may perhaps be related to greater resistance to disease, it cannot really be considered a reliable measure of health.

In contrast to the calisthenics and vigorous exercises of the West, traditional exercises in the Orient emphasize balance and flexibility over strength. The Oriental approach to health has always been to increase one's vitality and to ward off illness rather than to fight an illness after getting it. The ideal is to maintain optimum health and vitality so that diseases can be easily avoided. Yoga and Zen mediation rarely lead to an increase of physical strength, but they are receiving attention as excellent practices for increasing health and improving one's physical condition. Tai Chi, dance, and casual strolls do not increase one's muscular strength as much as they tone and balance the whole body. These are highly effective methods for learning to relax and release stress.

Sports originally served a vital role in liberating people from their work and bringing more fulfillment in their lives. Getting involved in some sports is indeed a meaningful way to spend one's leisure time. In this way, one's physical energies not used in work are liberated and the whole body is refreshed and revitalized. On the other hand, a competitive attitude is often engendered in group sports. This may be good as a harmless outlet for our aggressive drives, but many people become absorbed in the competitive aspect. Some people even become obsessed by the excitement of competing. It seems that all too often people become engrossed in the competitive aspect of sports instead of enjoying the recreational and relaxing effect of sports.

True health denotes an overall physical balance where one has the capacity of recovering quickly from the tension and imbalances created while absorbed in work or other activity. Suppleness implies the ability to recognize and release tension anywhere in the body. The flexibility of a person is one index of suppleness, yet this does not mean a person has to be able to bend all his joints to their extreme limit like some acrobat. One cannot really be considered healthy unless one's whole body, including the internal organs and nervous system, is functioning in a supple manner. What is more important, one must possess a "suppleness of mind." Only the exercises which serve to restore the mind-body balance in this way are truly worthy of being called "exercises for health."

Exercise as a Reflection on Life

Exercising is unnecessary for babies and animals, which are true to their own nature and live according to their instincts. This is why babies and little children are rarely considered to be in need of special exercise. In this modern age, however, exercising has also become a necessity for children since many of them are compelled to develop their intellectual abilities at the expense of their natural dispositions. Living in a highly structured society with work specialization encourages physical restrictions and unnatural lifestyles in children as well as adults. This creates distortions in the human body which was originally part of nature. The body thus distorted cannot be restored to a natural state without adding some healthful element. Exercising has been conceived as healthy activity for reestablishing a natural balance in life.

In contrast to religion and education, which are efforts to seek a better life by applying the mind, exercise is an attempt to find a better way with the body. It is therefore meaningless to just copy the outward forms or movements in exercise. Copying postures in exercise is a mental process of making the body conform to certain forms, but this inhibits natural movement and the free expression of the body. If you were to look at the photographs in this book and suppose that Imagery Exercises are similar to other types of exercise, you are missing the point entirely. The most important feature of life is not the external form but the internal dynamics which create and sustain the form. Diligent practice may enable you to copy the postures and movements perfectly, but this does not mean that you will learn to give expression to the life within you. It may be possible to obtain the desired results such as better health or appearance without developing this ability, but this is not so different from taking drugs to obtain relief from symptoms.

There is a deeper significance to having physical problems or beauty problems just as there is to having a disease. There has to be an underlying cause which relates to your life in general. Otherwise the problem is just a misfortune or injustice to you which simply has to be compensated for. It is far more constructive and creative to view such handicaps as an impetus for improving yourself. It is more engaging to use exercise as a way of becoming more aware of how life is motivating you to grow. Zen Imagery Exercise is founded on the principle of meridians, which comes from an Oriental perspective on life. Experiencing meridians as the flow of life energy or a special feeling of tension during stretching exercises allows you to become aware of your own body type or the condition of the meridians. To really experience your imbalance and understand its underlying cause, it is necessary to allow your body to move without conscious control and to become aware of the dynamics of life energy within yourself. Feeling the energy imbalances in your body through movement will in turn lead to an adjustment in the balance of energy. Your interaction with this fundamental aspect of life can serve as a guiding principle in your life, and the imbalances you become aware of can be understood as a reflection of your own life. Since you will come to understand how these imbalances relate to your life through exercising, you will be able to apply this in your daily life to come up with ways of preventing such imbalances from occurring. The most important thing to learn is that the pain or physical problems which occur in one part of the body as the end result of imbalances is not the fault of that part alone. Thus you should not become overly concerned about alleviating just that one problem.

It should therefore be obvious that forcing yourself in some way to correct an imbalance, or otherwise bending or stretching a certain part forcefully, is not the answer. The part or problem we become consciously aware of is the result of an imbalance, and the cause of the imbalance usually goes unnoticed. The problem in a particular part just points to a larger imbalance somewhere else, and we must learn that attempts to deal with only the apparent problem rarely leads to lasting improvement in the body as a whole. Even when physical problems are corrected individually, if this is not integrated within the body as a whole, the body soon returns to its original condition. On the other hand, a variety of problems can be alleviated by dealing directly with the root cause to restore the overall balance. The simple principle of moving in the direction which is the easiest and exhaling completely at the limit of each movement serves to relax the whole body and strengthen weak areas. Once the energy deficient parts become replenished, the circulation of energy is improved throughout the entire body and problems disappear of themselves.

Listening to Our Body

The conveniences of this modern age have a tendency to limit our freedom and creativity in equal measure to their availability and convenience. Things in our world today are conceptualized as nothing more than "objects" by our language and rational perspective. Although this makes it simpler to deal with the world around us, it has stifled the changeable or "living" aspect in everything. Words differentiate various aspects of our world and define their characteristics so that things of a similar nature can be grouped together to create a sense of order. It can be said that our language developed hand in hand with our "conscious mind" or our intellectual capacity for making fine distinctions. The society we live in is a product of our language and intellect, and these are predominant forces in our life.

Although our bodies do not always work the way we want them to, we generally manage to obtain some degree of control over our bodies by means of our rational perspective. Nevertheless, it is a mistake to view our bodies as consistent and tangible objects. The tendency of treating our bodies as objects probably originated with the widespread acceptance of the perspective offered by the science of anatomy and physiology. The contemporary rational attitude is to view the human body from a physical perspective based on the concept of anatomy, even when contemplating relative matters such as life or health.

The Japanese physicians who were first exposed to Western medicine were amazed at the accuracy of the Dutch anatomy texts when comparing them to the corpses they dissected. This anatomical model was dramatically different from their traditional Oriental understanding of the body. Western medicine, which was founded on the accurate portrayal of the physical structure of corpses, may be convenient for understanding the body, but its preoccupation with accuracy in detail has caused the loss of freedom and creativity necessary in dealing with the phenomenon of life. Even though Oriental medicine is not founded on an accurate anatomical model, it possesses an excellent therapeutic paradigm which deals with the phenomenon of life more appropriately.

Unfortunately most Oriental medicine practiced today applies very little of this creative approach conducive to life. In acupuncture treating symptoms by the use of standard acupuncture points has become the norm. The traditional holistic approach to health, which included truly excellent exercise regimens, has largely disappeared. Recently in Japan the exercise system developed by Professor Michizo Noguchi,* who suggests that we should listen to what the body wants, has been called a breakthrough which goes beyond conventional understanding of health and physical fitness. Oriental medicine, however, has been practiced for thousands of years by paying attention to the subtle indications of the body.

The purpose of traditional Do-In exercises is not merely to mimic various animals or to control the movements of different parts of the body. The real purpose is to move the whole body in unison with a mental picture which captures the quality of these movements. I developed Zen Imagery Exercises in order to revive the essence of traditional Oriental practices and provide a method for exercise and self-help therapy in the home. The foremost principle in Imagery Exercises is to *move the body according to what the body wants*. Trying to consciously control the body is not effective. You should not try to learn these exercises quickly by just copying their external features. Otherwise you may miss the point of these exercises entirely.

The concept of "oneness of mind and body" is so familiar to the Japanese that it is almost taken for granted, yet in the West, where people have been raised with a clear distinction between the mind and body, people are often quite surprised when they first come in contact with this idea and eagerly ask how they can experience this unity themselves. When told that meditation is the best way to experience this, many Westerners begin to meditate diligently. The Westerners who become convinced that learning a particular aspect of Eastern culture will lead to a deeper understanding usually attempt to experience this firsthand.

Those who claim to teach "oneness of mind and body" today do it after a fashion, but this is no easy task. A person would have to be truly enlightened to continually maintain this state of mental and physical integration. Thus, even Oriental people rationalize the discrepancy between this ideal and the reality of their unintegrated lives as just the normal state of affairs. Most people make the mistake of believing that knowing intellectually is the same thing as understanding and think that the "mind" is no more than the conscious mind. People usually excuse themselves as "only being human" when things do not go according to the dictates of their conscious mind, and they fail to seek out the underlying cause. We must each work to experience for ourselves those things the masters have been teaching.

The first steps necessary for this process will be explained with the way to breathe. Although all of us have been breathing since the day we were born without giving it

---

* Professor Michizo Noguchi is the head of the physical education department of Tokyo Fine Arts University and is the originator of a unique system of exercise known as "Noguchi Taiso" (Noguchi Exercise System). In this system the body is viewed as a basically fluid entity and movements are made by picturing natural phenomenon such as a waterfall. Professor Noguchi is the author of many Japanese books on the subject of exercise.

much thought, it can be incredibly difficult when we try to breathe as instructed. You may at times think that you control your body with your conscious will, but the more you try to consciously control your breathing, the more it becomes awkward and uncomfortable. As soon as an action that was once simple and habitual is made conscious (or broken down into parts), it does not come as smoothly and easily as before. This phenomena does not take place just in sports or the performing arts but occurs even with everyday movements.

When we speak of movement, however, the tendency is to think of just the physical aspect of movement. From an Eastern perspective, the activity of the mind is inherent with any movements because of the concept of "oneness of mind and body." When considering movement, the dynamics of the psyche should rightly be the central issue. The concept of holism implies that the mind and body work together as one. The function of integrating movements to form one uniform action is actually more in the domain of the unconscious.

It is common knowledge that man is a conglomeration of billions of individual units of life called cells. The only reason all these cells come together to support the life of one human being is because they come under the control of the "mind" at some level. Our internal organs do not move by conscious control, but their functions are coordinated by some internal intelligence. Our emotions or mental state have a direct influence on the function of our body, and our language is full of such expressions as "his blood boiled with rage." When we are restless and our heart beats out of control, mostly the heart is reacting because we are unable to calm our mind down.

Balance in our physical body is contingent on a balance between the mind and the body. Suppleness of the body indicates a flexible posture physically and mentally. Exercises up until now have been preoccupied with physical movement, and the vital role of the mind has been largely ignored. The conventional approach to exercise does not lead to true health where a wholeness in life is the aim.

Until the most basic posture for a human being—standing upright—becomes suddenly impossible because of an injury such as a "slipped disk," people rarely pause to reflect on the value and significance of standing. Even then, many people just blame their bad back and fail to appreciate what they had. Some people knowingly contend that since the human frame was not originally designed for standing upright, low back pain is nothing but the lot of man. This is akin to stating that sickness is just our fate. Standing upright on two legs is a unique posture which is not maintained by any other animal. This is truly amazing and wonderful when you think about it. We tend to overlook this marvelous evolutionary development which liberated our hands and enabled the creation of civilization.

According to Professor Noguchi, man became able to walk upright and to free both hands only after learning to walk on two feet by alternately freeing one leg. Holding the body up against the pull of gravity with the lower limbs created the standing posture and enabled the free use of our arms. This opened up tremendous new possibilities. The development of mankind took a dramatic leap when we learned to liberate our upper limbs.

Exercise has been defined by Professor Noguchi as "an activity for exploring who we really are through the clues gained by moving our body." He further explains this concept as follows: "Words giving meaning to exercise must come from our own awareness of our body. The effect of these words (or images) on our body can then be used to seek answers to questions of our mind. No satisfactory definition exists for what exercise is and there is no need to prematurely impose a restrictive framework."

Dr. Yoshinaru Fujioka, a Japanese social psychologist known for his work on the subject of mental images, also states as follows: "It is incorrect to consider mental imagery as not being a valid area of scientific study because there is no precise definition of what mental images are. A working definition of images can be gradually formulated in the course of studying mental images."

If we consider this statement in light of the nature of life as discussed earlier, this empirical approach stands to reason. Man has investigated the many and varied phenomena of nature in an attempt to define life, but we always come back to the basic question, "What is life really?" Nonetheless, everyone has the awareness of being alive. In fact, nothing could be alive without this basic awareness. Both health and exercise are only possible because we are alive. The key to health and longevity is to use exercise of the mind and body as our clue in coming to a greater awareness of what it means to be alive.

Answering the question of what life is about has been the foremost aim of religions and philosophical schools since time immemorial. But modern science has set this vital question aside for the very end. We should not leave this all important question in the hands of "experts" and accept their hypotheses. Living is a crucial issue for every individual and each person should try to experience life as fully as possible in order to personally come to a realization of "*this* is what it means to be *alive*!" Words only describe one facet of phenomena. Life as a whole can never be described by words. You must realize that Zen Imagery Exercises are offered so that you will be able to use, not those words and images you learn, but those words and images that issue from your innermost being that belong to nobody else but you.

Awareness and Movement

Our body is able to maintain a healthy equilibrium of physiological activity by each meridian performing its proper role or function, and for this to happen, Ki or life energy must constantly circulate through each one of the meridians in an orderly sequence. Disease results when there is stagnation of Ki somewhere along the course of these meridians. Even if something is done to improve the flow of this energy at the point of stagnation, as long as the basic cause of the stagnation is not removed, the disease will recur because the root cause of the problem remains. Finding a quick solution for removing the symptoms in the affected area may make it seem as if the problem has been solved, but this cannot be regarded as a true state of health.

Imagery Exercises are done in a specific sequence to facilitate the flow of Ki in proper order through the body. The chief organ responsible for the circulation of Ki is the heart which is regarded as the sovereign of all organs in Oriental medicine. The function of the heart can be regarded as being similar to that of an individual's awareness.* Awareness works to bring together many different elements to form a unified whole. Awareness acts as the center to which various component parts are drawn and organized around to make a distinction between self and nonself. When drawing a circle, usually the center is decided first and then the circumference of the circle is drawn around the center. In the case of an organism, however, both the center and periphery form simultaneously.

Single-celled organisms are a combination of many different components, but multi-cellular organisms, which are composed of many cells, are also able to function as one organic unit because of an awareness which unites them into one organism. This can be compared to a large number of people working together for one purpose, or to people joining together to become "one in body and spirit." Instinct is one word used for this unifying aspect of awareness which is an inborn trait in animals. Jean Henry Faber (1823–1915), who studied insects with complex instinctive behavior, observed many things which even seemed miraculous. But he also found that introducing some unlikely obstacle in the environment of insects caused their instinct to lead them completely astray. Faber called this the "ignorance of instinct." Instincts are ignorant because those things which are not likely to occur in nature are not taken into account. Instincts only work to ensure the survival of the species as a whole in a given environment under specific conditions.

Life, having originated as one facet of nature, perhaps was endowed with the power to serve as an integral part of the whole of nature by bringing separate elements together. The special power to distinguish a part from the whole grew with the development of awareness, and organisms began to appear on earth that could freely adapt to contingencies by modifying their behavior to suit the circumstances. This is the function of our consciousness. The presence of conscious awareness is most pronounced in higher animals, but no one can really say that the lower life forms do not also have some measure of it. Anyway, in the case of human beings, the conscious mind—that portion of awareness which had been serving the needs of the whole—developed so far as to come to dominate instinctive awareness. Through the work of human consciousness things that never before existed in nature were created, and socialization, language, and work specialization eventually lead to the rise of civilization. However, in this day and age the creations of man, having gone too far in the direction of the conscious mind, are becoming farther and farther removed from the essence of life.

Life originally arises from a place where there is no life and in time again returns to a place where life no longer exists. This whole process of creation and destruction may be called the function of life. The role or significance of something identified as a separate part only becomes completely clear when it is perceived as a part of a whole. Yet our conscious mind has taken over awareness (the part of our mind which works to create a whole) and has come to view itself as the master of awareness. Those areas beyond the scope of our conscious mind have been defined as our unconscious. Our awareness, which is largely related to our unconscious, seems

* The word awareness is used in this book for the Japanese word *kokoro*, which also refers to one's mind and emotions. In Imagery Exercises *kokoro* refers to the essential feature in all forms of life which integrates an organism into a whole and enables it to function as an individual.

to function more effectively as a coordinator and integrator when it is not bound by the constraints of our conscious mind.

Since words developed out of the need of the conscious mind to distinguish things, naturally they are most suited for explaining matters pertaining to the realm of the conscious mind. To be logical is to be consistent with verbalized concepts, and rational thought takes place within the medium of words. The expressions used by Western people are suited to explaining the physical world because the self and others are clearly distinguished. In Japanese, however, expressions tend to emphasize the inner meaning, or the "heart," of things so the meaning is sometimes vague to outsiders. Nevertheless, there are times when a less rigid use of words is more useful because it can be a means of heart to heart communication conveying things which are beyond words.

Movements are always performed as a whole sequence of actions and are thus largely unconscious. Though the term "unconscious movements" may suggest those of a drunk or a sleep walker, what is meant is that the conscious mind normally only directs the beginning and end of movements and is not involved in the execution of every detail of the movement. The conscious mind only functions in a limited spatial range and works mostly in fixed time frames. Our mind has a hard time following the fine details of our movements through a continuous time sequence.

When a new series of actions are learned, first the entire sequence is broken down into parts so that each part can be learned individually, but the actions cannot be called learned until a person is able to put them all back together as a whole without conscious deliberation. Those movements which are still controlled by the conscious mind remain awkward, while those movements one is accustomed to are more smooth and require the minimum amount of effort.

The conscious mind acts, almost against nature, to distinguish parts, but this has made it possible for us to adapt to rare situations which would never occur under normal circumstances. Yet if an acquired ability is to be utilized repeatedly, the conscious element must be disposed with so the ability can become habitual and unconscious. Many assume that muscles under our voluntary control are moved by our will, but in order to make delicate movements, the unconscious participation of many muscles is required since each and every muscle cannot be controlled at any given moment. A group of movements is perfected only after each individual movement is integrated so that it complements the whole process.

When it is said that an exercise should be done rhythmically, or in balance, or with a smooth flowing motion, it all means that the exercise must be done less consciously. The conscious mind must be employed when learning new movements based on a specific standard which is intended to have a specific effect. Such exercises may at first sight seem to be useful and effective, but they are removed from the true essence of the movements. The motivations for exercising may vary, but each individual must experience the essential unity so as to enable spontaneity without the need to be conscious of every little distinction. The movements should ideally be practiced repeatedly so the details can be learned naturally as one performs them so that they become one's very own.

This is the important point on which most books on exercising have so far been in error. The authors of these books are not to blame because the intellectual element in society stresses the need for logical and comprehensible explanations. Thus explanations of exercises invariably have to be based on principles of Western medicine and psychology. Many authors of exercise books no doubt became aware of some aspects of such rational explanations which do not exactly comform with or convey their own experience. Nevertheless, perhaps since they are so confident in their method, authors leave it up to the reader to full in the gaps. Therefore most people who read the book never recognize the real cause for this discrepancy between understanding and practice.

Work and Play

Although work is not always enjoyable, most of us work for the pleasure we get from obtaining the things we need to live. Enjoyment in work also comes from knowing that one is doing something useful. There are those who contend that work should be done for the enjoyment of it. According to the "law of results" in psychology, even those tasks which appear meaningless can be performed with increased motivation when clear results are seen from one's efforts. When the results are hard to see, however, motivation is quickly lost. Job satisfaction which comes from seeing the results of one's work is very important for most people.

Work is activity pursued when there is some need to be fulfilled in life. The purpose of work is primarily to satisfy certain needs. "Satisfaction" is a state in which all needs are fulfilled and people are free to relax and enjoy themselves. Generally when people are enjoying leisure, most of their needs have been met for the time being. This is why leisure, or playing, by its very nature, is a pleasurable activity. Play also means that there is some leeway. The need for a little "play" exists not only for living things but for machines as well. When the parts in a machine are fit together too tightly with no room to spare, even a small jolt will cause it to break. This same principle applies to working and setting schedules because tight schedules are not only exhausting but are likely to be disrupted by the smallest delay or miscalculation. This is why extra time is figured into work schedules and break times are provided during work. In almost all work situations some free time is allotted when one does not have to do anything. This allowance for taking time out can be called "play."

As mentioned before, insects, which live according to highly specialized instincts, sometimes display the "ignorance of instinct" when their environment changes drastically. With higher animal forms, although the process of becoming an adult takes longer, there are greater behavioral options. In other words, there is a greater amount of "play" for an individual to learn the skills necessary for survival. By this token, for human beings playing is the "work" of children. Although playing is not strictly necessary for living, children learn an amazing variety of things by playing. Children thus unknowingly prepare themselves for their roles as responsible members of society.

Setting an ample amount of time aside for play even after becoming adults, most of whom must work for a living, provides an extra margin for staying well adjusted. New personal growth is also possible through the fresh inspiration found in moments of recreational activity. This is why every society has adopted some form of recreational activity as an integral part of adult society. Sports originated from this need for recreation. Nevertheless, the growth of competitive and professional sports seems to have caused a commensurate loss in its recreational value. Ideally sports or recreation should provide a feeling of satisfaction or joy just in itself. One should be free to do things the way he pleases in play or recreation, and this way there is the possibility for continuous experimentation and discovery. It is important for people to have some wholesome activity that liberates them from work, which often tends to become repetitive and mechanical. This way people can re-experience what it really means to be alive.

Taking part in recreational activities in one's spare time is very important for mental and physical health. It provides an outlet for one's creativity, and this freedom leads to greater advancement in other areas. Leisure adds a new dimension of imagination and creativity to our work. Our intellectual capacity developed in the process of evolution where life was liberated from the bonds of instinct to enable greater versatility in adapting to changes in the environment. Thus, the basic nature of our intellect is to seek greater freedom and further evolutionary development. Instincts, therefore, can be compared to work where the basic tasks in life are performed almost automatically, while the intellect can be compared to play because it is always seeking and creating new possibilities. Modern civilization is the product of just this kind of "play" and it has given us an entirely new way of life. Be that as it may, the play which was supposed to open up new possibilities in our life has in many cases been turned around so that individuals are instead compelled to conform to certain modes of behavior.

Our intellect, which at one point in our development brought forth greater freedom and creativity in work, has now removed the element of play from work in order to make work efficient and cost effective. Work has been tied down to the single purpose of making money. Work for the vast majority of people has become an activity where routine tasks are performed in a prescribed manner. The body is continually made to perform the same tasks in the same way and this is considered more efficient and economical. In most lines of work today, one's intellect is largely subservient to mechanical production methods which require tasks to be performed almost as automatically as instinctive behavior.

Fortunately, most people still have some opportunity for play in their spare time, but such recreational activities often tend to be uniform and ready-made, so very little freedom and creativity is exercised. Also sports have become professions and in many respects amateur and recreational sports have been patterned after professional sports so that the outward form or appearance has become more important. Thus many sports no longer serve as recreational activity done simply for the pleasure of it. With the orientation of sports mostly being on its external features, many people have forgotten their need to seek out new possibilities in life.

Studying the design of our body, it is obvious that it is a very versatile apparatus which far exceeds the performance levels normally required in life. It is said that most human beings use only a fraction of their potential, and our physical performance is no exception in this. No matter how perfect a body we are endowed with, just like our brain we either use it or lose it. By developing these physical potentials in a well-rounded manner, we can make use of the surplus capacity available to excell in various endeavors.

While the active use of our physical capabilities promotes their development and makes the body perform more efficiently, always using the body in one set way makes the balanced development of our physical potential difficult. This can be compared to eating an unbalanced diet because the body is unable to function properly despite having an ample amount of calories. One of the characteristics of life is that too great a burden on only one part will cause the whole body to suffer. One of the basic problems with living in this modern age is that individuals tend to become fixed early on in their life by their academic and athletic performance. Imagery Exercises are an excellent way to regain a balance, which is most important to adults since they tend to apply only a portion of their mental and physical potential.

How to Keep at It

One must practice Imagery Exercises regularly in order to realize the benefits of greater health and well-being, but there are always obstacles to starting a new program like this. The obstacles which keep people from practicing long enough to obtain appreciable benefits are usually internal rather than external. In Japan, a person unable to continue something for more than three days after deciding to start is called *mikka-bozu* (quitter after the third day). This come from the traditional wisdom that whether one can continue practicing something after resolving to do so often depends on whether one can make it beyond the third day. Somehow there always seems to be a sudden drop in motivation around the fourth day, no matter what you decide to start. This loss of motivation is particularly devastating when something is taken up for superficial reasons such as simple curiosity, not wanting to be left out, or just on someone's recommendation, without a full understanding of why it is beneficial and really necessary.

The human mind works in such a way that there is always an inherent dichotomy like that of Dr. Jekyll and Mr. Hyde. This is why, behind the decision to undertake something, there always lurks an attitude of wanting to quit. Behind all the reasons for starting something new, there lie excuses to rationalize quitting. When a person is about to start something, only the bright side is seen, but no one imagines there is also a negative side lying hidden within oneself. This negative side only shows up after one's interest begins to wane. This is not to imply that everyone has a weak character lacking in willpower and perseverance. It is simply that the human mind has a two-sided nature which acts as a safety mechanism. If people were able to stick to every decision, there would be the danger of persisting even after realizing a mistake and people would be incapable of reconsidering the suitability of their decision.

Therefore, whenever a person makes a "firm decision," reasons are always present for going back on the same decision. This is why no matter how determined a person is to stick to a decision and even tells others about it, there is always a "safety valve" ready so that a person can quit easily once it becomes clear that it is not what is really desired. For this reason a new approach is required to adopt a resolution and stick by it. The bootstraps approach of dogged perseverance and "sticking by one's guns" may work for a few, but those who succeed this way are a small minority.

So how does one stick with a program after deciding to start it? First of all, it is crucial to persist with it for at least a week. In this time you must seek and instill an understanding in both your mind and your body of why you really want and need to do it. Once your body feels how good the program is, your body will demand that you continue the program.

It is interesting that anything which is truly necessary for a person somehow always gets done. This does not mean that everything necessary always gets done. The point here is simply that in a broad sense, the really necessary things in life are enjoyable and make one feel good. Once we learn that something can be pleasant and enjoyable, we have a way of finding time for it. Instead of dismissing this as an obvious point, it would be well to take a deeper look at this basic rule of motivation which every one of us is subject to.

Chapter 2

Imagery, Breathing, and Relaxation

The Opposite Approach

Teachers of various traditional skills and crafts in the Orient have always found it difficult to explain their method with words and this is why they often resort to the use of various analogies. Things which are not expressed in clear and logical terms, however, tend to be regarded as pretentious or as being a case of beating around the bush by people of this day and age. A tremendous amount of work has already gone into introducing Oriental culture in a way that is more comprehensible in terms of Western concepts by expressing things in a more straightforward fashion. Nevertheless, even if things seem simple when put into words, they can prove impossible to execute in practice. When it comes to the actual mastery of a skill, there is very little a teacher can do except point the way and let a student pick it up on his own. Otherwise the skill one learns always requires a conscious effort and remains awkward and unnatural, just as when something is learned only superficially.

Advances in the field of psychology in recent years have made it a great deal easier to accomplish this goal of explaining Oriental concepts. Scientific investigation into human psychology, which really began only in the last century, has been tremendously fruitful. Psychology progressed beyond the study of the conscious mind into the realm of the unconscious to shed light on the workings of the deeper recesses of our mind. The rapid development of psychology in the past century started with psychoanalysis and psychotherapy and eventually expanded to include humanistic psychology and parapsychology. It can be said that psychology has now reached a turning point in its inquiry which is leading toward an understanding of the unconscious. The time is ripe to turn this whole concept around. The very term unconscious was derived from the past emphasis on the study of the conscious mind. It has now become abundantly clear that the unconscious encompasses a much wider spectrum of the human psyche than the conscious mind.

Viewed in this light, it can be understood why attempts were made so often by teachers in the Orient to convey their real intention by seemingly incomprehensible allegories and allusions. It may be too much to ask of people today to accept without question such elusive analogies and descriptions which require intuition. While this may be all right for those who have studied disciplines from the Orient such as yoga, Zen, Aikido, Do-In and Chinese medicine, those uninitiated individuals attempting to learn and apply these ideas on their own are bound to experience great difficulty. For the average person nonrational explanations cause the most important part of the teaching to be misconstrued and thus the real meaning is lost.

I am proposing an approach that fills this gap in understanding between the East and West. It is the "opposite approach" which is an attitude toward living based on

Fig. 2

The Conventional Approach			The Opposite Approach		
Conscious	$\longrightarrow$	Unconscious	Biosphere	$\longrightarrow$	Individual organism
Knowledge	$\longrightarrow$	Practice	Practice	$\longrightarrow$	Understanding
Parts	$\longrightarrow$	Whole	Mental image	$\longrightarrow$	Body posture
Individual movements	$\longrightarrow$	Overall form	Movement of whole	$\longrightarrow$	Modify parts

the Oriental way of thinking (Fig. 2). Rather than intellectualizing about this alternative approach, it would be more useful to experience what I mean by trying out Imagery Exercises for yourself. The main purpose of all this preliminary discussion is to motivate you to put the exercises in this book into practice at the earliest possible moment. I feel these explanations are important in getting people to take up this new approach with a positive attitude and a correct understanding.

As it may be inferred from the title of this book, the key element of this approach is the use of "imagery," or mental pictures. The subjects of mental imagery and visualization in the field of psychology have only recently begun to receive serious attention. Although the application of visualization or "imagery" may still be limited in psychology, this approach has been proven through the centuries in the Orient and elsewhere as being invaluable for arriving at a clear understanding of truths directly related to life.

So far no agreement has been reached in academic circles concerning the exact definition of a mental image. However, it is only the Western scientific approach which holds that nothing can start until all the terms are clearly defined. In the Eastern approach, people strive for a tacit understanding of things which are beyond description in order to come to grips with their reality through actual experience without resorting to the use of words. In fact one essential characteristic of anything pertaining to life is that it cannot be understood in real terms other than through direct experience. Therefore, to make the best use of this book on Imagery Exercises, it is suggested that everything you learn be put into immediate practice so that you can experience the full depth of what is being taught. The theoretical background for this approach can be augmented in the process of application to reinforce what you have learned through experience.

Imagery in Movement

Breathing is normally an unconscious and automatic act. Nevertheless, since respiration can be controlled voluntarily to speed up or slow down breathing or to make it shallow or deep, controlling one's breathing through breathing techniques serves as an effective way of regulating the autonomic nervous system. Most breathing techniques have the common aim of inducing physical and mental relaxation through deep and quiet respiration. While a variety of breath control techniques are taught based on different approaches and perspectives, very few of them seem to work so well in actual practice. One guru in India is said to have refused to teach his special breathing technique until a person had studied with him for over a month. Apparently, he was very aware of how difficult it can be to correctly master something which seems so simple.

Although all traditional crafts and disciplines can be copied in their outward form, it takes long years of training with a teacher to master such a skill (achieving perfect synchronization of breathing and movement). It would be wonderful indeed if traditional Eastern approaches for enhancing our health and well-being could be learned through a few simple explanations. The problem with Western linguistic expression is that, while providing a detailed understanding of the shape or structure of things, it does not always effectively capture the essence of things.

Many people, even after having mastered a certain art or skill, still make the mistake of believing that one's breathing must be consciously controlled in order to learn the skill. Consciously controlled breathing, however, invariably becomes forced and unnatural. This seems to hold true for learning any kind of skill or movement. This is why I suggest that you start practicing the exercises in this book by employing the opposite approach, which takes such problems in learning into account. The whole point is to become involved in the entire process at once. Do not be concerned with trying to understand everything that is stated in the beginning. The concepts presented will make more sense after some practice. The basic approach in Zen Imagery Exercises is to visualize an image which guides your body through an exercise, rather than to consciously control your breathing and movements (Fig. 3).

Fig. 3

Overall picture of movement
↓
Directing Ki (intention)
↓
Performing the movement
↓
Correcting parts of the movement
↓
Getting a feel for the movement
↓
Graceful and effortless performance

Of course, it is quite possible to perform a certain exercise by conscious control. Nevertheless, there are clear limitations to conscious control. Compare, for example, the breath you take when you simply tell yourself "I will take a deep breath" to the breath you take when you follow a mental image of raising your arms over your head and getting a full stretch. You can see how the inhalation is much deeper and more natural with a full stretch. In the former case, your mind becomes fixed on the idea of breathing, so the mental picture is limited just to your lungs. The conscious mind does serve as an important link in creating the imagery for a particular movement, but it cannot command each and every movement. When we attempt to dictate each and every movement with our mind, these movements remain confined in the limited framework of these images. You must give up the notion that movements are made with just those parts directly connected with the movement and realize that all movements are made with the body as a whole.

Just as we are naturally alive right now, we are naturally breathing. Once we become conscious of our breathing, it is no longer natural, and we can no longer tell what the natural breathing was like. If you try to breathe deeply, then natural and truly deep breathing is not possible. Since we inhale naturally once our lungs are empty, we are not really meant to intentionally draw air into our lungs. Breathing should really start with the exhalation to prepare our body for the natural intake of air. Instead of exhaling all at once, however, exhale slowly and naturally as if voicing a sound for a long time. Perhaps now you can see how conventional methods have not been adequate for teaching such breathing techniques.

Imagery and Exercise

Professor Michizo Noguchi says that "the body, rather than moving by the control of the conscious mind, moves as a complete whole guided by mental pictures." In his exercise system the aforementioned problem with conventional approaches has been surmounted because the experiential aspect is emphasized and people are taught to be faithful to their own sensibilities. Although the Noguchi Exercise System is a great step toward popularizing more holistic exercise, it cannot be regarded as being 100 percent complete because it is based on a Western medical perspective. This is unfortunate because integrating the principle of meridians which has existed in the Orient for thousands of years would make this method more complete. This is not to imply that each approach to exercise does not have its own merits. Nevertheless, it seems that even with traditional Do-In exercises, in which "Ki is guided and balanced to stretch and limber the body," the exercises are often practiced without an understanding of meridians. Yoga also must have originally included some concept of the meridians, but only the outward forms of the *asanas* (postures) remain today and the theoretical framework for why the exercises are done the way they are seems to have been lost.

The reason this basic understanding was lost is because our culture overemphasizes the conscious mind and has become too materialistic. Even though we now understand and utilize material things with greater ease and facility, we have become very inept at coming to a direct understanding of life. In order to overcome this handicap, although the theoretical framework of Imagery Exercises is presented with words, these concepts must be integrated by practicing the exercises and correlating the ideas with your own experience and mental imagery. Exercises learned through imagery are the most true to life. Thus everyone can apply their personal experience and understanding to learn exercises with a direct bearing on life. The theoretical framework of Zen Imagery Exercises is not founded in the rational concepts of Western medicine, but instead is based on the empirical meridian principle from Oriental medicine. Thus it cannot be grasped from an intellectual standpoint alone. This is a holistic understanding of life handed down as wisdom of the ages, and it allows each one of us to recreate the "exercises of the ancient masters."

I developed these exercises so that people could liberate themselves from the fixed notions imposed by their conscious mind and rediscover ways to move their body in tune with their inner sensitivity. One of the main features of this approach is that proficiency is reached in these exercises through gaining a living understanding of the concept of meridians which has underpinned the development of Oriental medicine over its two thousand year history. My explanations of this concept may not be complete from the standpoint of specialists in the field of Oriental medicine, but will no doubt be further clarified by the work of those who have firsthand experience in this area.

Imagery Exercises may seem to be similar to other approaches in many respects, but its similarity comes from the common traits possessed by all life, and it does not come from copying the outward form. Even if a certain exercise or posture appears to be the same, when the exercise is performed based on the concepts presented here, the effects should differ greatly. It is only natural that this should happen because these exercises are designed to strengthen Ki, or the life force, within us. From the standpoint of life, the more something is truly original, the more chance it has of becoming universal. Zen Imagery Exercises is a new approach based on ancient Oriental knowledge and practices. It is important, however, that all the good features of conventional exercises be put to use in the process of learning these exercises. This way you will be able to better appreciate the value of each approach and understand the reasons behind their effectiveness. This will then bring about a transformation in the understanding and practice of the methods which you have learned previously. In other words, the results attained by all other methods available to this day are put to good use in Imagery Exercises.

Conventional psychology teaches that our mental images are constructed from information collected with our sensory organs. It is generally regarded that our dreams are all composed of material gathered from real life experiences, and this is taught as being the most plausible theory. Nevertheless, even though our eyes are similar in structure to a camera, they capture an entirely different image from that of a movie, and our ears hear something completely different from what is recorded by a tape recorder. Cameras and tape recorders do preserve very objective images and sounds, but after all, the individuals who judge this to be so are viewing and listening through the filter of their own subjective mental images. Although a purely objective picture completely separate from our subjectivity may exist, there is no way for us to confirm its existence.

Images are something which every individual organism possesses. This is generally different from imagination which originates and is maintained mostly on the conscious level. The amoeba, for example, has primitive images for its food and for enemies which all organisms possess for survival. Although such images for life are possessed by individual amoebas, they are common to the entire species because all amoebas possess a similar awareness. We as human beings tend to assume that everybody sees things in the same way, but there is no way for us to be sure that this is so. Even the meaning of words and symbols differ among individuals because these are all based on mental pictures in each individual. Society is able to stay together despite this because we are all under the impression that we perceive things in more or less the same way. Occasionally, however, we are quite surprised to learn how differently things can be viewed when we come into contact with a foreigner. There is a tremendous difference between the Japanese outlook on life and that of Westerners.

Even becoming aware of differences is in fact founded on having something in common: in the above case, a common awareness as human beings makes such a distinction possible. The Japanese have an understanding that awareness is a subjective thing with individual differences, but that awareness also brings things together to make one integrated whole. There is a word game or riddle in Japan which brings two entirely different things together and to which a third idea is added to reveal what they have in common. For example, for wheels and dice the idea that brings them together is that they both "roll."

From a logical perspective the two things first mentioned are completely different. The fixed notion about how different they are, however, can be put aside to recognize the essential oneness if there is an idea or awareness which brings the two things together. Japanese are aware through such riddles that one must look for the essence of things rather than view just the superficial features. When the conscious mind attempts to describe some image such as that of the Rorschach ink blot test, each individual comes up with something different. An experienced therapist can discern common attitudes or perspectives among various interpretations. The Rorschach test also reveals that particular societies share a common awareness. But these things can only be discerned because people have the means (essential oneness) to become aware of them.

Do not think that mental pictures are composed by your conscious mind. Naturally our conscious mind accurately defines images of the external world through our sense organs, but our consciousness is only a reflection of our state of awareness. Our conscious mind only enlarges one part of the total picture to bring it into focus. You must not forget that the source of mental imagery is in our awareness or unconscious. Thus practicing Imagery Exercises on a deep level means to give physical expression to one's essential nature.

Breathing and Movement

Just as the phrase "breath of life" is used all over the world, the word breathing is synonymous with being alive. It is only natural then that in order to live a balanced and healthy life one must learn the correct way of breathing. Ideally all methods for health should begin by teaching the right way to breathe, but this is easier said than done. In the first place, everybody breathes automatically all the time, and most people rarely if ever have any difficulty breathing. Breathing consciously just does not feel natural. No one breathes consciously all the time and, as a matter of fact, living for the most part is an unconscious process. Everyone has been breathing since the day they were born without receiving any special instructions from anyone. It is very difficult to modify behavior patterns which have been a habit for so many years. So even when a person does decide to learn a particular breathing method, it takes a long time to make it effortless and natural.

It is always difficult to grasp the gist of any special technique or skill. In Japan, the mastery of a skill is sometimes referred to as *kokyu o nomikomu* which literally means to get the breathing down. In any endeavor involving coordination, whether it is just a menial task or an artistic creation, the crucial part is always the breathing and rhythm (timing). Natural breathing automatically conforms with one's movements. When the execution of a new movement (technique) becomes natural, this means that the breathing is in perfect synchronization with the movements.

While there is no way of avoiding the difficulty involved in attaining a level of proficiency where the breathing and rhythm are smooth and natural, learning a new skill often seems to become more complicated than necessary. The main problem is that it is nearly impossible to convey the correct breathing and timing through the use of words alone. Essentially, each person has to discover the key elements in mastering any technique by himself. People who have succeeded in mastering a certain skill describe their approach by using words that they find meaningful in their own experience. What most people fail to realize is that these words, just as often as not, lead beginners astray.

When someone asks for directions over the phone, for example, the person giving directions may say something like "it's simple; all you have to do is walk straight and turn left at the corner and it's right there." Although these simple instructions seem to be enough for the person who knows the way, for one going there for the first time, there are plenty of places where one could get lost. If a newcomer gets a wrong idea about the location, he may go around in circles searching for his destination in the completely wrong place. Probably almost everybody has had a similar experience. Even a place that is very easy to find, after a person is shown the way once, can be practically impossible to find for the newcomer unless directions are given specifically with the newcomer in mind.

It is also typical for complete beginners to understand less and less, the more things are explained to them in detail. When it comes to teaching exercises for experiencing the "essence of life" most teachers do not give ample consideration to this crucial point. Words used to explain a particular set of movements normally focus on the representative parts of the overall image. Rather than learning successively by gaining a conscious control of every detail, it is better to learn movements by an overall mental picture of the whole action.

It is not enough when learning a new set of movements to be able to perform the movements perfectly. One can only consider the movements completely mastered when the breathing accompanying the movements becomes smooth and natural. Even when the breathing is controlled intentionally to match the movement, in the learning stages one tends to get the timing confused and lose the rhythm. The coordination of breathing and movement comes naturally, however, when the same movement is repeated over and over. Only then does the timing and rhythm start to feel just right.

As the saying goes, "practice makes perfect." This means that one should repeat the movements over and over until the timing and rhythm are perfected. Very few people teach that timing and rhythm are directly connected with one's breathing. This is because those people who have achieved mastery of a skill know that intentionally controlling the breath with this knowledge only hinders natural breathing and complicates the learning process.

Breathing is usually associated with taking in and letting out air from the lungs. For this reason many people regard breathing as only pulmonary respiration. The intake and release of air is not limited to just the lungs. In physiological terms external respiration with the lungs is viable only because there is a commensurate internal respiration taking place between individual cells and blood. The respiration of the skin also plays an indispensable role in sustaining life.

From another standpoint breathing is inseparable from a person's psychological state. In Japan the word *iki* is used for breath and Ki is a frequently used term which describes mental phenomena. Ki is also conceived as a force which becomes the power behind well disciplined action.

When people are taught about breathing, the first thing they usually try to do is to consciously control their breathing. When people learn a new breathing technique, they tend to think that all they need to do is to control the respiratory muscles with their mind just to get more air into the lungs. Breathing is the only life sustaining involuntary function in man that can be controlled consciously. Perhaps for this reason it is impossible to avoid the tendency of consciously controlling our breath when we become aware of it.

One reason breathing is under voluntary control is that it has the special function of integrating the whole body by adjusting its rate according to movements, especially when a new pattern of movements is being learned. After a series of separate movements have been learned by a person, breathing plays a vital role in bringing all of the individual movements together in a coordinated fashion. For a number of separate movements to flow together in sequence as one continuous movement, they have to be executed in one breath. Once any complex movement is mastered in this way, it can be performed at will with ease and grace without conscious control over every little detail.

Ki and Relaxation

The relationship between our intentions (mind) and actions (Ki) is aptly expressed in the Japanese language. Japanese people give small gifts with the words, "Ki (small acts) speaks for the heart." While a small gift or act does not fully represent one's feelings, it does convey something of one's sentiments. Generally Ki means an intangible and all perversive energy which exists everywhere. Ki is the power that animates life, and it is the force underlying the rhythm of nature, which in the human body is represented by breathing. Timing or rhythm is essential to get control of Ki. Although you can get a feeling for what Ki is like, Ki can never be pinned down. It can be compared to the atmosphere in general, such as the atmosphere of a place, the "air" about a person and especially one's feelings. As one illustration of how Ki works on a personal level, even when we are trying to "act normal" in some situation where we are trying to hide our feelings, we cannot completely conceal our feelings, and at the very least, people sense that there is "something" about our behavior which is unnatural.

Just like the phenomenon of life itself, Ki is hard to define precisely. Nevertheless, all living things draw this energy into their body and utilize it as energy indispensable for living. It is the work of the "mind," or awareness, which brings this Ki together. This function of the "mind" can be seen to operate in human beings on a basic psychological level where we easily remember things which please us, while other things which we try to keep in mind are often forgotten when our mind is distracted.

On the other hand, most of us have had the experience of not being able to get a certain thought or concern off of our mind even when we try to find distraction in sports or recreation.

It is difficult to really relax and unwind even though we may be convinced of the need to do so, because we are so used to assuming an aggressive posture in making our way through the hustle and bustle of the high-pressure society of today. This is the reason traditional Oriental practices such as yoga and Zen are now becoming popular around the world as ways to find relaxation and peace of mind. It has become recognized that being able to relax and move rhythmically is important in sports, and that relaxing enables better performance over extended periods of exertion. Our awareness works to concentrate on a particular thing and our conscious mind serves to add further emphasis by isolating a particular aspect so that we are able to exert our efforts in a specific direction. When it comes to relaxation, however, conscious effort alone is not enough. Trying to relax when you are tense rarely works, but all a person really needs to learn is that relaxing is just a matter of letting go.

There is a didactic poem in Japan which says "the Buddha (angelic) nature is to remain detached and free under all circumstances; fixation on anything, be it good or bad, is the nature of devils." The Buddha nature thus means to be free and without attachment to anything, to have no worries whatsoever, and to always have a smile on one's face (Fig. 4). The nature of a devil or demon is to be obsessed with something. Some demons are absorbed in evil deeds, but there is another kind of demon which becomes so obsessed with work that he even sacrifices his family life. If this world were to be viewed as a hell of sorts, it would be impossible for us to survive without becoming a devil after a fashion. Every morning many of us must leave our happy home behind and turn into somewhat of a demon to go to work. If we fail to do this, our loved ones might starve. But still it is not right that we continue to play the part of a work obsessed demon even after we get home at night. Once we return home, we must let go of our concerns of work to once more become a loving family member. Being a parent also requires a person to be like a devil at times. Doing homework more often than not takes an effort. Thus we may have to hound our children like the devil to fulfill their academic responsibilities. The parents' devil-like role is only a temporary one, however, and the permanent state we are all striving for is that of an angel. This is an attitude in life where we are smiling naturally and spontaneously.

Fig. 4 Angelic and Devilish Natures

Angelic	*Devilish*
night	day
relaxed	tense
unattached	obsessed
free and at ease	fixated
cheerful	serious
peaceful and restful	division and struggle
eternal and boundless	temporary and limited
unconditional love	distinguishes good and evil

Even though it may be in the devilish nature to become preoccupied with something, nothing can be accomplished without some degree of fixation. Even our muscles must become stiff and rigid in order for us to use our strength. However, if muscles are tensed before they need to be, or if any tension remains after relaxing them, the next task cannot be accomplished as well. This is why relaxation before and after exercising is so important. How can we completely relax and release all our tension? When told by someone that your shoulders are tense, your shoulders tend to become even more tense as you become conscious of them. In this case what you must do is to first tense up your shoulders intentionally and then relax them. You will find that your shoulders relax quite easily this way. Relaxing is a matter of letting go, so becoming more conscious of something is not the answer.

We often see athletes lightly exercising before they are about to begin competition. This is the best way to relieve the psychological pressure before competition. By doing something else, one's attention is temporarily diverted so that one does not become too intent on one thing. One of the best ways to relax and loosen up is to lightly move the body and breathe freely and easily. When we become tense, our breathing becomes shallow and our attention becomes fixed on one thing or place, and as a consequence our body becomes rigid and stiff.

All one really needs to do to let go of tension is to exhale slowly and completely and then resume breathing naturally and freely. When only the immediate area that is tense is massaged in order to relieve tension, this only serves to increase the tension in the long run. Tension in the neck and shoulders can become a real nuisance when one's attention becomes fixed on the stiff part of the shoulder and remains there. The best way to release such tension in your shoulders is to guide your attention away from your shoulders once you are finished using your arms. In other words, your attention must be shifted to another part. By the same token, after using your head for a certain length of time, your arms and legs have to be moved to bring your attention back to the rest of your body.

The reason exercises have become a real necessity for people in this day and age is because of the preponderance of jobs and lifestyles which demand that one's attention remain unnaturally fixed or preoccupied. There are limitations to just trying to relax by ordinary means because the established pattern of preoccupation (fixation of attention) prevents people from really letting go of their concerns. This is a crucial point which we must keep in mind when considering ways to relax.

Releasing Tension

It is necessary that one learn to release tension in order to improve the circulation of Ki and obtain a balance in basic bodily processes. Tension denotes a condition of being tight or contracted. While tension is a natural condition in response to certain situations, it usually indicates that one has become biased or preoccupied about one thing. Tension can inhibit the circulation of Ki in the body, and this is why tension is undesirable.

Naturally, when we are about to undertake something, we must direct our Ki (attention) to that object and then become tense to exert our energy for that chosen objective. The problem is that some people become so involved in their work that they are unable to set it aside and relax. Ideally the doing of work should be followed with the "undoing" of relaxation. The "undoing" of action can be described as letting go, loosening, taking off, untying, and opening up, as well as the resolution of a problem. If undoing goes too far, however, everything created by doing could be lost, spoiled, or destroyed. So undoing without any awareness is not desirable either.

Another important point in releasing tension is that you should not make a special effort to do so. You cannot really undo tension while you are trying to do something about it. If you feel tension and try to release it, just the intention of trying to get rid of it will create more tension. You should instead allow the natural solution to take effect by assuming a relaxed attitude of waiting for the tension to go away by itself. The circulation of Ki is always best when you are completely relaxed and your mind is not caught up with anything. Just relaxing and resting, however, is not sufficient to correct imbalances because the pattern of tension induced by our lifestyle tends to keep us in the same state, and the adjustments necessary for our particular type of imbalance are not made.

When you notice, however, that some part of you is tense, it is important that you just relax and leave it up to the body itself rather than become overly concerned about that particular manifestation of tension. We must give ourselves up for a while to get back in harmony with the totality of life. This is the ideal attitude for recreating a balanced and whole state mentally and physically. The condition of being totally relaxed or undone can be likened to the Buddha, or angelic, nature, where one has transcended everything to become totally detached from things of the world. The nature of Buddha is to bring salvation and peace to all beings equally. There is a tremendous feeling of release when the body is completely relaxed and everything becomes evened out. Allowing the dynamics of the whole to work out tension means to give attention to those parts which are often ignored. This is the reason the Western approach of exercising the body to build muscles, limber the joints, and improve circulation is not adequate for understanding how tension can be released through exercise.

Recently the concept of nonstrenuous exercise is becoming increasingly popular in the West. The appeal of this approach comes from the realization that improving muscular strength and flexibility of joints in a mechanical fashion by vigorous exercise does not necessarily lead to good health. Nevertheless, few people really understand why nonstrenuous exercise stressing relaxation is good for health. It is known that traditional exercises of the East like yoga, Do-In, and Tai Chi are some of the best examples of nonstrenuous exercise. It has been found that these quiet forms of exercise are very useful for improving the function of the internal organs and the autonomic nervous system. Even so most Western people have yet to realize that the Eastern concepts, which embrace the phenomenon of life, have given us methods of exercise with potential far surpassing the limited scientific approaches to exercise.

In order to really relax or undo tension in a particular area, one must first find the obstruction which is related to a deficiency of Ki, and then find a way to release the tension and blockage of Ki. The Ki deficient area, which is lacking in energy, is never clearly apparent. Therefore, it requires a certain "intuition" to find such an area. This "intuition" is the ability to see and sense the whole as one. It means to perceive the dynamics of the whole body instead of becoming preoccupied with individual parts.

In order to do this, we must give up or let go of our preconceived notions or ideas. In other words, it requires that one be able to set aside one's ego and narrow self-interests.

Imagery Breathing

Almost everyone has the preconception that breathing is to breathe air in and out of the lungs and think that this can be done consciously by simply moving the respiratory muscles. Some approaches for health emphasize abdominal breathing, and deep breathing is supposed to be accomplished by moving the abdominal muscles. There is nothing wrong with such an approach, but this causes a person to become preoccupied with the abdominal muscles and could produce undue tension in the abdominal wall. In some Oriental exercises one is taught to concentrate on the center point just below the navel, the so-called *tanden* or *hara*, but most people find it difficult to pinpoint exactly where this is. The *tanden* has been explained as the center point of an imaginary sphere superimposed on the pelvic cavity, but many people find this difficult to understand. Placing the center of gravity in one's pelvic region and balancing all movements around this is said to be important in coordinating movements of the whole body. Be that as it may, it is not so easy to get a feel for this.

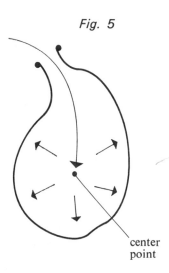

Fig. 5

center
point

For the sake of learning Imagery Breathing set these Oriental concepts of centering energy aside for the moment and just picture your whole body as one big balloon (Fig. 5). A simple way to conceptualize the lungs would be to imagine a balloon hanging inside a bottle with the mouth of the balloon overlapping that of the bottle. The balloon inflates naturally when the internal pressure of the bottle is reduced.

To do Imagery Breathing, however, you must visualize not just the lungs but the whole body as being one large balloon. This image has little to do with the anatomical or external features of the human body. In the Noguchi Exercise System, it is taught that our body is simply organs and bones suspended in an aqueous solution which is contained in a big sack of skin.

In terms of how it actually feels to be living and breathing in our body, however, even the oversimplified description above may still be too concerned with physical structure. Just close your eyes for a minute and experience what it feels like to be inside your body. Aside from the feeling of weight on the hips when sitting, or on the bottom of the feet when standing, the only thing that can be felt is some vague boundary between the body and outside. No individual structures such as the muscles, bones, or organs can be felt. Perhaps all that you can feel is the slight movement of expansion and contraction caused by your breathing. If any particular part comes to your awareness, this indicates an abnormal condition.

Ignore any such sensations for the time being and just imagine air coming in and filling up the balloon that is your body. As air comes in, the balloon will expand on all sides; the center of this force pushing out to all sides is the *hara*. There is no exact center point as such; all you need to feel is a focal point in the center of your lower abdomen that seems to be the point from which the air is expanding outward.

In Imagery Breathing our bodies should be visualized as being something like a balloon. If you do not like the image of your body as a balloon because it is too flimsy and apt to break, you can imagine it as being like an inflatable vinyl doll instead. What would be even more realistic as an image of the body would be to picture the seams in this vinyl doll at the back where the spine is. The back does usually feel much less elastic. If this all seems too complicated, you can just visualize your body as a large plastic bag shaped something like the one shown in the figure below (Fig. 6).

Now that you have a living image for your body, gradually expand your body from the bottom up as you inhale and keep inhaling until you are completely filled to your head. Stop your breathing momentarily and allow your limbs to fill out with the air pressure which has been built up. Then as you begin to exhale and allow this air to escape, imagine that you are slowly shrinking like a balloon. After the balloon is empty, just pause and relax briefly in the deflated condition. This is all there is to Imagery Breathing. The body is visualized as a balloon or vinyl doll and the *hara* is the center from where air pushes outward.

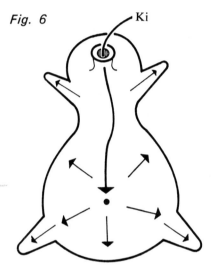

Fig. 6   Ki

Although psychology deals with the conscious and the unconscious, there is no adequate explanation when it comes to mental images. All our behavior is a result of either conscious or unconscious motivation, and of these two, behavior controlled by our conscious mind or intellect is considered to be the most advanced. But when we think about it, organisms have always behaved in an effective manner to adapt to their environment from the very beginning—long before there was any distinction between conscious and unconscious. This adaptive mechanism or "mind" must have somehow been integrated with the whole organism to fulfill its purpose. We can suppose that the amoeba has a "mind" or image suited to an amoeba and behaves accordingly. It is conceivable that a particular image or behavioral mold is a result of the integration of a certain organic structure with the life energy animating it. In Japan this energy is called Ki. All organisms as manifestations of life are kept alive only by existing within a greater order of life. Nevertheless, each individual organism possesses an independent image and is under the impression that it is acting on its own.

Although we have classified organisms into a hierarchy according to their structure and external appearance, when it comes to the actual feeling or subjective perception of being alive, it may be possible that amoebas and human beings are basically no different. The possibility of human beings being essentially the same as amoebas may be easier to comprehend when comparing the awareness of an newborn infant to that of an amoeba. The environmental conditions and level of adaptation are naturally of a higher order and far more complex for an infant than for an amoeba. However, as far as the fundamental issue of living is concerned, man is nothing more than another variation on the same theme of life; essentially there is no difference. The need to follow an image for characteristic behavioral molds is the same for an amoeba as it is for man, and in both cases the image serves as a mold which disposes the body to move in certain ways whenever energy is directed.

Conscious awareness must have developed in the course of evolution so that the orientation, or the focus, of this image could be refined to open up new possibilities and offer a greater range of choices. This was most likely to offer more freedom in altering patterns of behavior for adaptation. Yet the basic mechanism of using imagery to guide behavior has remained essentially the same all through evolution. Nevertheless, we human beings tend to believe that we can control all our actions with our conscious mind. The reason for the difficulty in getting the timing (breathing) just right when first learning a new set of movements lies precisely in this misunderstanding. It seems that everyone has completely overlooked the vital role of imagery in integrating separate movements into a continuous whole.

Once you begin to practice Imagery Breathing and repeat it over and over, you will come to realize how the action of exhaling and inhaling comprise one whole unit or "image" as one breath. Although it is really more natural to exhale first and then to inhale, when a person breathes consciously, the inhalation always seems to come first. Since Imagery Breathing is designed to make things simple, the inhalation is put first and therefore, Imagery Breathing begins by the body filling up with air (see Fig. 7). Stopping the breath after filling up completely is just for providing a brief pause. When the breath is stopped consciously, there is a tendency to hold the breath. This is the reason a mental picture where air continues to fill out the arms and legs is visualized after the intake of air is stopped. After a brief pause, the air is allowed to escape by itself until the body is completely emptied. Then one relaxes and pauses breathing momentarily before letting air flow back into the body.

The center of gravity or the focal point of Ki is the center point of an organism. In Imagery Breathing, the focal point of Ki is the center of the belly rather than the chest. The best way to breathe fully is to be aware of this center point in the lower abdomen by fixing your attention on this area.

So far I have explained breathing only in terms of letting air in and out, but I chose to explain it this way just to keep things simple. The exchange of life energy, or Ki, with the atmosphere has therefore been described by the word "breathing." Essentially the same thing is taught in most other approaches to breath control, and the exchange of vital energy is described simply as breathing mostly because of the ambiguity of Eastern terms. Nevertheless, some people may become confused when told to draw a deep breath down into their lower abdomen (hara), because in terms of human anatomy air cannot go below the diaphragm. Would it seem any more strange if we talked about amoebas breathing? Just as fish have their special means of respiration, amoebas also have a way of breathing as an animal species.

The real benefits of breathing techniques are usually misconstrued just because

Fig. 7

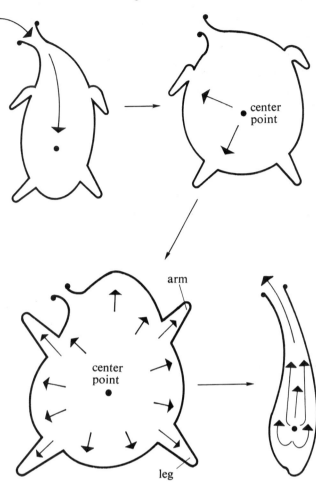

A—The balloon begins to fill up from the bottom.
B—The balloon expands with air pressure from the center.
C—Arms and legs fill out during pause in breathing.
D—Air is released until the balloon is completely empty.

respiration is usually understood only as the absorption of oxygen and the release of carbon dioxide. The lungs are by far the most efficient organs for respiration, but a more primitive form of respiration through the body surface still remains intact in humans as skin respiration. Considering breathing as just a specialized function of the lungs is a misconception resulting from Western medicine, which places too great an emphasis on anatomical features. Since breathing is the most visible manifestation of the exchange of Ki with our environment, it is often used to illustrate all other types of energetic exchanges. Ancient people most likely experienced and understood breathing as taking in the vital energy of nature. If you only recall what it is like to have a big yawn, it is easy to understand how, instead of just the respiratory organs, your whole body is involved in breathing.

The breathing techniques taught in Zen and yoga for quiet meditation are very useful for mastering Imagery Breathing. In meditation special attention is paid to breathing to induce deep relaxation so that one may experience a more profound level of existence. This kind of breathing is usually much slower and deeper than that when one is sound asleep. Individuals who live life at a frantic pace in this modern age and accumulate stress stand to gain a great deal from learning this kind of breathing technique. If you practice Imagery Breathing in a relaxed and unhurried manner whenever you have some time to yourself, this will give you a deeper appreciation of what it means to be alive, which will also give you greater pleasure in living.

The images or models presented in this book for breathing or for exercises do not have to be copied down to every last detail. The important thing is that your body quietly takes in and then lets out Ki, the energy of the universe. The often used image of expelling impure or unclean air and drawing in fresh and pure air is not so useful. Clean and dirty are no more than our subjective judgments. For plants the air we breathe out is good clean air full of life giving carbon dioxide.

In ancient times Chinese said that people near death breathed through their nose only, while sick persons breathed with their shoulders, and ordinary people breathed with their chest. Wise men were said to breathe with their belly, and masters from the soles of their feet. This means that the lower the focal point of one's breathing, the more an individual has *ochitsuki* (Japanese for settled or stable Ki) or composure, and the more he can breathe with his whole body. Abdominal breathing is what wise individuals strive for, but even this is not the ultimate way to breathe. The ideal to work toward is a mental image of drawing in and sending out Ki from the tips of our fingers and toes. The images presented in this book are simply suggestions. Mental images which are alive and dynamic are never quite the same for any two individuals, and this is how each and every living entity retains its unique and individual characteristics.

Chapter 3

The Principles of Meridian Exercise

Health in the Orient

The *Yellow Emperor's Classic of Internal Medicine* (*Neijing*), consisting of two parts, the *Suwen* and *Lingshu*, is the oldest text on Chinese medicine and many people even regard it as being the Bible of Oriental medicine. This text deals mainly with the fundamental theories underlying the application of acupuncture and moxibustion.*
In one section of the *Suwen*, the Yellow Emperor asks the court physician, "Why do physicians treat the same sickness with different methods?" The royal physician Chi-Po responds, "Treatment varies according to the region in which the sick person lives." Thus in the *Suwen*, the origin of different remedies is attributed to the differences in climate, diet, and lifestyle in each region (Fig. 8). According to the *Suwen*

Fig. 8   Origins of Chinese Medical Practices

	North	

cold steppe (dairy products)
chills, coughs—*Moxibustion*

West	Center	East

mountainous region (meat)
organ dysfunction—*Herbal medicine*

plains and cities (varied diet)
paralysis, alternating chills
and fever—*Do-in and Ankyo*

ocean side (fish and salty foods)
boils, abcesses—*Surgical instruments*

	South	

humid flat lands (fermented foods)
spasms, cramps—*Acupuncture*

* Acupuncture and moxibustion are two different methods of treatment in Oriental medicine which utilize acupuncture points. Acupuncture involves the insertion of needles and moxibustion involves burning small amounts of moxa on or near certain points. In Japanese and Chinese, one word is used to mean both acupuncture and moxibustion. The constant use of both words in English is cumbersome so only the one word acupuncture is used to refer to both acupuncture and moxibustion.

surgical tools originated in the east, acupuncture in the south, herbal medicines in
the west, and moxibustion in the north. The origin of Do-In and Ankyo (exercises
for health) are attributed to the more cultured people in the central plains, who ate
a varied diet.

Do (導) of Do-In means to open up channels and facilitate the movement of energy
along specific routes. *In* (引) of Do-In means to move and stretch one's limbs to
achieve this purpose. In *Ishinpo*, Japan's oldest medical text, Do-In exercises are
described as being effective in dispelling various ill Ki and reinstating healthy Ki.
An (按) of Ankyo means to massage the energy channels to balance the flow of Ki,
and *Kyo* (蹻) means to raise the limbs with smooth movement of the joints. Ankyo
can be compared to the various manipulative techniques in existence today. In
both Do-In and Ankyo the purpose is to improve the circulation of Ki, which is
the foundation of life. In the case of Do-In, however, this is done personally by
physical movement and exercising, while in the case of Ankyo it involves massage or
manipulation by another person, similar to shiatsu or other forms of therapy for
adjusting the body's alignment.

In Japan there are also the words Brahman Do-In and Indian Anma (massage)
which indicate that Do-In and Ankyo were originally brought to China from India.
These, rather than being therapeutic practices, originated more as spiritual practices
for attaining eternal youth. It is written in classics that "Do-In is a method practiced
by ascetics and Taoists of old which enable a person to stay young and strong and
develop supernatural powers and attain eternal youth. By practicing this everyday
without fail, a person can live to be more than a thousand years old and exist side
by side with wizards." Do-In is known to have included breathing techniques for
calming the mind through breath control together with spiritual exercises and meditation just as in Zen and yoga. In addition to these practices, the Taoists advocated
body work, both alone and with assistance, using pressure, friction, and structural
alignment techniques, as well as the alchemical concoction of elixirs.

Why is it that the various methods of therapy in Chinese medicine are all attributed
to outlying regions while Do-In and Ankyo alone are ascribed to the heart of China?
It is possible to assume that the various folk remedies practiced in the outlying regions came together in the central region and that these practices were organized into
a medical system based on the principle of meridians discovered through the practice
of Do-In and Ankyo. The remedies involving the use of various implements and substances were each developed individually by trial and error based on their effectiveness. The principle of meridians, on the other hand, most likely originated as a
complete system from exercising which involved experiencing the movement of energy
in the whole body. The discovery of the meridians was possible because of the per-
ceptiveness of the ancient Chinese and their deep understanding of life based on a
close relationship to nature. This could be the reason the principle of meridians contains the fundamental perspective for viewing all aspects of life, and it can be used
to explain and systematize a variety of different methods.

In spite of Do-In and Ankyo being given the central position among Chinese
medical practices because of their contribution of the meridian principle, these exercise systems became increasingly obscure in the course of time. Very few practices

which resemble Ankyo remain in Japan today except Anma massage, in which the skin is rubbed and muscles are kneaded to work out tension. Do-In eventually developed into a cult of mysticism using various esoteric methods to seek eternal youth. All that remains of Do-In today is a number of health practices which have become removed from the fundamental principle of meridians.

The contention of some historians that the mysticism of ancient China is not exactly the same as Do-In and Ankyo is not completely unfounded. According to the "Yiwenzhi," an index of publications in China some two thousand years ago, there were 7 schools and 216 texts for acupuncture, 11 schools and 274 texts for herbal medicine, 8 schools and 186 texts concerning sexual practice, and 10 schools and 205 volumes on remedial exercises such as Do-In. Among all this literature, only the 18 volumes of the *Yellow Emperor's Classic of Internal Medicine* remain today. Confucius wrote as follows about remedial exercises: "The purpose of exercises in mysticism is to preserve the essence of life by seeking expression in outward form. A person must continuously exert his will to remain calm and harmonize the forces of life and death, and not hold any worldly concerns in his heart. Even so, there seem to be those who make a business of teaching methods for longevity and increasingly these practices are taking on the disguise of deceptive mystique. These are not the teachings of the wise men of old."

Thus, even in the time of Confucius (around 500 B.C.) the practices of mysticism were diverging from the original teachings. "Preserving the essence of life by seeking expression in outward form" seems to relate to the "movement of essence* and the transformation of Ki" mentioned in the *Yellow Emperor's Classic of Internal Medicine*. In any case, what started out as a dynamic approach for fathoming the essence of life soon became a mystical practice reserved for occultists.

The "movement of essence and transformation of Ki" is described as being an ancient approach to health, not relying on acupuncture or herbal prescriptions. Many of the approaches to health propounded today are no less deceptive or mystical than those of ancient China. I have long felt the need to revive the correct way of exercising for health as originally taught by the sages of ancient China. After much study and reflection I arrived at the conclusion that the roots of shiatsu can be traced all the way back to Do-In and Ankyo in ancient China and that the very reason such exercises for health were given the central position among all forms of therapy in China was their role in the discovery of the meridians. I am now convinced that the principle of meridians is far more fundamental and universal than applied in acupuncture. This conclusion also became the basis for my discovery that all twelve meridians exist in each limb. The modern version of Do-In and Ankyo presented in this book as Zen Imagery Exercises are founded on an understanding of these twelve meridians. I am certain that these exercises are true to the spirit of the original "mystical practices" taught by the sages of old.

* In Oriental medicine essence is the ground substance which makes all organic life possible. Essence is derived prenatally from one's parents and after birth it is obtained from the nourishing elements in the "Ki of heaven" (air) and the "Ki of earth" (food and water). The kidneys are the vital organs which store and release the refined essence necessary to the body.

There is a set of traditional Chinese exercises called Wuchin, or "the exercises of five animals," which is said to have been invented by the ancient Chinese physician Huato (A.D. 110–207). The five animals imitated in these exercises are the tiger, deer, bear, monkey, and bird. The following is written concerning these exercises: "The aim of Wuchin is to prevent aging by stretching the body and flexing the joints. Diseases can be effectively alleviated through these exercises. When one is not feeling well, it is beneficial to take the time to do these exercises and work up a sweat. By the time one's forehead is covered with beads of sweat, the body will be light and one's appetite will have returned. If these exercises are done regularly, the eyes and ears will remain clear and one's teeth will stay firm past the age of ninety."

In Hatha Yoga the postures of various exercises are named after such things as a standing tree, a cobra, a plow, a fish, and a ring. These postures are not named like this simply to make them easier to remember. Rather it is by using these names and utilizing their images that one can avoid the mistake of performing these exercises with too much emphasis on one part of the body. Also holding a certain posture for a while has the beneficial effect of enhancing the function of the meridians. The main aim in yoga as well as in Zen Imagery Exercises is not to copy postures or movements in part, but to form an image of the entire movement so as to facilitate the flow of energy through the whole body and enhance the function of the meridians.

Zen Imagery Exercises is an Oriental approach to exercise, done in a slow and relaxed manner, compared to the Western approach of strenuously exercising to build strength. If the Oriental approach of not forcing movements and not being concerned about the flexibility of individual parts sounds new and strange to you, it just means that the Western approach is deeply ingrained in you. In contrast to Western civilization, which developed through struggles to overcome harsh natural conditions, Oriental cultures generally developed in more temperate climates where being in the right position to receive the dispensations of nature was all that was necessary for a good life. It is not hard to see how such a difference developed in attitudes toward health in the East and the West.

Meridian Exercises

The "meridian exercises," which I originally developed based on the precept of "oneness of mind and body," have become quite popular as a unique method for health, and I have received many reports about their wonderful benefits. Meridian exercises are also being performed in foreign countries by groups engaged in the practice of Zen and shiatsu, and these exercises have gained widespread acceptance as preparatory exercises for meditation.

The real purpose of this book is to get the reader to place the primary emphasis on practice rather than theory and to go deeper into theory only after experiencing these methods. Therefore, the significance of the meridians should be studied in depth later. The concept of meridians is nevertheless basic to Oriental medicine, and when illnesses are treated by applying the principle of meridians, great benefits can be obtained from their seemingly unexplainable effects. What the meridians really are is still a mystery, even to those who practice Oriental medicine.

In the classics of Chinese medicine it is written that the meridians are the flow of Ki and Ketsu.* What was really meant by Ki and Ketsu is difficult to say, but I consider them to be something akin to the gaseous and liquid states of the essential matter on which life is based. These words mostly refer to functional states, or the dynamics of energy, and not physical substances. When we recall that Ki is a central concept in the Oriental perspective which addresses life (instead of inert matter), it is inferred that life was viewed in terms of flow and circulation (of energy).

The Imagery Exercises, which are all meridian exercises, are a way to experience this dynamic of life through exercise. The meridians are a concept that is completely foreign to Western medicine, which is based largely on the detailed study of physical structure. Traditionally meridians were held to have functions but no substantial structure because they cannot be seen or felt by most people.

There is said to have once been a staunch materialist who carefully dissected a corpse from head to toe and announced that he found no soul. Even the existence of life itself would be difficult to prove just by dissection. The soul can be regarded as a manifestation of life for the very same reason that it does not show up in the dissection of a dead body. In a similar way, the meridians also being untraceable anatomically give evidence that meridians are very intimately connected with the phenomenon of life.

As stated earlier, everything that lives possesses some kind of awareness of being alive. One way to objectively interpret the condition of a living entity is its posture. All the different varieties and functional modes of living things can be distinguished by characteristic postures. In human beings, posture reflects people's attitude and reveals their intentions before action is taken. Posture changes with the movement of Ki, so the state of Ki can be observed in a person's posture. Since Ki moves before the body does, when this initiative is "nipped in the bud," the action itself is checked. When Ki is "held up" because movement is inhibited, it can become stuck or obstructed as pent-up energy. This in turn can cause stiffness in the part that was meant to be moved and other movements become clumsy and awkward as a consequence.

In Japanese becoming overly concerned or obsessed with something is referred to as "Ki becoming captivated." When Ki becomes stuck in one place, the flow of Ki throughout the entire body is affected. Disease results when such obstructions in Ki reach a certain order of magnitude. For this reason, in Japan tension and stiffness have traditionally been referred to as the cause of all disease. The deterioration of a physical function is called a functional disorder, and it is easy to understand how further deterioration in function will eventually become manifest as an organic or structural disorder. For the person with the stiffness or muscular tension, this condition is difficult to recognize in the early stages. Furthermore, there are few books available which will tell you which functions were impaired in the first place to cause the stiffness. These meridian exercises are a simple way to find out for yourself.

---

* Ketsu (Xue in Chinese) is often mentioned together with Ki to refer to the flow of energy and fluids in the body. Ketsu can sometimes be interpreted to mean just blood, but it often refers to other liquid constituents of the body.

What Are the Meridians?

The reason the concept of meridians (otherwise known as channels and collaterals) is difficult to grasp for some people is probably due to its association with acupuncture and moxibustion. Meridians can best be understood as pathways for the circulation of Ki, or subtle energy, which exists in everyone. Aside from acupuncture, Do-In, Anma (traditional Japanese massage), and Chinese herbal medicine all aim to cure sickness and restore health by improving the flow of energy along the meridians. The central concept in Oriental medicine is that all physical problems are a result of obstructions in the flow of Ki and that restoring this circulation serves to cure all diseases.

The word Ki is all pervasive within the Japanese language and it is generally used in reference to one's physical, emotional, or mental state. A few examples are, *kimochi* (feeling; literally "how one holds Ki"), *genki* (to feel well; literally "to have essential Ki"), and *kinodoku* (pitiful or, "injurious to one's Ki"). This concept of Ki or subtle energy is not only confined to that in human beings but also encompasses all phenomena in nature. This is exemplified by the Japanese words *tenki* (weather; literally "Ki of heaven"), *kuki* (air; literally "empty Ki"), and *denki* (electricity; literally "Ki of lightening"). Thus Ki can be understood as an expression for the dynamic interplay of living forces in nature as well as in human beings. The reason the concept of Ki, which pervades the Japanese language, became disassociated with the idea of the circulation of energy along specific channels in the body is due in part to the high degree of specialization in acupuncture.

The circulation of Ki is something which takes place in all forms of life. Therefore, this concept can be applied to a primitive single-celled animal like the paramecium (Fig. 9). The protozoans display movement in their protoplasm and this movement ceases as soon as they die, although their cellular material remains intact for a while after death. It has been suggested that the movement of protoplasm in higher animals extends beyond the limit of the cell membranes to constitute a primitive system of overall regulation, which came before the development of the circulatory, nervous, and endocrine systems for regulating the whole organism. It can be assumed that this

Fig. 9

single-celled organism

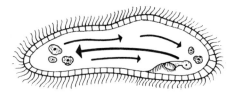

The movement of protoplasm enables:
- transport of cellular material
- transmission of biological information
- basic life functions (e.g., ingestion, elimination, locomotion)

primitive system remains functional in the more highly evolved forms of life. The primary reason such movement of protoplasm has not been studied in depth for large and complex organisms is due to the difficulty of observing this movement while they are still alive.

Meridians and the movement of protoplasm in a single-celled organism are the same thing called by different names. We can regard amoebas as also having meridians, since amoebas live by the movement of protoplasm and exist as independent living entities. Amoebas perform the basic life functions of locomotion, ingestion, elimination, and reproduction, and are also capable of defensive reactions like higher forms of life such as human beings. All these basic life functions depend on the working of the meridians. This implies that the movement of Ki, which sustains life, is revealed in an observable form by the structure and movement of the body.

We all know that animals move by the concerted action of the nervous and musculoskeletal systems. Yet primitive organisms without these structures are capable of locomotion as well as other basic functions. The action of Ki is one thing all organisms have in common. Thus even the more complex mechanism of movement in human beings is subject to the action of Ki. The biochemical and biophysical mechanisms set into motion by the action of Ki are related to specialized structures to effect a division of labor, and this enables us to carry out various vital functions including movement.

The insight of the ancient Chinese drew attention to the action of Ki, and this was eventually systematized into twelve meridians grouped into six Yin and Yang pairs. Viewing the embryonic development of animals, the inseminated egg develops from a most simple functional and structural form into a blastula, which consists of an ectoderm, mesoderm, and endoderm (Fig. 10). This model provides a clue as to why the action of Ki may have been classified as it was into six pairs or twelve meridians.

Fig. 10   Embryonic Development

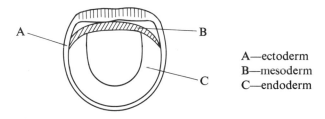

A—ectoderm
B—mesoderm
C—endoderm

One definition of a living organism is that it has some form of boundary which separates its internal and external environment and that this membrane serves to protect the integrity of the organism. In the early stages of embryonic development in higher animals, the mass of stem cells curl up and form a pocket (to contain a small portion of the outside) and the result is the endoderm (which later becomes the internal organs). The part of the embryo which remains directly exposed to the external environment forms the ectoderm (later to become the skin), which serves to provide information about the environment. The mesoderm consists of the area between the inner and outer layers and provides structural support (later becom-

Fig. 11   The Functions of the Twelve Meridians

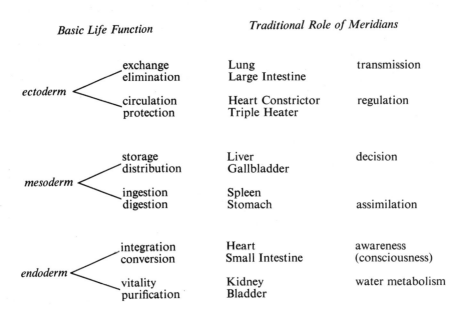

Basic Life Function		Traditional Role of Meridians	
ectoderm	exchange elimination	Lung Large Intestine	transmission
	circulation protection	Heart Constrictor Triple Heater	regulation
mesoderm	storage distribution	Liver Gallbladder	decision
	ingestion digestion	Spleen Stomach	assimilation
endoderm	integration conversion	Heart Small Intestine	awareness (consciousness)
	vitality purification	Kidney Bladder	water metabolism

ing muscles and skeleton). These three layers are just structural specializations of three basic modes of functions which exist in the most primitive single-celled organisms. These three modes of function represented by the ectoderm, mesoderm, and endoderm are thus foundational to all living things.

The ectoderm serves as the interface between the external environment and the organism (exchange, elimination) and communicates to the inside any changes on the outside to protect the body (circulation, protection). The mesoderm serves not only as structural support but also as the mechanism for movement. So on one hand the mesoderm is concerned with the intake and distribution of the energy source—food—(ingestion, digestion), while on the other hand it controls this vital supply of energy by distributing and storing it throughout the body (storage, distribution). The endoderm works to convert and integrate energy taken in from the environment (conversion, integration) and further regulates functions in different parts of the body by controlling the supply of energy and variously activating or inhibiting each part (vitality, purification).

The twelve meridians in Yin-Yang pairs are responsible for six basic modes of function which can be further divided into twelve essential functions as shown in Fig. 11. Six of the essential functions are associated with the six Yang meridians and organs, which are related to the more superficial areas of the body, and the other six functions are associated with the six Yin meridians and organs, which are related to deeper areas in the body.

The Lung and Large Intestine Meridians control exchange of Ki and elimination, while the Heart Constrictor and Triple Heater Meridians provide circulation and protection. These four meridians, which are related to the ectoderm, interact with the external environment. The Spleen and Stomach Meridians are associated with ingestion and digestion, while the Liver and Gallbladder Meridians control the storage and distribution of energy and nutrients in the body. These four meridians, which are related to the mesoderm, support the physical structures on the inside and outside and function in connection with physical movement. The Heart and Small Intestine Meridians are responsible for integration and conversion, while the Kidney and Bladder Meridians supply vitality and purify essence. These four meridians, which are related to the endoderm, coordinate the function of the various organs.

The order of energy flow through the above twelve meridians starts in the Lung Meridian and goes in succession through the Large Intestine, Stomach, Spleen, Heart, Small Intestine, Bladder, Kidney, Heart Constrictor, Triple Heater, Gallbladder, and Liver Meridians.

The order of energy circulation through the meridians is said to follow the principle of Yin and Yang. But no one has offered a satisfactory explanation of how the Yin-Yang principle was applied to determine the order of energy circulation through the meridians. The only explanation offered regarding this question is that the ancient Chinese found this to be so from their accumulated experience. Considering the sequence of meridians to be a mystery wrapped up in ancient Chinese philosophy, however, does not get us anywhere. One of my aims in this book is to explain the vital role of the meridians in all aspects of life and to make them more comprehensible in terms of contemporary concepts and thinking. The rationale behind the order of the meridians becomes clearer in the process of learning how they are each related to essential functions. Understanding why the energy circulates through the meridians in the order it does allows us to appreciate the profound insight the ancient Chinese had into the fundamental principles of life.

It has been scientifically established that the development of a new organism is marked by the formation of a membrane or cell wall, which separates its internal environment from the external environment. The function of the Lung and Large Intestine Meridian in exchanging life energy (Ki) across such a membrane or skin can be understood as giving them the first role in life. Also, considering that the Lung Meridian governs the function of respiration, which is one of the primary ways to confirm the existence of life, it seems natural that this pair of meridians come first.

The Stomach and Spleen Meridians, which come next, perform a vital role in keeping an organism alive by digesting food. It makes sense that these meridians are next in line of energy flow since digestion and assimilation of food taken in from the environment is an absolute necessity if an organism is to continue growing. The Heart Meridian, which controls the entire organism from the center, comes after the Stomach and Spleen Meridians. At the same time as an organism forms a boundry between itself and the external world, it must form a center within itself. Under the control of the heart with a central integrating function, digested food is converted into usable substances for the body. The Kidney and Bladder Meridians, which follow, facilitate the further refinement of digested materials to transform them into vital components (essence) necessary for various organ systems. After this, the Heart Constrictor and Triple Heater Meridians carry out the will of the Heart Meridian by transporting the refined substances to all parts of the body to nourish and protect it. The Liver and Gallbladder Meridians are last in line, and they store these substances and release them where necessary to meet physiological demands. One cycle of energy circulation through the meridians is complete when the energy from the Liver Meridian returns to the Lung Meridian. Here respiration is adjusted according to the functional state of all the other meridians and organs and the whole cycle is repeated.

In the *Yellow Emperor's Classic of Internal Medicine*, all the Yin organs* are equated to top officials in the imperial government. In Chinese philosophy the ideal government serves the people to make their labors fruitful. This is quite different from the usual notion of the government being an authority which exercises power to control and regulate people's lives. Traditionally the emperor of China held the position of supreme power, but his real responsibility was to bring peace and happiness to the lives of his subjects. In China the best government was regarded as that which allowed people to pursue happiness in their own lives. In the ideal society people would rejoice in their ruler by saying "Your Majesty, there is nothing that is not possible for us." When the emperor was no longer able to serve this role, a revolution would occur and the "Mandate of Heaven" would go to someone else. Even the highest position of emperor was just an official position, so naturally all lesser positions existed only to serve the nation as a whole.

Problems in the execution of official duties are sometimes misconstrued as being the fault of the official (organ). If disease were to be considered from the standpoint of Western medicine, the role of organs (officials) would be more important. In this case the meridians would exist as channels for adjusting any dysfunctions in the organs, and acupuncture points would be the points most effective for this purpose. However, the exact opposite is true when the traditional Chinese analogy of the body as a nation is applied. Physical problems begin with imbalances in the supply of Ki (motivation) to the cells of the body (citizens) along the meridians, and consequently an organ (official) is held responsible and its function becomes impaired. The resultant physical disturbance in turn demands that the whole body pitch in to rectify the situation. This is the correct viewpoint regarding the true relationship between meridians and their corresponding organs.

* In Oriental medicine there are twelve organs which correspond to the regular meridians, thus six of them are Yin organs and the other six are Yang organs. The Yin organs are dense or solid organs while Yang organs are hollow organs. The five Yin Organs, the lungs, heart, spleen, liver, and kidneys, are the primary organs in Oriental medicine.

Chapter 4

The Function of Meridians

Lung and Large Intestine Meridians

Fig. 12

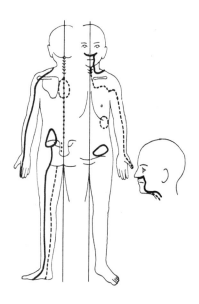

----- Lung
——— Large Intestine

The Lung and Large Intestine Meridians (Fig. 12) are associated with the functions of exchange and elimination. This, in other words, is to cope with the external environment and take in the Ki (energy) of nature and to eliminate those substances which have become unnecessary. There is a Yin-Yang complementarity between these meridians because the lungs take in the fine essence of air and the large intestine processes grosser materials. Both of these meridians lie close to the surface of the body to play the vital role of exchanging energy with the outside world. Abnormalities in these meridians generally appear first in the skin or nose. A person's complexion is also closely related to his vitality or state of health, which is dependent on proper respiratory function. The lungs and large intestine are also associated with the whites of the eyes as well as the throat, the anus, skin respiration, and the pores (excretion of sweat).

The lungs take in from the external environment the vital Ki component essential for survival and refines and distributes this to activate the adaptive response of the body. This function is seen most clearly in the process of respiration, where oxygen exchange and elimination of carbon dioxide takes place. Respiration, in turn, is closely related with brain function and exerts a profound influence on one's state of mind. In the classics of Oriental medicine the role of the lungs is equated to that of a Prime Minister, who is responsible for managing external affairs as well as keeping order in domestic affairs. This was an ingenious way of describing respiration as being essential to internal regulation while also being intimately connected with outward action. The Lung Meridian comes to its end point at the tip of the thumb. Thus, when the thumbs are clenched, Ki is withheld and when they are held wide open, it becomes easier to breathe deeply and the person feels more expanded.

Fig. 13

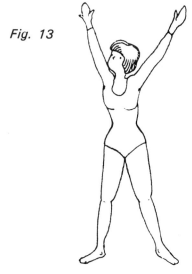

When imbalances occur in the Lung Meridian, one often becomes depressed and the chest starts to feel congested. There is a loss of vigor and one may begin to sigh. The head feels heavy and the back and shoulder area become stiff. Melancholy sets in and one tends to remain closed off from others. Eventually one will experience dizziness and coughing as respiratory diseases such as colds, asthma, and bronchitis set in. Gas poisoning and convulsive fits in children are also associated with the Lung Meridian.

The large intestine aids the lungs and functions to process and eliminate food substances taken into the body. This is the action which serves to clear obstructions of Ki. In the classics of Chinese medicine the large intestine is called the "official of transmission," and its role is that of an official who transmits the will of the Prime Minister by expressing it in terms of practical action. In psychological terms withholding of emotions, or keeping one's feelings to oneself, has an effect on the large intestine. The release of gas when this happens can symbolically be interpreted as letting go of one's pent-up emotions. When the function of the Large Intestine Meridian is impaired, one has difficulty in finding psychological release, and since this tendency is often accompanied by shallow breathing, the lack of exercise only increases this tendency. This in turn leads to physical symptoms of constipation, chilling of extremities (poor circulation), and too much blood going to the head (hotness of the head and dizziness).

When imbalances occur in the Large Intestine Meridian, one tends to lose motivation and there is insufficient intake and elimination of Ki due to lack of exercise. This condition eventually leads to diseases of the respiratory tract, which includes the nose, throat, tonsils, and windpipe (trachea). It can also cause chills and rigors, chilling of the lower abdomen, and diarrhea. One's complexion tends to become pale and his skin becomes sensitive and susceptible to infection. Furthermore, hemorrhoids, bloodshot eyes, pain and difficulty in moving the thumb, and a feeling of weakness or pain in one's back, are all associated with imbalances in the Large Intestine Meridian.

When the action of the Lung and Large Intestine Meridians are pictured as movement of the body, the mental image of a person stretching and yawning to get a deep breath can be conceived as representing the action of Ki in these meridians (Fig. 13). When the above posture is assumed, the tension that forms in the body is along the lines of the Lung and Large Intestine Meridians. In acupuncture, several key points are chosen for needle stimulation along these meridian lines to restore the balance of Ki. In Imagery Exercises the entire length of these meridians are stretched to balance the Ki.

Spleen and Stomach Meridians

The Spleen and Stomach Meridians (Fig. 14) are associated with the functions of ingestion and digestion, which involve the intake of food for nourishment and the processes of digestion and assimilation. The "spleen" of the Spleen Meridian is considered by some authorities on Oriental medicine to correspond to the pancreas in modern terms, but more than this, the spleen traditionally included the function of all organs secreting digestive enzymes. The "stomach" of the Stomach Meridian also does not indicate just the gastric organ, but corresponds to the entire digestive tract from the mouth to the jejunum (upper part of small intestine) in Oriental medicine. In physical terms the condition of the Stomach Meridian is manifested most readily in the lips and muscles, and in the eyelids when one is drowsy. The muscles in this case include such things as the esophagus, breasts, ovaries, fatty tissues, and muscles of the upper and lower limbs.

Fig. 14

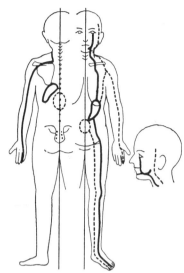

The Spleen Meridian, while centered on the pancreas, also includes the function of all the organs which secrete digestive enzymes (the stomach, gallbladder, and small intestine, as well as the mouth). The Spleen Meridian also relates to reproductive glands in woman (the mammaries and ovaries). The cerebral cortex is also in a way related to digestion because facts are digested by thinking. This concept gave rise to the notion that lack of exercise and too much thinking cause a reduction in the secretion of digestive juices, which in turn causes poor digestion.

When there are imbalances in the Spleen Meridian, one has a tendency to think and worry too much as well as to always feel hungry and crave food. Such people are restless and eat quickly and do not get enough exercise. Also, they love sweets and foods with high liquid content. And because they constantly crave food, they often eat between meals. Also they constantly become drowsy and feel like taking naps. In such cases there is a lack of gastric juices and the mouth is often dry and sticky. Such people commonly experience pain in the back or in the knees, and this causes difficulty in sitting or standing. In some cases fluid collects in the knee joints. Poor function of the spleen is also associated with distortions in the shoulder joint, and this often leads to conditions such as "frozen shoulder."

Fig. 15

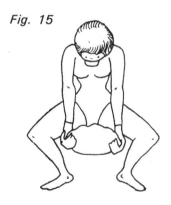

The Stomach Meridian inside the body is related to the entire upper digestive tract from the lips through the oral cavity, esophagus, stomach, and duodenum to the jejunum. The stomach, in facilitating the functioning of these parts, relates to eating, exercising, and production of body heat as well as reproduction for women. The development of the breasts and a layer of subcutaneous fat in women are among the many changes occurring at puberty. These particular changes are made possible by the function of the Stomach Meridian which controls appetite, lactation, and the function of the ovaries to some extent.

When imbalances occur in the Stomach Meridian, one becomes overly conscious of the stomach, and appetite is influenced by one's mood and the type of food. Such people have a tendency to worry over minor details and tension builds up in their neck and shoulder areas. Their legs feel heavy and they get cold below the knees; they also yawn a lot and get tired easily. When people like this overeat, they belch a lot, have hyperacidity, and feel distension of the stomach. They are prone to prolonged colds with nasal congestion, rhinitis, and coughing. Sores at the corner of the mouth are a sign of inflammation of the stomach lining and they also appear along the course of the Stomach Meridian. The pit of the stomach (epigastric area) becomes hard and puts pressure on the heart to cause pain in the cardiac region.

In the Chinese classics, the spleen and stomach together are likened to an official who controls the grain storehouses. This was intended to mean that these meridians control the body's intake of nourishment. When the figure of a person squatting down to grab and lift up something heavy is pictured, the lines of tension which form in the body at this time can be considered as the Spleen and Stomach Meridians (Fig. 15). In other words, this posture represents the action of Ki when picking up a large piece of food, wherein blood circulation increases to the joints and muscles involved and one is in an excited state of anticipation.

Heart and Small Intestine Meridians

Fig. 16

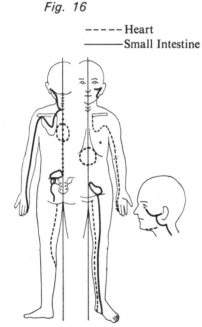

----- Heart
——— Small Intestine

Fig. 17

It may seem rather odd to those who first learn that the Heart and Small Intestine Meridians (Fig. 16) are joined as a Yin-Yang pair in Chinese medicine. The heart and small intestine may appear to be virtually unrelated when viewed strictly from the standpoint of present day anatomy and physiology. From ancient times, the heart has been considered as the seat of the soul (consciousness). Possibly this was because the heart closely reflects one's emotional state, such as by beating faster when excited. On the other hand, the effect of strong emotions on the lower abdomen (*hara*) has long been noted in Japan. This is evident in the Japanese language, with expressions such as *hara-ga-tatsu* (to get angry; literally "for the stomach to stand up"). Emotional outbursts do in fact cause a reaction in the lower abdomen. It is also known that a large amount of blood collects in the abdominal cavity during shock as a natural reaction to prevent possible blood loss. In terms of embryology, the vascular system develops first around the digestive tract of the embryo and one portion of the developing blood vessels eventually grow to form the heart. The theory that blood is produced in the small intestines, advanced by Dr. Kei-ichi Morishita, a Japanese biologist, also supports the classical Oriental viewpoint that "food becomes one's blood and flesh."

The Heart and Small Intestine Meridians can therefore be understood as occupying a central position in the body and as being associated with the functions of "conversion and integration." The Heart Meridian works to integrate the external stimuli received by the body and to effect a response. The small intestine receives food introduced into the body from the outside and converts this into a usable form. In this way, these two meridians regulate the function of the entire body. The Heart Meridian "converts" the input from the five senses into appropriate internal responses and thus controls the whole body as the center of Ki and Ketsu. This motivating and integrating function of the Heart Meridian can be felt in oneself most distinctly as the beating of the heart.

Imbalances in the Heart Meridian are associated with nervous tension due to shock or fatigue, which produces tightness in the solar plexus area and causes one to worry excessively. Some people with this condition become obsessed with the notion that they have cancer because tightness of their tongue causes them to stammer or because they have difficulty swallowing and must clear their throat constantly. When the energy in the Heart Meridian is unbalanced, there is a tendency for blood to rush to one's head and for the palms to become sweaty. People like this tend to have heart problems.

The function of the small intestine is to convert food into nutrients to produce blood and tissues and to control the whole body by providing nutrition. The Small Intestine Meridian also aids the Heart Meridian by keeping Ki down in the *hara* area to maintain calmness and composure. When there is anger, shock, or anguish, blood collects in the lower abdomen and becomes congested. The stagnation of blood here produces symptoms of low back pain and chilling of the lower extremities, especially among women. Thus the Small Intestine Meridian is also related to the function of the ovaries and maintaining menstrual regularity.

Imbalances in the Small Intestine Meridian are associated with holding things inside, such as withholding anger or otherwise being in a state of shock. Such mental states can cause a stagnation of energy in the neck and shoulder area, and a person becomes fatigued easily and often experiences low back pain and cramps in his legs. Bowel movements are often irregular due to problems in digestion and assimilation. Imbalances in the Small Intestine Meridian affect the function of the ovaries in women and this causes menstrual disorders, migraine headaches, and neurotic symptoms associated with new mothers.

The condition of the Heart and Small Intestine Meridians is reflected in one's complexion, tongue, and the corner of the eyes. In the Chinese classics the heart is called the "sovereign of the organs where awareness (consciousness) originates." The small intestine, on the other hand, is referred to as "the organ which receives and transforms nourishing substances." According to the Chinese way of thinking, the sovereign or the emperor is not necessarily the most important person. The role of the emperor is to take responsiblity for the nation at large by residing in its capital and keeping a watch over the whole country so that appropriate steps can be taken to deal with influences from the outside. As already stated, when this role can no longer be served by the emperor, a revolution takes place and the old emperor is ousted and a new one takes his place. This same situation is analogous to one's heart when going through drastic changes in life—the individual has a change of heart or turns over a new leaf.

The small intestine aids the heart by performing the practical function of taking in gross energy (food) and converting this into blood and flesh. When the action of these two meridians are described in terms of a posture, that of sitting cross-legged with the arms folded across the chest as if deep in contemplation is most appropriate (Fig. 17). The lines of tension which form in this posture are on the inside of the arms and legs. In other words, the Ki (intention) is held within for a certain period to prepare for switching into an active mode.

In the principle of Five Phases,* the Heart and Small Intestine Meridians are classified with the element of fire just as the Heart Constrictor and Triple Heater Meridians are. The Heart Constrictor and Triple Heater, however, are the "minister fire" and assist the work of the heart and small intestine, which are the "sovereign fire," in much the same way as ministers assist the emperor in his duties.

Kidney and Bladder Meridians

Fig. 18

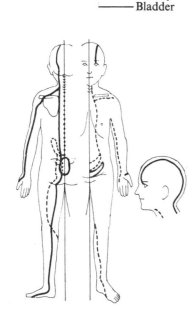

The primary function of the kidneys in Western medicine is regarded as being the formation of urine, but the kidneys also work to maintain a homeostatic balance in body fluids as well as to rid the body of impurities and regulate the metabolic components required by each organ. The kidneys and bladder, from the standpoint of Chinese medicine, include the function of the adrenals and the autonomic nervous system, as well as that of the reproductive organs. The kidneys in particular are held in the Orient to be the most vital organs along

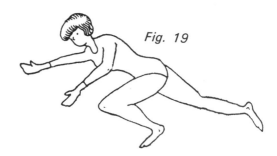

Fig. 19

with the liver. The kidneys are considered to control the essential energy throughout the whole body. Thus the kidneys and bladder together perform the function of supplying vital energy and purifying body fluids.

The kidneys, in their greater sense, work to regulate the constituents of body fluids and supply essential components to all parts of the body, and control the whole

* The Five Phases, otherwise known as the Five Elements, is a philosophical system which, together with the Yin-Yang principle, is the fundamental conceptual framework of Oriental medicine. The Five Phases are wood, fire, earth, metal, and water, and all phenomena in nature can be classified under one of these phases. The most important feature of the Five Phases is the mutual relationship of each phase variously promoting and inhibiting the activity of related phases.

body through hormonal regulation. This also relates to sex hormones and one's response to stress (adrenals). The kidneys purify the blood by isolating and eliminating those substances poisonous to the body. The right kidney reflects the condition of the adrenals and the endocrine system, and has traditionally been referred to as the "fire of the life gate." Dysfunctions in the right kidney are associated with fatigue and hotness of the head. The left kidney reflects the condition of water metabolism and regulates urine formation, and it is referred to as the "water kidney." Dysfunctions in the left kidney are associated with edema (swelling) and chilling of the extremities.

Imbalances in the Kidney Meridian (Fig. 18) are associated with the psychological symptoms of being phobic, or excessively fearful, and being easily startled. Such people tend to be anxious and work compulsively, but they lack the perseverance to finish what they start. They also have a tendency to overdo things and to overreact to everything. In terms of physical characteristics, their skin tends to be dark and lacking in tone and is prone to swelling. Their lower abdomen and back often feel cold, and cramps in the leg are also common. In addition, their head may feel heavy with lack of sleep, but still they are unable to sleep soundly. Also their abdomen is hard and their arms and legs may feel hot. Impairment of kidney function is also indicated when the ability to grasp firmly is greatly reduced in the morning. There can also be a bitter taste in the mouth or a strong odor in the mouth, and the skin becomes susceptible to infection and eczema. Nosebleeds also occur frequently in people with kidney dysfunctions.

The Bladder Meridian is associated with the workings of the autonomic nervous system through the pituitary gland, which functions in conjunction with the entire endocrine system. The Bladder Meridian therefore controls the reproductive function and the uterus, as well as the organs of elimination which collect and excrete liquid waste products after the filtration (purification) of body fluids.

Imbalances in the Bladder Meridian are associated with a large amount of nervous tension and overreaction. The muscles down the back often become very rigid while the lower back area feels weak. Imbalances in this meridian cause painful sensations in the inside corner of the eyes (next to the nose), headaches, or a throbbing sensation in the back of the head. Further, there are varied symptoms caused by dysfunctions in the autonomic nervous system. For some people there is a creeping sensation up and down the back, or there is excruciating pain in the lower back. Oppressive headaches from the back of the head to the arch of the nose are common, and at times the back becomes twisted by pain and contraction in the muscles. Sometimes a sensation of chilling extends from the lower abdomen down to the legs, and the frequency of urination either increases or decreases. On occasion, this leads to cystitis (inflammation of the bladder), in which the lower abdomen feels distended and painful with a full bladder and a feeling of urine retention persists after urination.

The Kidney and Bladder Meridians have traditionally been associated with the bones and teeth, the pupils of the eyes, the reproductive organs, and the hair on the head. The condition of these meridians is also said to be clearly reflected in the function of the ears. In the Chinese classics the kidneys are referred to as "strong and capable ministers from whom technical ability and expertise are derived." Thus the kidneys were understood as the organ which facilitates the work of other organs and enables them to perform their various functions. The bladder is likened to "a governor of a state capital from which the water flows." Thus this organ was thought to be like a local governor who works to adjust the supply and demand in outlying areas. In this sense both the Kidney and Bladder Meridians act like supervisors over the function of various other organs. When the action of these two meridians are described in terms of a particular posture or movement, that of "getting off to a start" seems most appropriate (Fig. 19). This posture is just like that of starting to run a race. When one assumes the "ready . . . set . . . go!" posture at the starting line, the Bladder and Kidney Meridians can be felt as lines of tension which form through the whole body.

Heart Constrictor and Triple Heater Meridians

Fig. 20

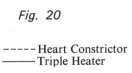
- - - - - Heart Constrictor
——— Triple Heater

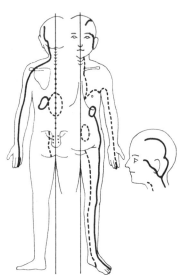

There has been some confusion even among practitioners of Oriental medicine as to exactly what the Heart Constrictor and Triple Heater Meridians are supposed to represent. We can get a more precise understanding of these meridians by carefully considering what the classics of Chinese medicine have to say about them. Also these meridians can be compared to the Heart and Small Intestine Meridians which also belong to the "fire phase" in the Five Phases. In other words, the will of the sovereign organ, the Heart, is conveyed throughout the entire body by the Heart Constrictor, while the nutrients absorbed by the Small Intestine are transported to every corner of the body by the Triple Heater. By these processes the body is integrated and filled with vitality and is able to defend itself. In this way the Heart Constrictor and Triple Heater are best understood as being involved in the functions of circulation and protection.

The Heart Constrictor is considered by some as being equivalent to the pericardium, the membrane which covers the heart, but if the Heart Constrictor really works to assist the central coordinating function of the heart, as written in the classics, it has to be viewed as being related to the central circulatory function including the heart, the aorta, and all the major arteries and veins, not to mention the lymphatic ducts.

Fig. 21

The Triple Heater Meridian, which forms a Yin-Yang pair with the Heart Constrictor Meridian is described in the classics as "having a function but no form." Some people therefore conclude that the Triple Heater is just some physical function unrelated to any specific structure and fail to recognize its real significance. In contrast to the Heart Constrictor, which is related to the central circulatory function, the Triple Heater controls peripheral circulation and lymphatic flow. This means that the Triple Heater is also closely related to the skin, mucous membranes, and serous membranes which are supplied by peripheral capillary and lymphatic networks.

In traditional Chinese medicine, the body is divided into three areas, each with its own "heater." A "heater" is an area of heat production (center of metabolic activity). Thus the Triple Heater is also a traditional classification of metabolic activity (generation of heat) in the organs located in the top, middle, and bottom sections of the torso. In this system the chest cavity, the upper half of the abdominal cavity (above the navel), and the lower half are respectively governed by the top, middle, and bottom heaters. So the Triple Heater consists of three parts, each of which have a distinct function.

The Heart Constrictor is closely associated with emotional responses because it assists the heart by taking care of the actual work of the central circulatory function. This not only includes the function of the heart and pericardium, but the activity of major blood vessels and lymph ducts. The Heart Constrictor carries out the will of the Heart and is involved in blood circulation which regulates the distribution of nutrients. Thus the Heart Constrictor is able to inhibit or stimulate the functioning of all the organs.

Imbalances in the Heart Constrictor Meridian are associated with exhaustion from concentrating too hard, working too long in the same position, and haziness of the head. People with this problem often find it difficult to relax, and blood rises to their head to cause hotness of the head, while their extremities become cold. Sometimes there is discomfort in the pyloric region (area above the navel), rapid pulse, abnormal blood pressure, or pyrosis (heartburn). In more serious cases, attacks of angina pectoris occur. Also symptoms such as insomnia, palpitations, shortness of breath, and fulgurating (pricking) pain, or a sense of oppression in the chest, are common.

The Triple Heater is associated with the mesentery, that is attached to the small intestine, which serves a vital role in assimilation. The Triple Heater also regulates the actual distribution of nutrients to the extremities by its control of peripheral circulation. Imbalances in the Triple Heater Meridian are associated with an inability to relate well to others and being overly defensive and always having one's guard up. This tends to make a person tense and stiff all over. This causes the forearms to be tense and rigid and for the fists to be constantly clenched. The head often feels heavy as if it were covered with something. Such people are oversensitive to changes in the environment and are adversely affected by sudden changes in temperature and humidity; furthermore, they tend to have allergic constitutions. Also the mucous lining of their nose and throat is hypersensitive and their lymph nodes swell easily. They constantly get colds and their eyes as well as their throats are affected. Aside from this, there is a sense of oppression in the chest and the abdominal wall and the skin surface in general is hypersensitive, causing ticklishness, itching, and oversensitivity to pain. Eczema and urticaria (nettle rash) are also common. With this constitution edema occurs readily, and sometimes the arms as well as the back of the head feel numb.

In Chinese classics the Heart Constrictor is described as "a palace official from whom pleasure and mirth are derived." The role of the Heart Constrictor in conveying the intentions of the heart or giving expression to the emotions is thus emphasized.

The Triple Heater, on the other hand, is described as "the official in charge of water works. In China, historically, controlling the water of the rivers has been held as being of prime importance in governing the land, and similarly the Triple Heater Meridian has the vital job of regulating the water metabolism in the body. The basic function represented by the above two meridians is to circulate nourishing Ki and protective Ki to the central and peripheral areas of the body. If these meridians are described in terms of a posture, that of crouching down in the cold and hugging one's body (to prevent the loss of heat) and rubbing oneself on the arms and legs to keep warm serves as a good illustration of their function (Fig. 21).

Liver and Gallbladder Meridians

The Liver Meridian (Fig. 22) is clearly associated with the liver, which is regarded even in Western medicine as being a vital organ. The Gallbladder Meridian in turn is associated with the gallbladder. The wider significance of the Gallbladder Meridian, however, is more closely tied to the Oriental concept of "gall" as being the source of strength and resolve. The functions of the gallbladder, including the storage and release of bile, are naturally part of the many functions of the Gallbladder Meridian. But in physiological terms, the gallbladder may be more closely associated with the function of the endocrine system. The Liver and Gallbladder Meridians can be regarded as sharing the functions of storage and dis-

Fig. 22

------ Liver
——— Gallbladder

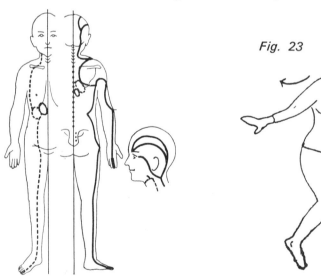

Fig. 23

tribution, or of determining the distribution of vital energy by their action of storing and releasing essential substances.

The liver works to store nutrients and secures the vital supply of energy required by the body to remain active. It also augments the blood supply and breaks down and detoxifies harmful substances. The primary overall function of the liver is to keep an individual full of vigor. Imbalances in the Liver Meridian are associated with loss of vitality, sudden spurts of motivation followed by extreme fatigue, bad temper, and easily being disturbed by noise. Also the letdown after emotional arousal, heightened emotional sensitivity, and a tendency to raise one's voice are associated with liver imbalances. In terms of physical symptoms, one's eyes lose their sparkle, everything takes on a yellowish tinge, and one experiences dizziness upon standing. There is an unexplainable decline in sexual performance or occasional outbreaks of fever as well as problems in the prostate and testicles. Otherwise, there are the symptoms of pain in the sacrum and coccyx, hemorrhoids, tension in the flank region, a sense of pressure in the right hypochondrium (area below ribs), loss of appetite, nausea, and headaches.

The gallbladder controls the distribution of nutrients throughout the body, and it controls the amount and balance of digestive enzymes (including saliva, pancreatic juice, bile, and intestinal enzymes) as well as hormones from the thyroids. The gallbladder is also the organ related to decision making and it decides the response or course of action. Imbalances in the Gallbladder Meridian are associated with becoming overly concerned about little details, being frightened out of one's wits, or losing sleep over not being able to make a decision. Also in this case the eyes get overworked and there are symptoms of eyestrain, yellowing of the eyes, accumulation of mucus in the eyes, blurring of vision, and increased ocular pressure. Another tendency is not taking enough time to eat so the release of bile is insufficient and either constipation or diarrhea results. Also the skin becomes yellowish, the joints in the arms and legs become stiff, and the body as a whole becomes rather rigid. In addition there are the following symptoms: heartburn, occasional nausea in the morning, distention of the stomach, tension in the shoulders with occasional sharp pain in the side (costal neuralgia), spasms and pain in the biliary tract or stomach, hyperacidity, duodenal ulcers, and coughing accompanied by phlegm.

The condition of the Liver and Gallbladder Meridians have traditionally been considered as being reflected in one's eyes and nails, but symptoms of imbalances in these meridians quite often appear in the flank region. Further, these organs are associated with the iris and vision, tendons (especially the Achilles tendon), the sexual organs and sexual response, as well as the movement of various joints.

In the Chinese classics the liver is likened to "an army General who decides strategy." This means that, like an army General, the liver has command over how the vital energy supply of the body is to be used. The gallbladder is called "the impartial officer who makes decisions." Thus it presumably carries out the will of the General by making actual decisions out on the front line. Impartiality is important here because otherwise the original aims could become misconstrued and the planning and strategy (of the liver) would be rendered useless.

When the functions of the Liver and Gallbladder Meridians are described as a posture, they can be likened to a posture in which one looks this way and that to decide which way to go (Fig. 23). It stands to reason that both of these meridians are related to the sides of the body. As a result, the energy of these meridians come into play when the body is turned to either side, as is the case when trying to decide which way to go.

Chapter 5

Basic Exercises

How to Practice the Basic Exercises

My main goal in developing Imagery Exercises was to get people to experience the essence of what it means to be alive and so confirm the profound concepts of Oriental medicine for themselves. Daily practice is indispensable if one hopes to gain an insight into the theoretical aspects presented in this book. The time of day the exercises are done matters very little so long as they are not forgotten and are fitted into your daily routine without fail. If you decide that the best time for doing these exercises is before going to bed, you must be sure to set time aside for them because no matter how beneficial Imagery Exercises are, just knowing about them does you little good. If you decide that the best time for doing these exercises is right after waking up in the morning, you should be sure to wake up early enough. Since the Basic Exercises require very little time, you should make a point of getting right out of bed to do them. If you wish to do them after taking care of some other work first, you may do this also, but unless you set a definite time to do these exercises, they are likely to be forgotten. They can be performed between household work or while on breaks at work, but it must be kept in mind that some space is needed to sit and lie on the floor. You may also choose to do these exercises right after returning home from work before doing anything else. The main point is to make the Basic Exercises a routine and not to forget to do them. There is no need whatsoever for any mechanical devices or special equipment. These exercises can be started and ended at anytime you wish. All it really requires is that you make up your mind to set aside a little time every-day for these exercises.

The easiest and quickest way to begin these exercises is to start with Imagery Breathing in the standing position. Just stand relaxed with your feet apart slight more than shoulder width and place your hands over your lower abdomen to feel your breath in your lower abdomen. After breathing this way for a minute or so, begin Exercise "A," the stretching of the Lung and Large Intestine Meridians, and continue through all six of the Basic Exercises (see Fig. 24). After that lie on your back and finish up with Imagery Breathing (Exercise "Z"). All you need to do after finishing the exercises is to lie down on your back and relax with your arms and legs spread out comfortably. You should experience yourself as being totally relaxed from head to toe, and just keep your awareness on your breathing and how your body feels. It is essential to do at least this minimum routine once a day without fail.

If you are not pressed for time and want to get the maximum benefits from the Basic Exercises, you can include the stretching of the Conception and Governor Vessels (Exercises "p" and "q") before starting the sequence of exercises from "A" to "D." This will allow you to better synchronize your breathing and movements as you go through the Basic Exercises. Also, stretching the Conception Vessel gives added stimulation to all six of the Yin meridians, and stretching the Governor Vessel gives stimulation to the remaining six Yang meridians.

All you need to do is to follow the instructions and do the Basic Exercises in the order given. This will ensure that you get the maximum results even with the minimum amount of exercise each day. The whole sequence of the Basic Exercises can be done in as little as five minutes, but they are most beneficial when practiced more slowly and attentively. It is best to allow at least ten minutes and to take your time in doing these exercises.

In these meridian exercises, rather than going through each exercise in rapid succession, it is best to take your time after getting in each stretched position in order to experience how the energy flow in the meridians concerned is being facilitated and how the tension is being worked out. Therefore, you should try to quietly experience the sensation which lingers along the meridians after finishing an exercise and returning to the original position. It is important to get a feel for what these meridians are in your own body as a "living sensation," rather than just as something depicted in diagrams.

In order to do all the exercises smoothly in sequence, you must learn how to move your arms and legs into position for the next exercise before beginning to shift your center of gravity to effect the stretch. Pay the most attention to what goes on inside your body and do not become overly concerned with external form because this will cause all your efforts to be expended in keeping your arms and legs in the right place and the more important sensation of the meridians being stretched will be lost. Always keep your attention on your breathing and be sensitive to how your body is responding to each exercise.

Fig. 24   Order of Meridians

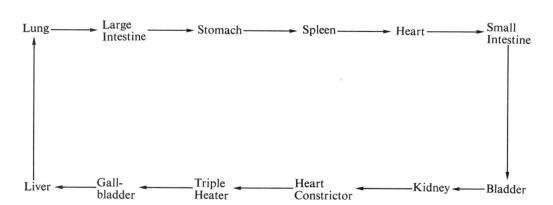

Exercises "Z" and "I" (Starting Positions)

In order to do these exercises, first you must become aware of your body and experience your breathing as "the breath of life." To do this, lie flat on your back and relax completely and begin Imagery Breathing as explained before (Fig. 25). Simply direct your attention to what it feels like to be in your body at this moment. It is better in the beginning to close your eyes to keep from being distracted by external stimuli. Once you become accustomed to lying completely relaxed and still while keeping your attention focused on breathing through your *hara*, it does not matter whether your eyes are open or closed. In yoga, this first exercise is called *Shavasana*, or the "corpse pose."

Fig. 25

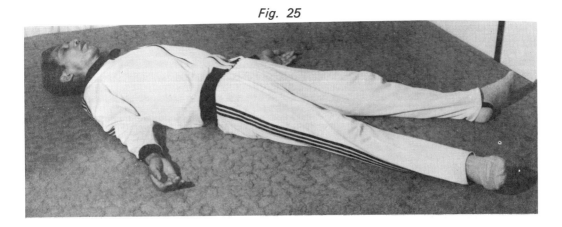

I recommend that you make a habit of relaxing totally with Exercise "Z" before going to sleep every night. Those who have difficulty in getting to sleep should regard the time before falling off to sleep as an ideal time to practice Exercise "Z." Be creative in developing a mental image that works the best for you to relax completely and breathe slowly and deeply through your lower abdomen. When you hit upon the right mental image, the process of getting to sleep will become a most pleasant experience, and it will consistently lead to deep and restful sleep.

This posture should be the beginning and ending position for all Imagery Exercises. It can even be said that the ultimate aim of Imagery Exercises is to be able to do Exercise "Z" perfectly (i.e., to totally relax). This is why I recommend that you always end whatever exercise you do in this way. Also, since "the end is always a new beginning," it makes sense to both begin and end all exercises in this fashion. By doing this, you can better compare how you feel at the beginning and end of exercising and thus confirm the changes brought about through the exercises.

When beginning the Basic Exercises, do Exercise "Z" for at least as long as it takes to complete several deep and relaxed breaths, and then stand up and continue breathing the same way in the upright postion (Figs. 26 and 27). By standing this way you can feel how the energy for movement comes up from the bottom of your feet. No movement can be done correctly when your feet are unsteady or when you are slightly off balance. As long as the feet are firmly in contact with the ground, move-

Fig. 26

Fig. 27

ments in the upper part of the body can be performed with grace and ease. Aside from your stance, if your pelvis is unstable or unsettled during the exhalation of Imagery Breathing, you can lose your balance when the breath is emptied and your abdomen is relaxed. Professor Michizo Noguchi says that "our waist is our second foundation."

What is meant by the "waist" in this case is the *hara*, the focal point of energy in our lower abdomen from which the Ki in each breath ebbs and flows. A sensation of fullness or weight should extend from the center point just below the navel down to your feet to firmly support the whole body. In order to really *stand* in Exercise "I," not only must your feet be firmly on the ground, but the center of your Ki (the focus of your physical presence) must be poised in the center of your lower abdomen. If you become too conscious of your feet, "your Ki will be set on end," to borrow a Japanese expression, and this will cause you to feel restless and uneasy. As a result you will find it difficult to stand in one place for any length of time. You will find it easiest to maintain your balance and composure by standing with your feet about shoulder width apart and feeling your energy as being settled in your *hara*.

Exercises "p" and "q" (Conception and Governor Vessels)

There are twelve regular pathways for the circulation of Ki on each side of the body in the traditional meridian system. These twelve meridians are grouped into six Yin-Yang pairs in relation to basic life functions as explained before. In addition to the twelve regular meridians, traditional Chinese medicine has eight extra meridians, which are special pathways for Ki. The Conception Vessel and Governor Vessel are exceptional among the extra meridians in that they have independent points* which are located on the center line in the front and back of the body. The most exceptional feature of these two meridians is that they regulate the flow of energy in all of the regular meridians. The Conception and Governor Vessels are said to respec-

---

* Independent points are acupuncture points which belong primarily to one meridian. All the regular meridians have independent points, but most of the extra meridians do not. Meridians without independent points share points which belong to other meridians.

tively serve as reservoirs of Ki for the Yin and Yang meridians.

Fig. 28

In other words, this means that there are six extra meridians (vessels) aside from the twelve regular meridians (six Yin-Yang pairs). Above these meridians are two extra meridians of major importance, the Conception Vessel and the Governor Vessel. The Basic Exercises should appropriately begin with the stretching of the Yin Conception Vessel and then the Yang Governor Vessel. Since your body is made ready for movement by standing upright from the reclined position in Exercise "I," it can be said that the energy in your body has been shifted from a Yin (passive) state to a Yang (active) state. Just standing up, however, only creates possibilities for movement. Nothing is actually set in motion yet, and therefore your Ki is still basically inactive. To activate and extend your Ki, picture your *hara* moving forward as you lean back. Place both hands against the back of your thighs in a relaxed way to give support as you lean back and let your head tilt all the way back (Figs. 28 and 29).

The lines of tension produced along the center line of the abdomen is the Conception Vessel. This is the flow of Ki which regulates all the Yin meridians. By stretching the Conception Vessel, in a sense, you open yourself up to the outside world and external influences are received without resistance. The Conception Vessel is a meridian running along the center line on the front of the body which has twenty-four independent points beginning at the perineum and ending right in the middle of the lower jaw. For our purposes,

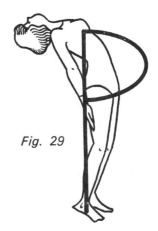

Fig. 29

however, it is easier just to conceive of this meridian as the line of tension produced when leaning back with our belly pushed forward.

After leaning back to stretch the Conception Vessel, imagine that you are moving your *hara*, the center of your physical presence, toward your back. Then make your body bend forward as if you were trying to put your head between your legs and reach both arms around your thighs (Figs. 30 and 31). The line of tension which forms down the center of your back is the Governor Vessel. The Governor Vessel has twenty-eight independent points and begins at the tip of the tailbone and goes up and around the top of the head to end up at the midpoint of the upper jaw. The tension along the Governor Vessel is felt most strongly when you inhale. During the exhalation Ki is released and the whole body relaxes.

In stretching the Conception Vessel, the belly is pushed forward and the chest is expanded so, in effect, you open yourself up to the outside and release Ki. In stretching the Governor Vessel, you bend forward at the waist and place your hands around your thighs so that your face is hidden and your energy is drawn inward. These two

Fig. 30

Fig. 31

Basic Exercises represent the two most basic functions of life where the force of Ki is directed either to the inside or to the outside (i.e., drawing in or otherwise reaching out).

These meridian exercises should not be viewed merely as a way of stretching and limbering muscles and joints. Stretching in this context does not refer just to lengthening or pulling something apart, but is rather an act of extending or expanding which liberates the energy lying latent within you. These exercises should serve as a form of physical expression to release, through the act of stretching, those things which you have been holding inside. These exercises are an opportunity to get in touch with your body and give expression to your inner being through movement. You will get a better feeling for how these first two exercises should be done and clearly recognize the sensation along the meridians after practicing the full sequence of Basic Exercises.

Exercise "A" (Lung and Large Intestine Meridians)

To stretch the Lung and Large Intestine Meridians, stand with your feet apart slightly more than shoulder width. The tips of your toes should point naturally outward. Put your hands behind your back with the palms facing backward, and hold them together by hooking your thumbs together. Spread your fingers out so that your fingers point as much as possible in opposite directions. Keep your knees straight and think of your weight as going mostly on the base of your little toes and bend forward as you exhale. Stretch both arms over yourself, keeping your elbows straight (Figs. 32–34). When your body is stretched forward as far as it will go, quietly begin to inhale. A line of tension or stiffness will be felt along the back of your legs, abdomen, back, and arms. In Exercise "A" the line which has a tingling sensation or a feeling of distension corresponds to the Lung and Large Intestine Meridians. This sensation should not be felt as a result of using force to stretch these parts. As you inhale and your body becomes filled with Ki, what should happen is that you feel a line of tension develop along the course of the Lung and Large Intestine Meridians. This line of tension or stretch may be felt as being like a pulling sensation in the muscles. When you try to draw your arms forward by your own effort, the muscles become unnecessarily tense and the real line of tension becomes indistinct and hard to feel. Imagine that your arms are being pulled forward by someone other than yourself. Compare your stance with that of the picture. If any strength is brought to bear on one part in particular, this will prevent you from feeling the meridian lines. It is important to hold the mental image of Ki energy flowing from the center point of your *hara* out to your arms and legs.

In conventional exercises the tendency is to force a stretch or to add a bounce in the movement to increase the range of movement. It is true that your limbs will increase in flexibility if you can endure the discomfort of stretching them forcibly, but improvement in flexibility achieved in this manner is just a product of repetition. You must realize that stretching by the use of force is the exact opposite of what is intended in these meridian exercises.

In Imagery Exercises you have to develop and savor the feeling of a good stretch, and you should never attempt to force a stretch. Each breath must be exhaled slowly and quietly after every inhalation to aid a smooth and relaxed stretch. Usually it is difficult to bring on relaxation in a stretched position just by thinking about loosening up. But if you imagine that Ki is being released (like air leaking out of a balloon) as you slowly exhale, you will be able to feel your whole body slowly relax. When you inhale, you should be able to feel the lines of the meridians expanding even more after having been relaxed completely. You will again feel tension develop along the same lines. Then exhale slowly again and feel the relaxation come with the outgoing breath. Repeat this breathing and relaxation about three times in the position of Exercise "A" and slowly return to the upright position.

Fig. 32   *Fig. 33*

Fig. 34

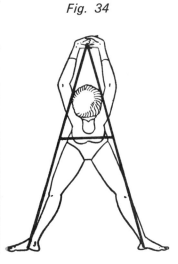

Exercise "B" (Spleen and Stomach Meridians)

To stretch the Spleen and Stomach Meridians, first you must sit in the Seiza position*
and then slowly lean backward (Figs. 35 and 36). As you lean down to the rear, move
your feet apart, out from under your buttocks so that your buttocks come to rest on
the floor. Since, for most people, the knees raise off the floor when laying all the way
back like this, there is no need to force them down to the floor. Just keep your lower
legs out to your side next to your hips so that you can keep your knees close together. After your back and shoulders are resting on the floor, stretch both arms over
your head, interlace your fingers, and turn the palms toward your head (Figs. 37 and

Fig. 35   Fig. 36

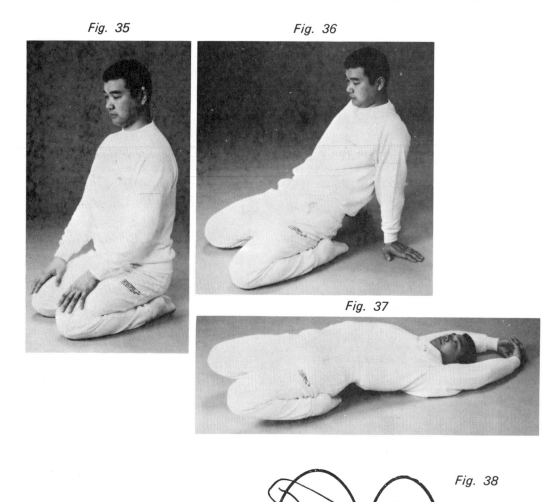

Fig. 37

Fig. 38

* Seiza is the traditional sitting posture in Japan where one sits erect with the legs folded under
the hips. Sitting in Seiza is becoming less common in Japan with the progress of westernization,
but it is still considered to be the most formal and ideal sitting posture.

38). Next breathe in and stretch your whole body so that it extends and straightens. This will naturally cause your back to raise up off the floor and your knees to spread apart; this is perfectly all right. The lines of tension that form down the front of your body and along the spine, as well as on both sides of the arms, correspond to the Spleen and Stomach Meridians.

If you let your knees spread far apart in this exercise, your back will reach the floor quite easily, but then the meridians will not be stretched fully. While your knees do not have to be kept together rigidly, you should try to keep them together as much as you can without undue effort. To make this easier, keep your feet out from under your buttocks and keep your back and hips against the floor. Once you get a good stretch all the way through your body, quietly breathe out as you relax your effort, and feel your whole body relax.

In other kinds of stretching exercises, parts which are not very flexible are often stretched forcibly. Even though this will stretch muscles and tendons, you will never feel the energy flowing through the whole body or learn to release Ki in the meridians and relax the lines of tension this way. It is actually very difficult to relax after forcing a stretch to the maximum limit.

The best way to release tension is to get a feel for what it is like to relax with Imagery Breathing, in which Ki is released with each exhalation. You must first develop a clear image of how Ki expands out from your *hara* and fills your whole body while doing Imagery Breathing in the reclined position. Ki should fill your lower abdomen and expand outward to your limbs as you inhale and then it should flow out as you exhale to leave you feeling completely relaxed. The tension in your body will go away naturally as you stretch slowly and gently with this mental picture. You can feel yourself loosen up as you do this.

The main point in Imagery Exercises is not to force a stretch, but to instead allow the stretch to happen a little bit at a time with each exhalation. Inhale after each complete exhalation while remaining in the fully stretched position reached as a result of having released Ki. As you inhale, you will once again feel an increase of tension in the same line of tension which relaxed slightly with the last exhalation. The same meridians as before fill up with Ki as you inhale and you can feel the tension build along the same lines. Remain in this position and feel the lines of tension after taking a deep breath, and then slowly let your breath out.

How much you are able to relax with each exhalation depends entirely on the depth and smoothness of your breathing. It is difficult to discern the subtle difference between tension and relaxation in the meridians when your breathing is strained or uneven. One of the most important things in Imagery Exercises is to relax your whole body and to experience your own breathing after finishing each exercise. Even though you may think that you have relaxed completely, often there is residual tension where you are unable to let go and relax your muscles completely. If it were true that our skeletal muscles contract by our conscious control only, we should be able to completely relax all of our muscles at will. In reality, however, a great deal of tension remains even after we try to relax. The basic aim of Imagery Exercises is to get a feel for that force within us which coordinates our muscles above and beyond our conscious control.

Exercise "C" (Heart and Small Intestine Meridians)

To stretch the Heart and Small Intestine Meridians sit on the floor and place the soles of your feet together in front of you by bending both knees out to the side. Draw your feet in toward yourself as close as you can by grasping them around the toes from the bottom (Fig. 39). Then bend forward while exhaling, keeping the thighs down as far as possible (Figs. 40 and 41). Ideally your forehead should reach your toes and both your elbows and knees should touch the floor, but there is no need to force yourself into this position. This is just a goal, and straining or forcing a stretch only defeats the purpose. This rule applies to all Imagery Exercises.

Fig. 39

The movement of bending forward will naturally come to a stop at the place where your body is stretched to the limit. Pause here and breathe in to fill up with Ki, and your body will begin to tighten up from your *hara* out to your limbs. The lines of tension that form in this position are the Heart and Small Intestine Meridians. These exercises are designed to stretch specific meridians to the greatest extent possible so when you breathe in, you should be able to feel the full length of the meridians being stretched.

Fig. 40

Fig. 41

Greater emphasis is placed on getting the form right in other methods of exercise, which are designed to increase circulation by working the muscles and joints. In calisthenics, one's attention naturally becomes focused on just those parts involved since all movements are made willfully. Imagery Exercises also require conscious control to get the body into each position. But once the position is reached, the object is to let go and do Imagery Breathing and just observe what goes on in your body. When breathing in, tension increases naturally and this tension is most pronounced along certain lines. At times this sensation extends from one end of the body to the other. It is most important that you experience the meridians in this way as something distinct from muscles and nerves.

You can feel for yourself how the line of tension begins to relax as you exhale. This is the sensation of relaxation accompanying the release of Ki. After each complete exhalation in the position of increased stretch, inhale and feel the tension build up once more along the same meridians. There is no need to be too concerned about reaching the ideal position. Just repeat this breathing and stretching routine several times in a row. The main requirement is to relax completely and reach the farthest point of the stretch at the end of each exhalation. No matter how much you try to relax and attempt to loosen up certain parts of your body, tension and stiffness will often remain in the neck and shoulders. When a person is told to relax his shoulders completely, chances are that he will become more tense in his shoulders because of having become more conscious of it. Autogenic training* is one way to learn how to relax intentionally through self-suggestion. By regular practice of Imagery Exercises, however, the ability to relax can be acquired automatically. As you continue practicing these exercises, each day your position will more closely resemble the desired form.

Exercise "D" (Kidney and Bladder Meridians)

To stretch the Kidney and Bladder Meridians, sit with your legs stretched straight out. While your heels must be kept together, there is no need to keep your toes together. Keep your knees straight and try to keep the back of your legs in contact with the floor as much as possible. Then bend your upper body forward and reach your arms out toward your toes (Figs. 42 and 43). Invert your palms to face outward to the arches so that the thumbs are turned down toward the heels.

This stretch of the Kidney and Bladder Meridians is very similar to the "toe touching exercise," which is a good indicator of overall flexibility and is often used to check people's flexibility. It is unwise, however, to simply regard flexibility as being tantamount to youthfulness without a real understanding of why flexibility is so important. Some people have trouble reaching their toes with their hands and the head remains far from the knees because their back is too rigid and the stretching action on the back of the legs is too uncomfortable. In other methods this stretch is some-

Fig. 42

Fig. 43

* Autogenic training is a therapeutic system of self-suggestion developed in the 1930s by Dr. J. H. Schultz of Germany. It is a self-training system involving the silent repetition of simple phrases aimed at regulating the autonomic nervous system and balancing physiological functions. Modified forms of autogenic training are widely applied today for stress related conditions.

times forced by jerking the head down with a bouncing movement or by having someone else push on the back from behind. There is no need whatsoever to endure pain to get a full stretch. Naturally it is better to be more flexible, but being flexible does not necessarily mean a person is healthy, and furthermore, it does not mean that the energy is flowing well along the meridians. Even flexible people, as limber as they may be, often have deep seated tension. When you force stiff muscles and joints to stretch, those particular muscles and joints become the focus of attention. Even though flexibility can be improved to some extent this way, it inclines a person to overlook the obstruction of Ki or the underlying dynamics which caused muscle tension and stiffness of joints in the first place. Stretching the lines of tension by slowly breathing and paying attention to the changes in the body as a whole is a much sounder way to work out tension and increase flexibility.

Bend forward as far as you can while exhaling in the position described above and then draw a deep breath. When Ki starts filling up your body, you will feel tension from your waist down to your feet and your toes will be drawn backward. Your head should hang down over your knees and your arms should be stretched forward to their limit. This will cause strong lines of tension to form, beginning from your hands and running along your arms then down and back along your legs to your feet. This is the course of the Kidney and Bladder Meridians. Although these lines of tension cause your body to be less flexible, it is not advisable to stretch them forcibly. When people try to do this stretch with too much force, it can cause muscle cramps in the legs.

The line of tension will be relieved automatically as you exhale slowly and completely. You can feel how the arms which would not stretch out any farther ease forward slightly. Try to get a good feel for how this stretch is effected with relaxation, because this stretch of the Kidney and Bladder Meridians, in particular, is one where the extra stretch after releasing Ki is quite apparent. This very same principle works in all other Imagery Exercises, and you will really be able to feel the difference after repeating this process two or three times.

Exercise "E" (Heart Constrictor and Triple Heater Meridians)

The posture of Exercise "E" for stretching the Heart Constrictor and Triple Heater Meridians is difficult for some people, so you must find the way that is the easiest for you to avoid straining yourself. The ideal sitting posture for this exercise is the lotus position of yoga and Zen meditation. In this position, the legs are crossed and each foot is placed on the other thigh. The "half lotus," where only one foot is placed on the other thigh, is also fine for this exercise. It is also possible to do this exercise simply by sitting cross-legged without placing either foot on the other leg. The closer your knees are to the floor the better, but do not force them. It really does not matter if the knees are raised slightly off the floor, or if one knee sits higher than the other.

Next cross your arms one over the other and grab the opposite knees (Fig. 44). The arm on the same side as the leg on top should go over the top of the other arm. For those who are right-handed it is generally better for the left arm to go over the right arm first, but it is best to assume the easiest posture first. Next bend as far

forward as possible and use your arms to
pull yourself down so your forehead reaches
down toward the floor (Figs. 45 and 46).
Rather than keeping your back straight,
bend forward and let your head hang down.
Just draw your body forward with the feeling of pulling it down toward the feet.

After exhaling completely and bending
down as far as you can, draw in a deep
breath. The lines of tension that form along
your back and down the outside of your
arms and legs as you inhale is the course of
the Triple Heater Meridian. The lines of

Fig. 44

Fig. 45

Fig. 46

tension on the opposite side, to the inside, is the Heart Constrictor Meridian. As you
exhale again you should be able to feel these lines relax. Repeating this sequence three
or four times should give you an idea of what it means to relax and stretch.

Exercise "F" (Liver and Gallblader Meridians)

To stretch the Liver and Gallbladder Meridians you must sit on the floor with both
legs extended out to either side. Relax and spread your legs as far apart as you can.
Some people are able to spread their legs all the way to almost form a straight line
with their legs, but for most people the legs form an obtuse angle. The important
thing is to keep your knees straight so that the back of your legs stay on the floor.
Your legs do not need to be spread apart any more than you are able to keep them
fully extended with ease.

Next clasp your hands high over your head and turn your palms upward. Straighten
your elbows and start leaning down to one side (Fig. 47). Bend down toward one
foot with your arm on the same side facing down (Figs. 48 and 49). Keep facing
forward as you bend down to one side. Instead of turning your torso to face the direction in which you are bending, face the front and bend down sideways. After bending

Fig. 47

Fig. 48

Fig. 49

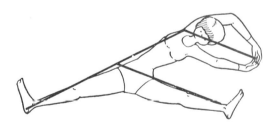

down as far as you can during the exhalation, slowly inhale. You should feel lines of tension form along the outside of the leg you are leaning toward, down the inside of the opposite leg, and along the side of your body that is fully extended, as well as along the front of your body toward the side which is down. These lines correspond to the Liver and Gallbladder Meridians. When you exhale completely, this tension will be relieved somewhat and the stretch will increase. As you draw another breath, the same lines of tension will form. You must not bend so far as to cause pain. If you become too preoccupied with bending, this will cause the backs of your legs to rise up off the floor, and the stretching effect on the meridians will be lost.

Sensing the line of tension form through the length of your body in this way is one way you can actually experience meridians for yourself. Releasing this tension with slow exhalations gives you a feel for achieving total relaxation. This relaxation does not occur when you begin by bending just as far as you can and attempt to relax after getting the maximum stretch. Instead of forcing a stretch, simply exhale until you are completely empty. When you reach this point, let go one last time and release all your Ki. This will automatically cause the line of tension to relax and your body will stretch a little bit farther. The relaxation and stretching effect tapers off after repeating this breathing and stretching sequence about three times. When this happens, slowly return to the starting position.

In the stretching of the Liver and Gallbladder Meridians, you should first check to see which direction you can bend easier and begin on that side. (Most people find it easier to bend to the right side.) After practicing this exercise over a period of time, the arm on the side you are bending toward will begin to reach your knee. Also you will be able to spread your legs wider and wider to more closely approach a straight line. The real purpose in these exercises, however, is not to attain the flexibility of a gymnast or ballerina. The most important goal is to find the best position in which you can feel the resistance or a tingling sensation coming from the line of tension forming along the meridians. The main objective here is to get a feeling for what it really is like to relax by releasing Ki and allowing tension to dissipate.

After completing the six basic meridian exercises in succession, just relax for a while on your back with your eyes closed (Exercise "Z"). Do not spread your arms and legs too far out to the side; just keep them comfortably apart. This position is called "the corpse" in yoga, which simply means to become entirely detatched from the external world. When you do this, your mind will begin to tune in to internal events of your body. You may begin feeling various sensations like tingling or buzzing along the course of meridians which can be regarded as energy flow. These sensations, instead of issuing from conscious awareness, have their origins in the inner workings of your body. When you quiet your mind and relax completely, you can actually experience this primal awareness of being alive come welling up from within.

Chapter 6

Complementary Exercises

Moving with Mental Images

By practicing the Basic Exercises regularly, you should develop an awareness of what it really means to let go and relax. In other words, you will come to grasp the essence of Imagery Exercises, which is to breathe out and allow the lines of tension in the body to relax. In this way stretching becomes much easier and flexibility increases effortlessly. The trick is to first fully feel the tension along the meridians, and then to relax all effort gently with the exhalation in order to effect a complete stretch. Repeating this full stretch three times for each exercise is sometimes enough to open up the pores in your body and warm you up almost to the point of sweating. Although the increase in flexibility will not be noticeable in just one day, you will be able to feel your body becoming more supple from one week to the next. This will be accompanied by an increase in the length of time you are able to let go and relax during the day. Instead of regarding Imagery Exercises as being useful just in the times you are able to exercise, learn how to apply them in your day to day activities.

The primary emphasis in this set of Imagery Exercises, which are meant to complement the Basic Exercises, is to learn to move with a mental image. Specific parts of the body are mentioned in describing the movements of these exercises just for the sake of convenience. Once you get the idea of what the exercise is like, however, it is important to move with a mental picture of your body moving as a whole. No one thinks about putting one foot in front of the other or swinging the arms when walking. This all happens together naturally as an integrated and smoothly flowing motion as soon as we are able to envision the whole act of walking.

The Complementary Exercises are especially useful for people who have difficulty with some of the Basic Exercises and are making slow progress or are unsuccessful in increasing their flexibility. This series of Imagery Exercises can also be effectively used as "symptom specific" exercises as will be explained in a later chapter. Interspersing these Complementary Exercises between the Basic Exercises should provide more tangible results and doing Imagery Exercises will become even more exciting.

Exercise "Y"—Taking Flight (Lung and Large Intestine Meridians)

Throw both your arms up and back with the mental image of spreading large wings. Stand on the base of the toes of one foot and draw the other leg back as if it were your tail wing (Figs. 50 and 51). Then bring the arms down with a big swooping motion and simultaneously jump forward onto both feet, or otherwise just bring your feet together. From this position (standing with your feet together with your arms down) throw your arms up and out (spread your wings again), and at the same time

Fig. 50

Fig. 51

jump forward onto the ball of the other foot with a thump. Simultaneously bend your knee and raise your other foot behind you. Repeat this sequence up to ten times imagining that you are a bird in flight. Be sure to breathe deeply as you do this exercise.

Start with the Basic Exercise "A," and next do Exercise "Y"; then try Exercise "A" once more. You will be surprised at how much easier the stretch in Exercise "A" becomes. If you attempt to stretch the lines of tension in your body by an effort of will as in conventional exercises, once you reach the limit, there is pain and resistance no matter how you try to stretch beyond this point. The more you try the less good it does. Because of this, many people are left disappointed and discouraged, thinking that their body is just not flexible. What one must do is to change the whole approach and make large movements involving the whole body.

Exercise "Y" is designed especially to stretch the Lung and Large Intestine Meridians so that pent-up energy can be released spontaneously. If you can, try leaping up lightly as if floating upward. Once you become used to this exercise, you will begin to feel as if you were really taking flight. This will serve to facilitate the flow of energy in the Lung and Large Intestine Meridians as well as to alleviate physical symptoms associated with these meridians.

Exercise "W"—Knee Lift (Spleen and Stomach Meridians)

Fig. 52

Exercise "W" is an effective way to stretch the Stomach and Spleen Meridians. First do the Basic Exercise "B," and next do Exercise "W"; then do Exercise "B" once again. This will have such a pronounced effect in improving your flexibility, you will probably be amazed at how quickly your body can become limber. To do Exercise "W," simply raise the upper half of your body to the upright position from the reclined posture of Exercise "B." In other words, sit with your legs tucked under your buttocks or folded at your sides (Figs. 52 and 55). The main thing is to get in a comfortable position like this. Next place your hands on both knees and begin lifting them up and letting them down alternately as if trying to walk (Figs. 53 and 54).

You may notice when lifting your knees that one is harder to lift than the other. Do not try to force this

Fig. 53

Fig. 54

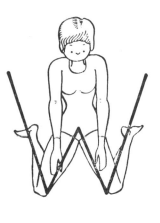

Fig. 55

knee higher. Instead, place your emphasis on lifting the more flexible leg as high as you can. When putting each leg back down, press it down into the floor with your hand. The trick in this exercise is to take each "knee step" slowly and surely as if you were climbing stairs. Take about ten to fourteen "steps" in this way. Not only will this make it easier for you to lean all the way back in Exercise "B," but it will make it easier to keep your knees together and get your back closer to the floor.

Exercise "U"—Seesaw (Heart and Small Intestine Meridians)

Exercise "U" is an effective way to stretch the Heart and Small Intestine Meridians. Exercise "U" also serves as a preventive measure against low back pain or "slipped disks." Sit on the floor in the same manner as in Basic Exercise "C" and bring the soles of both feet together by bending your knees out to the sides. Then place your hands under your legs above the outer ankle bones so that you are holding them in the palm of your hands and your elbows rest on the inside of your thighs (Fig. 58). If one knee sits higher than the other or one leg is more tense and harder to press down to the floor, begin by leaning in the direction of the more flexible leg by pressing down on the thigh with your elbow (Figs. 56 and 57). Then come back to the upright position and lean down to the other (more difficult) side, utilizing the momentum along with gentle elbow pressure on the inside of the thigh. Be sure not to force this movement. Use your weight to press down with your elbow on the easier side, but go lighter on the difficult side.

Fig. 56

Fig. 57

Fig. 58

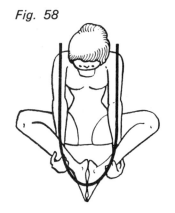

Your torso and head serve as the center of the "seesaw" and you push your knees down to each side alternately using your elbows. The trick is to use the full force of your weight on the side that goes down more easily and to go down easier·on the side that is more tense by just bouncing back in that direction. Repeat this exercise five or six times back and forth, and then try Basic Exercise "C" once more. You should notice a definite improvement in your flexibility.

Exercise "T"—Hip Walk (Kidney and Bladder Meridians)

The Basic Exercise "D," in which one reaches for the toes, may seem difficult for many people in this day and age who are full of tension and stress. There are a few people, however, who are able to reach past their toes with ease in this exercise. Seeing this causes some people to become discouraged at their own lack of flexibility. Sometimes this even causes people to give up on stretching exercises altogether. Conversely there are those who, in a zealous effort to increase their flexibility, get others to push down on their back so they can reach their toes. Even if people force themselves to become more flexible in this way, the hamstring muscles often become tense and sore. Also one can cause muscle cramps this way. For these reasons, few people persevere in practicing such forced stretches for very long.

The effectiveness of Imagery Exercises in improving flexibility, on the other hand, becomes quickly evident by practicing Exercise "D." In Imagery Exercises stretching

Fig. 59

Fig. 60

Fig. 61

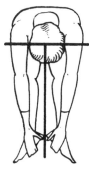

is relaxing and enjoyable. Through its practice, you will come to learn that, rather than forcing a stretch, relaxing the lines of tension while exhaling is a much better way of increasing flexibility.

To do Exercise "T," assume the same posture as in Basic Exercise "D" (Fig. 61). Then push each leg straight out in front of the other alternately. In other words, try to walk forward with your hips while keeping your legs straight. As you push forward with one foot, reach forward with the arm on the same side to move slightly forward in a coordinated manner (Figs. 59 and 60). Then reach straight out for your toes on the other side, and alternate this movement rhythmically on the right and left sides. Place emphasis on stretching on the more flexible side and shove yourself forward from the hips. Do this exercise five or six times on each side and you will notice a surprising increase in the amount of flexibility when you try Exercise "D."

Exercise "R"—Bear Twist (Heart Constrictor and Triple Heater Meridians)

It is not unusual to see a bear in a zoo pacing up and down the cage shaking its head from side to side. Probably it shakes its entire body along with its head to make up for its lack of exercise. People who have difficulty with Basic Exercise "E" must do Exercise "R." To do this exercise, stand with your feet open slightly more than shoulder width and grab the opposite shoulders with both hands. To decide which arm to place over the other, try out both ways to see which is easier just as in the Basic Exercises. Then grasping your shoulders the easier way, reach around as far as you can (Figs. 62–64). The upper half of your body must be tilted forward and your head should bend forward without effort. Imagine that the entire top half of your body is the bear's neck and shake it from side to side. Begin by stretching the side which has the arm on top by twisting fully in the opposite direction. You must twist to the point where the heel of the opposite leg begins to lift off the floor. Put strength in this heel to keep it on the floor in the same place.

Fig. 62

Fig. 63

Fig. 64

The Heart Constrictor and Triple Heater meridians are stretched along their entire length by this exercise. Go easier when twisting in the opposite direction. Simply swing in the opposite direction without using much force. This is the side which has greater resistance to this twisting movement so you should not force it to stretch. This is best done by using more force to swing in the direction of least resistance to twist your whole body as far as you can in one big movement and then to bounce back and twist in the other direction.

Exercise "S"—Looking Over Shoulder (Liver and Gallbladder Meridians)

In Basic Exercise "F" ideally you should be able to spread your legs apart to almost form a straight line. Unless you have practiced doing the "splits" from a young age, however, this is not usually possible. Also most people find it difficult to bend their body down to the side in this exercise so that the head reaches the knee. Nevertheless, there is no reason to feel that you have to be able to stretch this far. The purpose of Exercise "F" is to feel the lines of tension which form along the Liver and Gallbladder Meridians when attempting to approach the ideal position and then to breathe out and release this tension. When a person is so inflexible that no loosening up effect at all is felt with Exercise "F," person may get discouraged and want to give up on these exercises. In this case, a person should definitely do Exercise "S."

Fig. 65

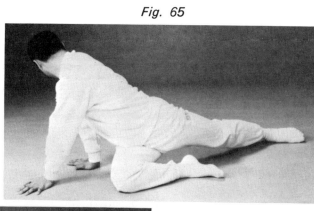

Fig. 66

Fig. 67

Start from the seated position of Exercise "F" with your legs spread open as far as possible. Twist your upper body in both directions to see which side stretches more easily and twist in the easier direction and look backward. Place both hands behind you on the side to which you twist without crossing them. Also bend your knee on this side and pull this foot in toward your crotch (Figs. 65–67). Stretch out the leg that is straight and try to keep the big toe and inside of the foot on the floor as much as possible. Tension should be felt to the tips of your fingers and toes. You should feel the tension the moment you give your body a full twist and look back over your shoulder. Exhale fully to release this tension and then switch sides to twist in the other direction, but remember to go gently. Do this exercise three times on each side, getting a full stretch each time. After this try exercise "F" once again. You will no doubt experience a substantial improvement in your ability to spread your legs apart and lean down to either side.

Exercise "Q"—Head Drop (Governor Vessel)

Continue from the seated position of Exercise "S" by spreading your legs apart as far as you are comfortably able. Keep your knees straight and do not spread your legs too wide. Clasp your hands together behind your head, interlacing your fingers. Then gently begin dropping your head down (Figs. 68 and 69). Instead of trying to bend your torso forward, just imagine that the weight of the hands on the back of your head is making your body lean forward naturally. When you try to bend forward with your torso, this causes the muscles in your body to tense up and the stretch is no longer smooth or natural. The Governor Vessel on the spine is best stretched by allowing the arms to pull the head down. Breathe with the emphasis on exhaling slowly. Relax the tension in your body with each exhalation so that your head droops forward a little more each time. Take your head down as far as you can without causing undue strain. Exhale and let go once more at the farthest point of the stretch and then slowly raise your head and body back up as you inhale. One full stretch in this manner is sufficient to improve the Ki circulation in the Governor Vessel.

Fig. 68

Fig. 69

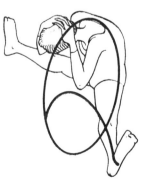

Exercise "P"—Belly Drop (Conception Vessel)

The starting position for Exercise "P" is a push-up. However, unlike the ideal push-up posture, where the body must be kept straight, in Exercise "P" the hips are raised a little so the body is slightly bent (Figs. 70 and 72). This position is much easier to hold for most people. From this position drop your belly or lower abdomen down to the floor (Fig. 71). Instead of bending your arms and going down as in a push-up, keep your arms straight and relax the rest of your body all at once. This will cause the belly to drop to the floor. By keeping your shoulders directly over your arms with the elbows locked, your arms will provide stable support even when the muscles in your arms are relaxed. Imagine that there is a lead weight in your belly, and drop it down to the floor. You may drop down slowly, especially if there is some uncertainty about this quick stretch on your back. But remember to drop down with the exhalation and to relax your whole body after you reach the fully stretched position. Tilt your head back and feel the tension in the Conception Vessel on your center line as you inhale. Exhale slowly and fully as you relax, and imagine that your belly is sinking into the floor as you draw your head back.

Fig. 70

Fig. 71

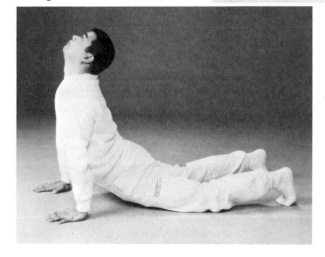

Fig. 72

Chapter 7

Work Exercises

Work Exercises are more advanced than the meridian exercises introduced before and their effects are more pronounced. It is important to undertake each new set of exercises with renewed resolve. Otherwise you will not get as much out of them as may be expected. What is more, without the anticipated results, you could grow tired of these exercises and give them up before they are able to have a significant effect. All these explanations are limited by the bounds of language. The key to success is persistence and getting a feel for the essential aspect of each exercise with your own body.

These exercises are named Work Exercises because they are conveniently done during the day at work. It is usually difficult to find the floorspace to sit or lie down at work so Work Exercises are mostly done in the standing position. These exercises are designed for working men and women as well as adults in general. Of course anybody can do these exercises, but one should have plenty of practice in Imagery Exercises by doing the Basic Exercises regularly. In the Work Exercises, a substantial force comes into play in each exercise at the stage of "releasing Ki" or the act of relaxing with the stretch. Therefore make sure you are mentally and physically prepared before undertaking the Work Exercises.

Exercise "X" (Lung and Large Intestine Meridians)

Both the Basic Exercise "A" and the Complementary Exercise "Y" for stretching the Lung and Large Intestine Meridians are done in the standing position. Exercise "X" is the same in this respect. Open your feet wider than shoulder width and stretch your arms out over your head to form a large "X" with your body. Place both hands on an overhead beam or bar, or otherwise on either side of a doorway (Figs. 73 and 74). Then lean forward and stick out your *hara* (center point) as if it were the center of a square kite that is being tugged by a string.

Fig. 73

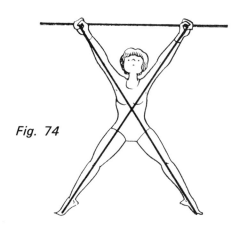

Fig. 74

When you stand on your toes and allow your belly to stick out this way, you will feel bands of tension in your chest, in your arms, and in the back of your legs as well. Bend your head back at this time to stretch fully and then return to the normal standing position and relax. You should not stretch so far as to cause pain. Imagine that the string attached to your belly is being alternately pulled and slackened to raise the kite in the sky. The lines of tension will progressively relax as you repeat this stretching exercise three or four times with this mental image, and your *hara* will feel as if it is being pulled forward naturally.

In addition to providing beneficial stimulation to the muscles and tendons, the pent-up energy which causes tension in the parts stretched is released. In our day to day life we work mostly with our arms in front of us, and we too seldom take a big yawn or stretch ourselves fully to expand our chest. Doing a big stretch like Exercise "X" all of a sudden without preparation can sometimes cause cramps, so be careful and slowly work up to the full stretch.

When you are fully prepared, lean forward with the feeling of being pulled from your *hara*. Draw a deep breath into your belly in this position and then exhale completely and relax your whole body (except the arms). Imagine that you are being pulled forward with a string and allow your body to arch as if you were a kite receiving the full force of the wind. After remaining fully stretched in this position for a moment, return to the standing position. The point of this exercise is to support your weight with your arms and allow your body to lean forward by its own weight. Do not arch your body forward by your own effort.

Exercise "O" (Spleen and Stomach Meridians)

This exercise was named Exercise "O" because a circle is formed with the arms and legs. The mental image to be used in this case is "lifting up food," which is a characteristic pose for the Spleen and Stomach Meridians (refer back to Chapter 4). This exercise corresponds to Basic Exercise "B" which stretches the Spleen and Stomach Meridians. It has the effect of increasing the appetite and improving digestion and absorption of food.

Begin by standing with the legs slightly less than shoulder width apart. Then bend over and firmly grasp above each ankle from the front. Squat down while grasping both legs and then stand up again with the intention of lifting up what you have in your hands (Figs. 75–77). Of course both hands are holding the lower legs, so what happens is the extension of the knees as the torso is bent forward. Nevertheless, one should not think of this exercise as being only a matter of bending and straightening the knees. Do it with a feeling of exuberance as if the object in your hands is a large piece of food which you have finally secured. When you use all your strength to pull up on your legs like this, it will cause your heels to lift up off the floor and you will be balancing on your toes.

Start with several gentle lifts so you can practice going up on your toes and staying in balance. Concentrate on your *hara* and lift from your pelvis; this will keep your body from falling forward. It is perfectly all right to step forward a few steps to stay in balance. After getting a little practice, begin to squat deeper and breathe into your *hara* before pulling up with force. Try pulling up on your legs about five times in

Fig. 75

Fig. 76

Fig. 77

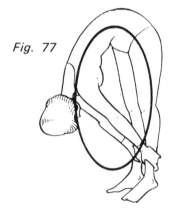

succession with as much force as you can. This is at least as much exercise as a short jog around the block. These who feel they do not get enough exercise can do this exercise up to ten times.

You must really use all of your strength to try and lift yourself up off the ground. For the last lift, pull up with as much strength as you can muster. First draw a deep breath into your *hara* and imagine that you are a weight lifter about to lift a great weight in one quick coordinated motion. Remain on your toes for several seconds after this last big effort and then exhale and relax. Put your heels back on the floor, squat down, and feel yourself relax all over.

Exercise "K" (Heart and Small Intestine Meridians)

Basic Exercise "C" for stretching the Heart and Small Intestine Meridians is based on the characteristic posture of a person in contemplation. These same meridians are stretched in Exercise "K" with a far more dynamic pose which somewhat resembles the letter "K." In order to do this exercise, first you must get a sturdy chair or box. It is also possible to do this exercise at the bottom of a flight of stairs. Start by putting the leg which is more flexible up on the chair or step (usually the left leg is more flexible). Keep the sole of this foot flat against the top surface. Extend the other leg

Fig. 78

Fig. 79

Fig. 80

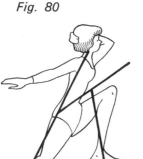

to the back and point the big toe out to the side so that the inside of the foot comes against the floor. Put your hands on the knee of the raised leg and gradually sink your hips down (Fig. 78). This will stretch the thighs on the inside. Let the pelvic area drop lower and lower so that the line of the Heart and the Small Intestine Meridians on the inside of the leg are stretched. Be sure to hold a full stretch for a short length of time rather than bouncing up and down in this position. When both hands are used to push the knee forward while lowering the hips, the line of tension to the inside of the thighs can be felt most clearly. The important thing in stretching meridians is to hold the mental image of stretching the whole body instead of stretching just the legs. This way tension in the leg muscles is minimized and the meridian lines can be felt through the whole body.

Next hold the back of your head with the hand on the side of the raised leg and raise the elbow as high as you can (Figs. 79 and 80). The Heart Meridian in the arm is stretched by raising the elbow up behind as much as you can. Extend the other arm straight out behind you and turn the little finger upward so that a line of tension forms along the Small Intestine Meridian which runs along the top of the arm in this position. Now drop your hips down as done in the earlier exercise so that the knee of the raised leg moves slightly forward. Feel your weight in your *hara* and simply let your own weight stretch your body, and experience the stretch along the Heart and Small Intestine Meridians. When you slowly exhale in this position the sensation of tension will begin to disappear. This means that the lines of tension have relaxed somewhat so your center of gravity can shift even lower. When you draw a deep breath in this position the lines of tension will reappear, so slowly exhale once more to relax them again. After repeating this deep breathing and relaxation about three times, do this same stretch with the other leg on the chair. After finishing both sides just stand in a comfortable manner and allow your breathing to return to normal.

Exercise "J" (Kidney and Bladder Meridians)

Exercise "J" corresponds to Basic Exercise "D," which stretches the Kidney and Bladder Meridians. Stretching by arching backward is not enough to completely release the tension and stress that builds up in the back after a long day at work, especially in those who have desk jobs. Arching the body backward becomes much easier after exercise "J" is performed to gently stretch the lines along the Kidney and Bladder Meridians that have been tense all day. The posture assumed in this exercise somewhat resembles an upside-down "J" so I named it Exercise "J" for convenience sake.

Fig. 81

Stand comfortably with your feet slightly less than shoulder width apart. Then relax the upper half of your body and bend forward. Then hold your legs with both hands. It is best if you could reach your hands down and around your calves, but reaching around your thighs is also quite acceptable. Instead of straining to bend forward, just use your arms to gently draw your head toward your legs. This will make your body bend down fully and naturally. Discomfort results when you try to bend all the way down at once using force. Relax once you bend down as far as you can comfortably go. When you feel the lines of tension, relax your arms, come up a little as you inhale and then slowly draw your head down to your legs as you exhale. Repeat this part of Exercise "J" about five times and feel the line of tension down your back and legs. Doing this will make you aware that the muscles in your back are tense and that this exercise creates a strong line of tension down the back

Fig. 82

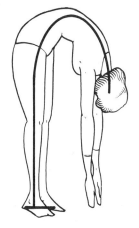

of both legs. There is no need, however, to force a stretch in an attempt to relax these muscles. Not being able to bend down very far does not necessarily mean that your legs are unduly stiff or rigid. It is usually just an obstruction in the flow of Ki in these areas which makes it difficult to extend fully.

After bending forward in this way by using your arms, return to the upright standing posture. The main point of the last part of Exercise "J" is simply to allow the upper part of your body to fall forward from the waist up. Normally when people bend forward this way, they reach down with their arms in order to bend just as far as they can. In the final stage of Exercise "J," however, your arms must be kept completely relaxed. Begin with your arms hanging loosely by your side and exhale from your *hara*. Slowly bend forward from your head, and lean forward by successively relaxing your neck, shoulders, and torso (Figs. 81 and 82). You can picture this action of bending forward as that of an inflatable doll deflating. Instead of trying to bend forward, just let your upper body be gently pulled down by the force of gravity.

Exercise "G" (Heart Constrictor and Triple Heater Meridians)

Fig. 83

Exercise "G" corresponds to Basic Exercise "E" for stretching the Heart Constrictor and Triple Heater Meridians. Those who have difficulty in assuming the lotus position* will find marked improvement after practicing this exercise for a certain period of time. Since the stretching effect in this exercise is quite powerful, however, you must take care to do the stretching gradually.

To do this exercise, lean your back and hips up against a wall, and let the wall support your weight. The surface of the wall needs to be smooth to do this exercise. Point your toes outward, bend your knees, and sink your weight down. Place one foot on the other thigh, just above the knee, and stand on one leg. Try out this position both ways (standing on each leg) to find which way is easier for you. Then do Exercise "G" on the side which is easier. Assume a stable posture standing on one leg with the other leg resting above the bent knee. Place

Fig. 84   *Fig. 85*

your hands on each knee and bend the leg you are standing on just a little more (Figs. 83 and 85). Your hips should sink slightly against the wall as you bend the knee more. In addition to stabilizing your position, the hands on each knee serve to spread your legs and stretch your inner thighs by taking the weight of your upper body. Do not bend the knee of the leg you are standing on all at once. Allow your hips to slide down gradually, and slowly bend your knees out to the side so as to avoid a sudden or excessive stretch.

* The full lotus position is the traditional cross-legged seated posture of yoga and Zen. The full lotus position is assumed by placing the right foot on the left thigh and bringing the left foot over the right to place it on the right thigh.

If the stretch becomes too difficult, just raise yourself back up by straightening the knee of the supporting leg.

Once you reach a stable position in the above mentioned manner, you are ready for the final portion of Exercise "G." Grasp both shoulders by crossing your arms. The arm on the same side as the leg you are standing on should go underneath. Bend your head forward and curl your body up somewhat (Fig. 84). The picture which comes to mind in this exercise should be one of withdrawing into yourself or hibernating. Inhale deeply in this position and then exhale slowly to relax your whole body as much as you are able. The weight of your body should cause your knee to bend more and make your body sink down a little more. Maintain this position and draw one more deep breath and exhale slowly and completely. You must be careful not to go too far and lose your balance or fall over. After breathing and stretching this way for about three times, raise yourself back up to switch the position of your legs and arms and do Exercise "G" by standing on the other leg for the same amount of time. After this, return to the standing posture with a feeling of expansion as if you were coming out of hibernation.

Exercise "L" (Liver and Gallbladder Meridians)

Exercise "L" corresponds to Basic Exercise "F" for stretching the Liver and Gallbladder Meridians. This exercise increases the flexibility of joints and elasticity in tendons for those whose bodies have become rigid and inflexible. Damage to tendons generally results from poor circulation of Ki in the muscles and tendons, and this

Fig. 86

Fig. 87

exercise serves to prevent injuries such as sprains and strains. Exercise "L" is recommended especially as a warm-up for vigorous sports.

In Exercise "L," one leg is bent while the other leg is extended straight out to the side. Lowering the hips and stretching the legs in this way with the hands placed above both knees is a posture often seen in warm-up exercises for

Fig. 88

stretching the back of the legs (Fig. 86). The aim of Exercise "L," however, is not just to stretch muscles and tendons, but to relax the tension along the meridian lines. Therefore there is no need to push down on the straightened leg to force it to stretch. The posture of Exercise "L" may be similar to other exercises, but the hands are placed on the legs only to keep your balance. Slowly lower your hips down toward the raised heel of the bent leg. The extended leg should be allowed to slide out as far as it will go without forcing or straining, but keep the tips of the toes on the floor. This exercise is also one which should be performed first on the side which is easier to stretch. Stretch the less flexible leg later. Be sure to support yourself with both hands placed above your knees to control the stretch and keep it from going up too far. Repeat this preliminary step in Exercise "L" three or four times on each side.

Once you become accustomed to this position, place both hands behind your head and clasp them together. Begin on the easier side, as determined by the first part of this exercise. Be careful not to lose your balance. Face the extended leg by turning your upper body slightly in that direction (Figs. 87 and 88). The palm of the hand on the side of the bent leg should cover the back of your head while the other palm should come to the side of your head so that the elbow stretches out in the direction of the outstretched leg. Slide the foot of the extended leg out farther while keeping the toes on the floor. Let your buttock rest on the heel of the bent leg. Ideally your buttock should come down slowly onto the heel while exhaling, but it does not matter if your buttock does not go down so far. Once you learn to relax your whole body quickly and completely, your buttock should come to rest on your heels smoothly and evenly so that you do not lose your balance. You will lose your balance if there is tension remaining in your body, so relax and be confident that your heel will hold your weight.

Chapter 8

Type Exercises

Imagery Exercises by Types

The treatment of diseases in Oriental medicine is to a large extent an intuitive process based on philosophical principles which seek out basic causes. Even when two people have the same disease with identical symptoms, individual differences in the person's constitution and the underlying cause of the disease are carefully analyzed to choose a treatment most suited to each individual. Remarkable results can be obtained when the most appropriate form of treatment is selected in this way. Chinese herbal medicine, acupuncture, and shiatsu are natural and holistic forms of treatment, and the most basic and important feature in all these methods is the "differentiation of syndromes" (diagnosis of meridian imbalance) used to decide the most effective treatment for a person.

In the "differentiation of syndromes" the signs and symptoms of a patient at a given time indicate the "vector," or the direction in which his condition is progressing, and this direction determines the treatment. These "vectors" can be categorized into six types according to the six basic functions or tendencies of life. As discussed before, these six functions are fundamental to all forms of life. Each of these basic functions developed into complementary pairs in the course of evolution, and each of these were classified by the Chinese into Yin and Yang pairs and systematized as the twelve meridians. Any deviation from the natural balance among these essential functions, or undesirable developments for normal functioning of life, can be corrected most precisely and efficiently by determining the "syndrome" or the particular type of meridian imbalance a person has at the time.

In contrast to the traditional Chinese approach, in Western medicine disease is analyzed systematically with scientific data which is primarily concerned with the manifest phenomena or the apparent effects of a disease. The classification of diseases in Western medicine is much more conducive to scientific study since it deals with visible or measurable phenomena. This view of the disease process, however, tends to be fixed in time with analysis only of clinically relevant symptoms and findings.

The "differentiation of syndromes" used in Chinese medicine contains a dynamic element of being a forecast of the future and it indicates the most suitable treatment in that instance. This insight is derived from keen observation of changes occurring as a result of the natural healing powers at work in the body. A patient's condition is classified into a "syndrome" by the type of energy or meridian imbalance existing at the time. In this approach, a person's condition is traced from the past up to the present so as to decide the direction, or "vector," in which his physical condition is inclined to progress. Thus, even though two persons may appear to have an identical problem, they are given different treatments when their physical conditions are progressing in different directions.

In a similar sense, the outcome of the same treatment or health regimen can vary widely from person to person. Commonly, exercise programs are claimed to be equally effective for everyone and individual differences are seldom taken into account. The limitations of such "universal" approaches are clearly evident, however, when considering the issue of nutrition. Man's diet varies considerably by climate and geographical location. If all diets were made the same, aside from not suiting people's tastes, the food would not be adequate or properly digested in all cases. The important thing, be it diet or exercise, is to get a variety most suited to yourself. In Imagery Exercises it is especially important to find out what our type is to choose the exercises which suit our own condition, instead of being satisfied with a standard regimen.

One of the simplest ways to classify human beings is by their gender. Although men and women are basically equal, they have inherent differences. It is clear that all things cannot be the same for men and women. Men and women develop in different ways physically even when they eat the same diet, so obviously our bodies use the same nutrition in different ways. Such a difference also exists in how our bodies develop with exercise. When women exercise, their bodies do not become muscular in the same way as men. The bodies of women retain their unique proportions even when doing the same weight training as men. The difference in the effect of the same exercises, however, is not really so profound. A basic difference between the sexes is reflected more in the attitudes and motivation for exercising. Men generally think of exercise as a means of improving their health and becoming more effective in their chosen area of activity, while women tend to view exercise in terms of their appearance or personal appeal. Naturally these attitudes are merely tendencies and they are not fixed in either sex.

Another way to classify people is by personality types, and this grouping is not specific to gender. Three basic types can be distinguished by disposition, or the physical, emotional, and intellectual orientations. These orientations also have a bearing on people's reasons for exercising as follows: the first type gets pleasure out of working and building the body, the second type derives joy in self-expression through movement of the body, and the third type finds satisfaction in following a plan and working toward a goal. Such orientations seem to stem from inborn dispositions. Depending on which type of person is teaching an exercise system, the presentation differs substantially according to their respective dispositions. Whether one can go along with the instruction depends to some extent on whether one can relate to the teacher's basic orientation.

The thing that is special about Imagery Exercises is that every person can choose the exercises which best suit one's own preferences and physical type, as well as schedule and personal goals. The main goal in practicing Imagery Exercises is to become more healthy and attractive by achieving a balance in the functions of Ki (meridians), which are essential to life. Therefore everyone must choose those exercises which are best suited to their own situation and practice them to reach a balanced and natural state of health. There is no need to do all the exercises in a routine way. You can skip over those exercises or moves which are strenuous or difficult in order to do only those exercises which are easier and more fun to do. The easy exercises are often the ones which are the most suitable and beneficial for you.

When performing the six Basic Exercises, most people find some exercises more difficult to do than others. Some exercises are more difficult because there is an obstruction of Ki in the meridians affected. In other words, the body is "stuck" in those places. I have already explained how relaxing and releasing Ki improves its circulation throughout the body. By doing the exercises for each of the twelve meridians to find out which ones are the most difficult to do, it will become clear to you where your body tends to get "stuck" and how it is out of balance. Also by noting your symptoms or physical problems and checking them against the symptoms associated with each meridian, you can learn which meridian is likely to have the greatest obstruction of Ki.

The reason the meridians were classified into twelve types in Oriental medicine is because all variations of life processes can be covered by twelve categories. In the Five Phases principle, all phenomena is classified into five categories, and this was further divided into the ten stems by the Yin and Yang within each phase. This classification seeks to divide things by their essential nature. The classification into six categories came from the Three Yin-Three Yang principle,* which follows changes occurring with time. The six categories of Three Yin-Three Yang were divided into Yin-Yang pairs to create twelve categories or the meridian system. This, in other words, means that there are twelve basic types of transformations that Ki undergoes in time. Some of you may be aware that the traditional Chinese calendar is composed of the combination of the ten stems and twelve branches. The ten stems were conceived from spatial relationships of the Five Phases (East, West, North, South, and Center), whereas the twelve branches were devised to trace temporal relationships (twelve months of the year). In the Chinese calendar these two systems are combined to express all time, dates, months, and years in terms of the sixty combinations of stems and branches. According to tradition, all life activities of man are subject to the natural Yin-Yang cycle of time; those who live in harmony with this cycle remain robust and those who go against it die before their time.

Restoring a Balance in Energy

In the Basic Exercises the main emphasis is on learning to relax the lines of tension to release blocked up energy by Imagery Breathing. The Complementary Exercises are meant to promote greater relaxation and to alleviate obstructions in Ki by the use of imagery. The purpose in the Work Exercises is to further enhance the circulation of Ki. In Type Exercises I will explain how to change or restore a person's energy balance by working with Kyo and Jitsu, which can be called the secret of Oriental medicine.

---

* The Three Yin-Three Yang principle is a traditional Oriental classification system in which diseases are divided into six basic stages to trace the progress of a disease. A pair of regular meridians are associated with each of the stages as follows:

    Small Intestine and Bladder   —Greater Yang
    Triple Heater and Gallbladder—Lesser Yang
    Large Intestine and Stomach   —Brilliant Yang
    Lung and Spleen   —Greater Yin
    Heart and Kidney   —Lesser Yin
    Heart Constrictor and Liver   —Absolute Yin

In all Imagery Exercises it is important not to force those movements which are difficult and to avoid stretches that are painful. Many other exercise systems including yoga emphasize this same point. But instruction is seldom given concerning how one should go about those exercises or stretches which are difficult to do. Just doing the difficult exercises over and over until they can be done correctly is a long process which requires great patience. All too often people become impatient and strain themselves, or give up altogether.

In Japan the phrase *kibun-o-kaete* is often used, and it means literally to change one's Ki (attitude) or to direct one's Ki (attention) in a totally different direction. (In everyday usage this phrase means a change of attitude.) An obstruction of Ki, or a fixation in psychological terms, can be relieved by redirecting one's Ki (attention) in a different and totally new direction. There is a strong tendency in us, however, to become preoccupied with only those things which command our attention. The more we are told not to worry about something, the more likely we are to worry about it. When it comes to stretching exercises, even when we are told not to force things and just to forget about the exercises that are difficult, if we have trouble with a particular exercise, it usually bothers us and we have a hard time accepting it.

This is like advising a person with insomnia "When you have trouble getting to sleep, forget about trying to get to sleep; just relax and accept things as they are." This type of advice is usually of little use. It is the insomniac's conscious mind which wants to sleep, and also it would be the conscious mind trying to forget about getting to sleep. As long as his mind stays fixed on the issue of getting sleep, his Ki remains stuck. Therefore this person must be shown precisely how to release the Ki which is stuck. The most effective way to redirect Ki is to do something completely different. This is exactly why people tend to seek recreation after work. Sometimes simply not working can be a form of recreation. Once we feel obliged to take part in recreation, however, it is no longer recreation in the real sense. The way to become free of any preoccupation is to direct our Ki (attention) toward something other than that which is occupying us. The Jitsu condition can be likened to the thing which preoccupies a person, while the thing that a person is not aware of can be called the Kyo.

The line of tension (muscular tension, discomfort, or a dull and heavy sensation) produced by stretching in a way that is difficult is referred to as Jitsu in Oriental medicine. The Chinese character for Jitsu (実: Shi in Chinese) depicts a house which is filled to capacity. In traditional medicine this denotes a Yang condition of fullness. It is easy to understand how movement would become difficult with a full house. Jitsu conditions are always treated with a Sha (瀉: Xie in Chinese) technique. Sha, or sedating methods, serve to "disperse" or transfer energy from one place to another. The most effective way to transfer excessive energy away from the Jitsu is to alter the balance of Ki by treating the Kyo. The Kyo, in contrast with the Jitsu, is an area lacking in energy, where there is little if any restriction in movement. The Chinese character for Kyo (虚: Xu in Chinese) represents a mound which is hollow in the center. Kyo or emptiness is something which is not very apparent and naturally this makes it difficult to find. The empty quality of Kyo is not meant to imply that there is nothing there, but rather, that it is hard to come to grip with because it is difficult to see and touch. Kyo is considered as being the Yin counterpart of Jitsu, which is a Yang condition. The Yin aspect includes all that which does not manifest as Yang.

Therefore, Kyo can be considered as the counterforce that gives rise to the Jitsu. The primary aim in Oriental medicine is to provide a Ho (補: Bu in Chinese) treatment for Kyo conditions. A Ho technique is one which collects or draws Ki where it is lacking. Drawing energy to the Kyo (tonification) is the most effective way to alter the energy balance and relieve the Jitsu condition. Here lies the marvel and mystery of the effectiveness of traditional Chinese medicine. This great principle is difficult to teach without a living example, but nevertheless I will attempt to convey its significance in the pages to follow.

The basic tenet in Oriental medicine is that "the deficiency of Ki is Kyo and an excess of Ki is Jitsu." Both Kyo and Jitsu are a result of the dynamics of Ki in the body. The categories of Kyo and Jitsu are also used to describe the overall condition of a person. A condition of being weak and deficient in physical energy is regarded as Kyo, and that of being strong and full of energy is regarded as Jitsu. Because Jitsu means an abundance of energy it is generally viewed as being more desirable than Kyo. Since Kyo is an insufficiency of Ki, which more than anything needs to be replenished, and Jitsu is a condition of overactivity which requires sedation both conditions can be considered as a deviation from the natural balance.

Strong stimulation and radical treatments must be avoided for Kyo conditions, but there is usually little danger in treating Kyo conditions as long as one exercises a reasonable amount of caution. People with Jitsu conditions are in more danger of being harmed by overdoing some remedy since they are more prone to overreact. Kyo and Jitsu can also be compared to differences in age. Younger people have the vitality to overcome most physical problems, but their condition can fluctuate drastically. Thus their condition can sometimes progress too far in the wrong direction. On the other hand, older people take much longer to recover from an illness, but their condition usually remains stable. Older people with diseases need more patient and undramatic efforts to replenish their reserve of energy. In the case of young people medical intervention can be more drastic and such powerful treatments often yield good results. This is because younger people generally have a surplus of energy which enables them to better withstand invasive or radical treatments. Also they are capable of resting and recovering more quickly.

In any case, Kyo and Jitsu, rather than being absolute principles, are relative concepts which are neither good nor bad in themselves. They are very similar to Yin and Yang in that they describe two opposite tendencies. The only difference is that Kyo and Jitsu describe the availability and functional condition of Ki, or vital energy. In the theory of stress set forth by Dr. Hans Selye, this same phenomenon—the distortion of Ki in the process of living—is described as resistance against stressors. Distortion of Ki does occur in response to stress as resistance against adverse stimulation, but the special significance of Kyo and Jitsu lies in the distinction of passively accepting adverse stimulus and actively resisting it. Kyo and Jitsu are concepts which aptly capture the reaction, or the distortion of Ki, in both its positive and negative aspects to more accurately describe the condition of living organisms. One simple illustration of this is fatigue. Suppose we become fatigued after working hard all day. The obvious physical reaction is one of fatigue, which we can feel. The other reaction is that the fatigue causes us to sleep well at night to recover our vitality.

A Jitsu area of the body is more visible and easy to find because it is tense and full of resistance to any force coming to bear on it. Thus, it can be felt as being stiff or hard to the touch. The person being touched often experiences this as some discomfort or pain. In contrast to this, a Kyo area is lacking in energy. This deficiency of Ki is not clearly apparent, and this makes the Kyo area difficult to locate. Something which is missing is difficult to pinpoint by a brief examination, but it becomes apparent when one looks all over for it and finds it missing.

Distortions or imbalances in Ki consist of both the Kyo and Jitsu aspects, and while the Jitsu which is full and brimming with energy is more noticeable, actually Kyo is what gives Jitsu its energy. When a Jitsu feature becomes manifest, it is a sign that a Kyo aspect exists somewhere else. People who put up a bold front are often hiding some weakness. In Japanese the word *kyosei* (empty force) means a bluff or a false show of courage. When people have real strength, they generally refrain from displaying it. Our stomach serves as a good illustration of the dynamics of Kyo. When the stomach becomes empty, our hands and mouth go into action to fill the stomach. When the stomach becomes full, our hands and mouth stop their activity and rest. If a person still wants to eat more after becoming full, this is a sign that he has an emptiness somewhere which has yet to be satisfied.

If Jitsu (tension) is resistance to forces throwing the body out of balance, it is also energy working to reestablish a balanced state of health. So imbalances can also be understood as a force for restoring harmony or balance (Fig. 89). By learning to identify Kyo and Jitsu, one finds the key to restoring harmony. Only by becoming fully aware of the various imbalances and distortions in your own body will you be able to find the way to correct them. Once you recognize imbalances, the simplest way to restore a balance of energy is to replenish the deficient Ki in the Kyo area. The Jitsu, or apparent condition, exists to indicate the presence of Kyo. Something has to be done about the Kyo before the Jitsu can be relieved. Since Jitsu, or the apparent problem, exists to signify the presence of Kyo, concentrating on the Jitsu to rectify the situation means the Jitsu is prevented from doing its job, and consequently resistance increases and the symptom is aggravated.

Fig. 89

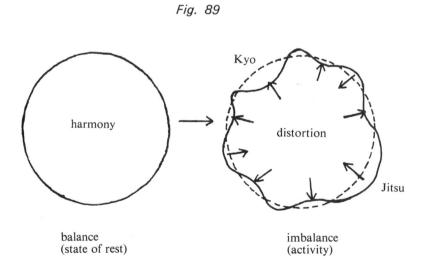

balance
(state of rest)

imbalance
(activity)

The primary treatment principle in Oriental medicine is Kyo Jitsu-Ho Sha (虚実補瀉: Xu Shi-Bu Xie in Chinese), which is to reinforce the Kyo and disperse the Jitsu. The rule in Imagery Exercises, where instead of forcing a movement one always moves in the direction of ease, is founded on this fundamental principle of balancing the Kyo and Jitsu aspects in our body. The body most readily corrects itself when we avoid pain and work with, rather than against, the dynamics of our energetic system. Even if a structural adjustment is made forcefully to correct a distortion, the body naturally resists such intrusive stimulus, and the correction usually does not have a lasting effect.

The presence of pain and resistance in a particular movement tells us the body does not want to move in that way, and it is pointless to force it. Be that as it may, the passive approach of just leaving the problem alone to let it take care of itself is also unsatisfactory. The Jitsu aspect exhibiting pain and other symptoms is letting us know that there is a Kyo aspect somewhere else. The role of the Jitsu aspect is fulfilled only when the energy deficient Kyo aspect is tonified (reinforced) and pain and symptoms are thus alleviated. Therefore, while you must not use force to do stretches and movements which are difficult for you, you still have to take steps to make such movements easier. Otherwise the Jitsu aspect, or difficulty in movement, is unable to find relief from its role of calling attention to the presence of Kyo.

When the same movement is done to the right and left, the side which is more difficult is Jitsu. Therefore the other direction, in which movement is easier, is performed repeatedly with Imagery Breathing to draw Ki over to that side. This is done because the direction of ease is related to the Kyo aspect which is deficient in Ki, and repeating the movement on the easier side serves to replenish Ki on that side. After doing this, movement to the Jitsu side clearly becomes easier. The easing of the Jitsu condition gives proof that the Kyo has been tonified.

When you do all of the Type Exercises, you will find a few that are more difficult to do. By going through the whole series of exercises, the Kyo aspect will be tonified without your being aware of it, and each exercise will become easier as a result. It is always useful to do the Basic Exercises first to get a general idea of which meridian groups are Kyo or Jitsu. Then when you do the Type Exercises, you can narrow them down to a few exercises that are most difficult for you. Then you can single out another Type Exercise that is easy and allows you to relax and increase flexibility. Instead of trying to improve your performance on difficult exercises, find an exercise among the easy ones which serves to relax the tension that is causing the difficulty. There is always one exercise which works best for this purpose although this may be hard to figure out in the beginning. Take your time and find the exercise which makes the difficult stretches easier. You will eventually learn to appreciate the surprising effect of the Type Exercises in relieving Jitsu symptoms.

Becoming Aware of Imbalances

All people see things with their own particular bias. People automatically put themselves in the center when judging relative matters such as ahead and behind or above and below. People also make themselves the standard when judging the size of things whether big or small. Even when we do not use ourselves as the standard, invariably we impose our own standards when we judge something. Even abstract qualities like health, beauty, and happiness are decided by our own standards. This is the same thing as every individual being alive just because each individual has an awareness which places him in the center. And since everybody is viewing things from different vantage points, no one really has the correct perspective in an absolute sense. All individuals have no choice but to have a biased or distorted view of things. Death can be regarded as something which equalizes all things, while life can be said to exist only with an imbalance or distortion. Living can even be called the very act of creating distortions and imbalances.

The six basic orientations of life processes in animals (the twelve meridians in six Yin-Yang pairs) are a result of the imbalances created by movement. However, as long as an organism is able to shift smoothly from one mode to another, life functions proceed in a normal and balanced manner. Even though imbalances are a necessary part of life, if we become fixed in a position of imbalance or remain stuck in one mode, this will eventually lead to dysfunctions and disease resulting from the inhibition of other functions of Ki. In the Far East, those who displayed consistent power in all realms of activity without becoming attached to any one thing were called *shinjin* (true person). These were the sages and mystics who, like the floating clouds and flowing water, lived without becoming attached to things in the mundane world.

Be that as it may, for the ordinary person being alive means to have imbalances, and these imbalances follow the pattern of the six basic functions related to the meridians. Ideally all the basic functions should balance each other out, but it is difficult to strike a balance, especially in today's society with work specialization. Also, people are born with certain tendencies which predispose them to particular imbalances. Thus there are several levels of imbalances in an individual from inborn characteristics, acquired characteristics, and conditions resulting from one's current lifestyle. Imbalances like this eventually lead to disease when they go uncorrected.

Theoretically it is possible to identify the various imbalances, or the meridian type, of a person and return them to a perfectly balanced condition. But this is not really possible for the majority of people because of the dynamics which cause the imbalances to come into being in the first place. Even if a person were taught the best exercise for correcting imbalances, it would require a great patience and there would be obstacles in practicing it in just the right way. The probable outcome would be for a person to give up on the exercise before completely mastering it. It is more natural and the person is more likely to succeed if the initial effort is made relatively easy. Nevertheless, people always want to be told what is the ideal exercise, and they try to imitate any exercise that is claimed to be the best. The point is, no one exercise is ideal for everyone, and it takes time to find and correctly learn the exercise which best suits our special conditions.

In Zen Imagery Exercises, rather than offering one ideal set of exercises for everyone, the aim is to teach people to become aware of their own imbalance and learn the exercises which are best for them in this process. The key to adjusting your Ki imbalance is to find which exercise is the easiest to perform and which one causes you to feel the most tension along the meridians. Tension can be equated to an obstruction of Ki, and the primary cause of difficulty in movement is not the tightness in the muscles or joints themselves. The movement will become easy once the obstructed Ki is released. You can begin the process by relaxing the affected part as much as you can by a long and complete exhalation. There is no need to pull or force your tight muscles and tendons. A greater sense of health and well-being will come naturally as a result of learning to recognize imbalances in terms of the meridians and taking the time to release tension regularly. This will enable you to consistently maintain a balance in basic life functions and enjoy optimum health.

Exercise "a" (Lung Meridian)

Stand with your legs slightly more than shoulder width apart and hold both hands behind your head with the fingers interlaced. Draw your elbows back so as to open up your chest, and also look slightly upward. People put their hands to the back of their head and stretch this way naturally after studying or working intently. You may sometimes do something similar to this in a chair by stretching out your legs, leaning back on the backrest and stretching your arms back with the elbows bent. You can imagine this kind of a stretch as you do Exercise "a," which is very similar except that it is done in a standing position.

Next turn to either side and twist your body as far as it will go (Figs. 90–92). By comparing the movement in both directions, you will probably find that one side is harder to do or slightly more strained. After you decide which side is more difficult, twist repeatedly in the easier direction. Begin by arching your back in the easier direction and then turn your upper body slowly in that direction as you inhale. Keep twisting and stand on the heel of the foot in the direction of the turn. Come up onto the toes of the other foot as you continue inhaling. Hold the position of maximum twist as you exhale deeply and release Ki. Try to relax with the stretch. Your whole

Fig. 90

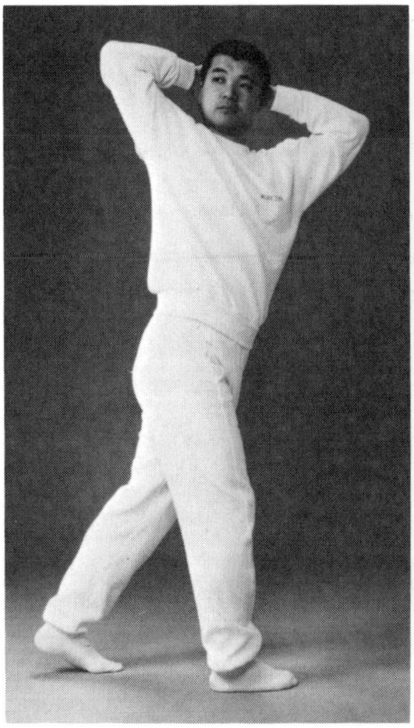

Fig. 91

Fig. 92

body will loosen slightly by exhaling this way and you will go a little farther than what you thought was the limit of the twist. Once more exhale deeply and relax at the limit of the twist, and this will allow you to twist even more. Repeat this breathing and stretching about five times on the easier side. Then do the same breathing and stretching about three times on the more difficult side to loosen up even more. Twisting in the direction which was more difficult, you will find that you can twist much farther.

Exercise "y" (Large Intestine Meridian)

After finishing Exercise "a," put the clasped hands behind your head on top of your head with the palms down. Bring your heels together and point your toes out in opposite directions. Bend your knees halfway and get into a stable stance with your knees also pointing out (Figs. 93 and 95). Next straighten out your legs, stretch your whole body upward, and stand on your toes (Fig. 94). Also straighten out your arms and turn your clasped hands over so the palms face upward. Look up and reach upward by straightening your arms out completely. Keep your hands clasped together but allow your thumbs to separate so that your index fingers receive the greatest stretch. Do this upward stretch while inhaling. After stretching completely with the inhalation, exhale and release Ki. This will make you lighter and you will be able to stretch even farther. Then slowly go down onto your heels and sink your hips down slightly by bending your knees. At the same time bring your clasped hands back down over your head.

Fig. 93   Fig. 94

Fig. 95

There are no right and left sides to this exercise, therefore repeat this same movement seven to ten times to repeatedly stretch and release the Ki in the Large Intestine Meridian along the whole length of your body.

Exercise "w" (Stomach Meridian)

Stand on one foot, bend the other leg behind you and grasp the back of the foot with your hand on the same side (Fig. 96). Stretch your free arm straight out in the other direction. Start off by trying this exercise on both sides to determine which side is easier to do. Then begin doing Exercise "w" on the easier side.

Fig. 96   *Fig. 97*

Fig. 98

As you slowly inhale, pull up on the foot raised in back of you so that the leg is stretched to its limit (Figs. 97 and 98). The leg you are standing on should be kept straight. The arm on the same side should reach straight out and up so that the little finger and ring finger are drawn back slightly. After inhaling deeply and stretching as much as you can in this position, exhale and release Ki to stretch even more. After doing this exercise about five times on the easier side, change sides and stretch the side which was more difficult. You will notice that stretching on the difficult side becomes noticeably easier compared with your first attempt. Your right-left balance should be improved substantially by putting an emphasis on moving and stretching the easier way and then doing the same movement just a few times more on the difficult side.

Exercise "b" (Spleen Meridian)

Sit on the floor with both legs extended straight out to the front and both hands on the floor behind and to the side of your hips so that your arms prop you up from behind (Fig. 99). This should feel something like sitting on a lawn and relaxing. Your fingers may be spread apart, and your feet can be placed comfortably apart. From this position slowly begin inhaling and feel yourself fill up with Ki and raise your belly up as high as it will go (Figs. 100 and 101). Naturally your abdomen will arch up and your head will come down. Arch your whole body upward and stretch your feet, but keep your toes in contact with the floor as much as possible.

After getting into this position with your belly pushed up as far as it will go, slowly exhale. You will feel your body relax slightly with the exhalation, so use this chance to arch your body up even farther. You should be able to push your belly up just a little farther. This stretches and facilitates the flow of Ki along the entire length

Fig. 99

Fig. 100

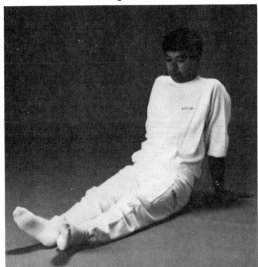

Fig. 101

of the Spleen Meridian. There is no movement to the right or left in this exercise, so the same stretch can be repeated seven to ten times to facilitate the flow of Ki in the Spleen Meridian.

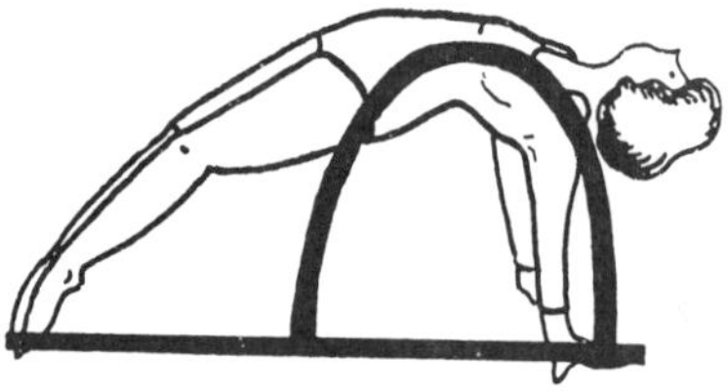

Exercise "c" (Heart Meridian)

For Exercise "c," it is best if you are able to assume the full lotus position, which is the cross-legged sitting position with one leg over the other used in yoga and Zen. If you are unable to get in this position, the half lotus or even just crossing your legs will suffice. Roll backward from the seated posture with your legs crossed and get into the shoulder stand position (Figs. 102–104). Prop yourself up by holding yourself in the back with both hands. Push your waist upward while staying in balance. The back of the head, shoulders, and upper arms become the foundation in this shoulder stand, but care must be taken not to strain your neck in this position.

When viewed from the side, the body curled upside down in the above manner resembles the letter "c." The entire length of the Heart Meridian is stretched in this position. If your legs are in the full lotus position, both legs will stay together

Fig. 102   *Fig. 103*

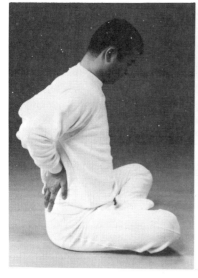

Fig. 104

with the knees stretched out to the sides. However, if you just have your legs crossed, you will have to make a special effort to keep your legs together and to spread your knees out to the sides. Inhale deeply in this position, and after you feel the line of tension, exhale completely and release Ki. This will relax your whole body and make it curl up even more. Inhale and exhale slowly once more in the same position before taking your hands from out behind you to return to the original seated position. After your breathing becomes calm and regular again, roll back into the same shoulder stand position and begin the same stretch by inhaling deeply. This stretch can be accomplished without much effort because of the pull of gravity. Nevertheless, this exercise is difficult for some people, and there is a chance of straining the neck when done suddenly or excessively. Five repetitions of this exercise is sufficient to improve the flow of Ki along the Heart Meridian.

Exercise "u" (Small Intestine Meridian)

Start Exercise "u" from the same cross-legged seated position of Exercise "c" and bring the left foot under the right leg over to your right side. Next move your right leg over your left leg so the right foot rests near your left hip joint. This way the right knee will be on top of the left knee in front of you and your feet will cross over to either side. Raise your right arm with the elbow bent and place your hand on your back, then reach your left arm around behind you and grasp your right hand (Figs. 105–107). Many people are unable to reach their other hand in this exercise at first, so try the same thing by reversing the position of the arms and legs. Decide which side is easier for you and begin Exercise "u" in the easier position.

Arch back slightly to expand your chest as you work to get a better hold of each hand with your fingers. The palm of the top hand should face in while the palm of the bottom hand faces out. Inhale deeply once you get a full stretch. Then exhale completely and release Ki in this position. This will relax your whole body and allow

Fig. 105

Fig. 106

Fig. 107

you to bring your hands even closer together. Repeat this breathing and stretching about five times. After this, do this same exercise in the opposite way for another three times.

Exercise "u" is modeled after the "ox" posture in yoga. It is said that this position cures headaches and insomnia, in addition to improving the sexual function. However, an explanation is seldom offered as to why this is so. The reason for these effects is more understandable to those who are familiar with the meridians because it is evident how this posture stretches and improves the circulation of Ki in the Small Intestine Meridian.

Exercise "t" (Bladder Meridian)

Sit with your legs out in front of you and bend both your knees upward. Next grasp the outside of each foot and pull them toward yourself so that your knees bend farther and come up to your chest (Figs. 108 and 110). Then, as you slowly inhale,

Fig. 108

Fig. 109

Fig. 110

straighten out your knees and extend your legs (Fig. 109). Keep holding onto your feet with your hands so that your upper body is pulled forward by the straightening of your legs. It is ideal if you are able to straighten your legs completely and your head comes down to your knees, but there is no need to force yourself into this position when there is too much tension in the back to do this. Even if your knees remain slightly bent, stretch your legs out to bend forward as far as you can while continuing to inhale. Pause in this position for a moment and then exhale and release the tension generated along the Bladder Meridian. You can feel the stiffness and tension relax momentarily, and your body should bend forward a little more. Return to the starting position by drawing your knees up to your chest. Next stretch out again while inhaling and then relax and stretch further as you exhale. You can repeat this sequence up to ten times.

In this modern age so full of pressure and stress, many people carry a great deal of tension in the Bladder Meridian, which runs down the back of the body. It is not so easy to just let go of this tension and relax. However through the practice of Imagery Exercises like Exercise "t," you can learn to relax both mentally and physically. The key lies in learning to release Ki (relax with a stretch) by exhaling fully with a clear mental picture of loosening up.

Exercise "d" (Kidney Meridian)

Begin from the same seated position as in Exercise "t" with your legs straight out to the front. Then roll backward and raise both legs back over your head so that your body becomes curled like a shrimp (Figs. 111 and 112). Instead of rolling back into

Fig. 111

Fig. 112

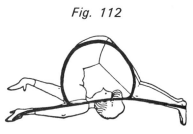

this position quickly, take your time and first lay down flat and then lift your legs up over your head in a steady motion. If you need support to keep your hips up in the air, you can place your hands on your back. The weight of your legs should make your toes reach down to the floor. Nevertheless, it is not important whether your feet touch the floor or not, so do not force them down. Those whose toes easily reach the floor can keep their arms on the floor to maintain their balance. When you feel the tension in your back and legs, exhale completely and release the tension as much as you can to loosen up a little more. After this go back to the original seated position and then roll back once again into this position. You will find that your body becomes more flexible and the exercise becomes easier with each repetition. Repeat this exercise slowly up to ten times.

This position is called the "plow" in yoga, and it is said to improve the function of the thyroid, spleen, liver, and kidneys as well as to stimulate the nervous system and increase vitality. In terms of its effect on meridians, this posture stimulates the Kidney Meridian the most. Often in yoga the need to keep one's knees straight or not to bend one's toes is emphasized, but there is no need to worry about these details in Exercise "d." Just breathe through your *hara*, and instead of forcing the stretch, just allow your own weight to stretch you.

Exercise "e" (Heart Constrictor Meridian)

Stand with your feet less than shoulder width apart and point your toes out as much as you can. Your feet should be in a straight line as much as possible, with the toes pointing in opposite directions. Bend your knees and squat down a little to get in this position. Hold your hands together behind you by interlacing your fingers and make the palms face upward (Fig. 113). Next, while inhaling slowly, bend your knees to squat down even farther and stretch your arms out and raise them behind you (Figs. 114 and 115). Since you have raised your arms up behind you, your body should lean forward and also your head should face down. Hold your breath momentarily after you reach the lowest comfortable position with your arms raised as high as you can. You should be able to feel the tension along the Heart Constrictor Meridian. After this, exhale completely and release Ki so you are able to squat down even farther and raise your arms even higher behind your head. There is no limit to how much you can squat down or how far your arms can be raised. The main point is for you to feel the relaxation of tension within the limits of your ability to stretch.

Exercise "e" improves the flow of Ki in the Heart Constrictor Meridian. In contrast with the Basic Exercise "E," which is a stretch for both the Heart Constrictor and Triple Heater Meridians, Exercise "e" is specifically for stretching the Heart Constrictor Meridian. A variety of mental images can be used in doing this exercise, but that of peering out over the edge of a cliff seems particularly appropriate. Just imagine yourself hanging on to a rope behind you.

Fig. 113   Fig. 114

Fig. 115

Exercise "r" (Triple Heater Meridian)

Stand with your feet a little more than shoulder width apart. Raise both hands over your head and hold them together by interlacing the fingers with the palms facing upward. Then bend down to either your right or left while turning your body slightly toward the back (Figs. 116–118). By doing this the Triple Heater Meridian is stretched all along the side of the body.

Fig. 116 *Fig. 117*

Fig. 118

The important thing in this stretch is for you to feel the stretch along the back of the arm down to your shoulders. You must bend into a position where this stretch extends down to the side of your body so that it can be felt all the way down the outside of your leg. You should also bend your head into a position where it connects with this line of tension to link the entire Triple Heater Meridian on one side of the body. If you make the movement by your conscious will alone, your muscles end up becoming the main focus and thus you will only be able to feel certain areas of muscular tension. The sensation of "tension" along the meridian can be felt by following the sensation in your arms and slowly bending and turning your body in a natural and coordinated fashion. Imagery Exercises are similar to Tai Chi in one sense because the sensation of Ki cannot be felt or followed unless the movements are made slowly and in unison.

Try this stretch on both sides to see which side is more limber. Begin by bending to the easier side and turn into position while drawing a deep breath. When the tension along the meridian reaches all the way down to your leg, exhale completely and release Ki, bending down a little farther as your body relaxes. Do not force this extra stretch; just allow it to happen. Repeat this stretch about five times on the easier side and then bend down to the other side about three times.

Exercise "s" (Gallbladder Meridian)

Lie on your side and then prop up your torso with the arm on the bottom. Next grab the knee of the leg on top from the inside with your free hand. Raise the top leg straight up and support it with your arm (Figs. 119–121). As you continue to raise the leg, slide the supporting hand from the knee up toward the foot. You should be facing the raised foot. Your bottom arm should be slightly to the front of you with the forearm and palm against the floor for balance.

As you slowly raise the top leg as high as it will go you should feel a line of tension form along your side and on the outside of your legs. This is the course of the Gallbladder Meridian. This line of tension will be felt most clearly when your legs

Fig. 119

Fig. 120

are spread with your pelvis turned to face the side rather than up at a diagonal. You should also stretch the arm that is holding up the leg as you stretch the leg. To do this, reach around the raised leg to grasp it as far up as you can.

Determine which leg can be raised or stretched more easily by trying this exercise on both sides. Start on the side which is more flexible, and inhale as you raise the leg as high as it will go. Exhale and release Ki, stretching a little farther. Repeat this exercise about five times and then change to the other side and repeat another three times.

Exercise "f" (Liver Meridian)

Exercise "f" corresponds to the triangle posture in yoga. Start by standing with your legs far apart and point your toes outward. Raise both arms out to your sides up to shoulder level with the palms facing down (Fig. 122). Then bending one knee slowly, lean down to that side while inhaling (Figs. 123 and 124). Go down so that you touch your toes on the side to which you are bending. Your arm on the other side should reach upward as you bend down in the opposite direction so as to point straight up when the other arm reaches the floor. You should continue to face forward as you lean down to the side. This way you will be able to feel tension along the Liver Meridian. Try this posture on both sides to compare the amount of tension, and begin on the easier side. Stretch to your limit as you inhale, and then exhale and allow the tension to relax somewhat so that you are able to lean down even farther in the same direction. Repeat this exercise about five times in the easier direction and

Fig. 122

Fig. 123

Fig. 124

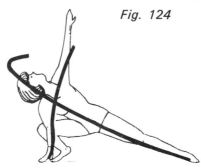

another three times in the opposite direction. Although we begin the movements on the flexible or easier side, the less flexible side is also affected so that it becomes much easier to move in the difficult direction. This should give you a feel for how your whole body is connected. It is wrong to consider the flexible side as being good and the less flexible side as being bad. They each play a special role in the overall balance of the body. Inflexibility is the result of obstructions of Ki. Once you learn to release Ki effectively, you will be able to experience for yourself how the lack of flexibility is often due to causes other than the condition of muscles, tendons, and joints. You must get a feel for the little extra stretch that accompanies the exhalation even after the limit of movement is reached. Each of the Imagery Exercises are repeated several times, not to force the stretch farther each time, but to feel the relaxation brought about with the release of Ki each time. Do not make the mistake of repeating these movements mechanically. It is most important that you sense the subtle changes taking place in your body with every breath as you repeat these movements.

Chapter 9

Imagery Exercises for Better Appearance

Exercising and Appearance

Standards for beauty or good appearance vary by the period and culture, but it seems that most standards of beauty are based on external appearance. There may be some variation, but generally several types of women are cast as "beauties" and anything that makes a woman closer in appearance to such models is considered to be "beautifying." Such stereotyping of good appearance occurs for men as well. A muscular build in a man is usually regarded as being attractive, but this comes from a time when the strength implied by a muscular build had real functional value. While many exercise regimens and beauty programs today are able to bring people closer to some stereotyped model of beauty, the effect of such programs are often achieved by ignoring the unique characteristics and needs of the individual.

Today in mechanical engineering, it is considered unwise to design the external form before building a machine. The most beautiful design is regarded to be a product of building a machine that can perform its function most efficiently. High performance machines such as race cars, airplanes, and rockets are most beautiful when they are built to perform at peak efficiency. This approach to designing machines reaffirms nature's design work which always produces a form most suited for performing certain functions. This can be regarded as natural beauty. The human body is a masterpiece among nature's creations simply because it is best suited to the wide variety of activities that human beings undertake. The culture in ancient Greece was based on physical education which had the objective of developing a well-rounded and perfect human form. Today our concept of beauty is mostly limited to certain superficial features and we seem to have lost sight of the essence of what constitutes a good appearance. Health, which can be called a process of wholesome growth both mentally and physically, is a prerequisite for real beauty.

In this sense exercising for the purpose of improving your appearance actually cannot be separated from increasing your physical capabilities in all areas of life. It is not truly beneficial to exercise just certain parts in hopes of building the features one would like to have. Exercises for making a person closer in external appearance to some ideal model is of questionable value for the person as a whole. The potentialities of human beings, both mental and physical, vary greatly from person to person. If the exercise is not suited to the person as a whole, the chances are that the effects will not be deep or long-lasting. Only those activities undertaken in response to a deeper need to find more fulfillment in life can bring about profound and lasting changes. For this reason, instead of exercising simply to improve your appearance, it is best to work on attaining the highest level of personal effectiveness in all areas of life.

Oriental medicine, which is based on the principle of nurturing life and the acceptance of diversity, holds that health and beauty as well as fulfillment in life lie in enhancing the process of life which is unique to each individual. To do this most effectively, people have to become aware of the basic orientation of their life processes, or what type they belong to. This type, rather than being a classification by superficial features, is a flexible definition of imbalances which occur from our mental and physical inclinations. Enhancing a person's beauty or attractiveness can therefore be regarded as a matter of getting one's entire mind-body process moving in the right direction.

I was one of the first persons to advocate the need for beauty treatments based on the Oriental perspective of life. Therefore I developed "beauty shiatsu" and explained its effects from the standpoint of meridians. Sometime later Oriental medicine began to receive attention as being effective for the purpose of beauty treatments. Perhaps the holistic approach of Oriental medicine, in which an attempt is made to treat the whole person, gained popular appeal. Nevertheless, these "beauty treatments" generally consist of nothing more than applying tsubo or acupuncture points in beauty massages. If people really wish to fully apply Oriental medicine for improving appearance, a person's type (meridian imbalance), which accounts for individual differences, must be the basic consideration from which to start. Types according to meridians are a representation of the essential tendencies in each individual, which relates to family and work environment as well as personal habits and attitudes. Such types are a classification of meridian imbalances which occur in everyone.

Ideally, a person should be totally balanced and have a well-rounded personality with no character flaws. Such a person would be able to lead a joyful life and work enthusiastically in harmony with others. Although it is possible to visualize such an ideal state and strive to live up to this, aside from being very difficult to keep up, such perfectionism could cause one to lose sight of something essential in oneself. In just the same way, although beauty or attractiveness is some ideal condition which we all would like to attain, it is also something which is impossible to standardize or measure objectively.

Overweight and Types by Meridians

Being overweight is by far the greatest of the concerns regarding beauty and appearance for the majority of people. In the animal kingdom a substantial part of waking activity is taken up by the search for food. Always being in a slightly hungry state is the basis for the agility, responsiveness, and beautiful appearance of wild animals. In civilized society the concern of hunger has diminished and instead an environment for overindulgence and excess caloric intake has been created. We can almost gauge the advancement of a civilization by the number of overweight individuals. In fact, obesity can be regarded as one of the biggest threats to our health today.

These days being overweight is thought to indicate a lack of self-control, and in some companies excessively overweight people are even considered unfit for managerial positions. Being overweight not only affects a person's appearance and physical condition, but also becomes the cause of various diseases. It is not absolutely certain, however, that all such physical problems would be resolved if only an overweight person loses weight.

The criteria for being overweight is derived from the average weight of people in a particular height category. This criteria, however, has no direct bearing on a person's appearance, ease and grace in motion, or sense of well-being. The main problem that must be addressed when having become obviously overweight is the unbalanced condition in one's life and the consequential susceptibility to disease. Therefore the effort to control one's weight should be identical to the attempt to restore a balance in one's life. In other words, it is one and the same thing as working to increase the level of one's health and well-being.

Obesity cannot be called a disease in itself, but it is a condition which leads to many physical problems, and in extreme cases it becomes difficult to carry out normal day to day activities. The cause of obesity stated simply is a surplus of calories from food intake in excess of energy expenditure. This surplus of calories gradually accumulates in the body as fat. In many cases overweight individuals are not even aware that they are eating too much, and quite often they do get a substantial amount of exercise. Even when a person is told to eat less and exercise more, this is not easy to do, especially if the person is not convinced that this was the problem in the first place. Furthermore, dieting can reduce a person's energy level and exercising too much all at once can put a strain on the heart, which can be dangerous.

The meridian principle, which Imagery Exercises are based on, is a concept rooted in Oriental medicine, and this meridian system is associated with basic life processes. Achieving a balanced state in this energy system yields health. The basic approach of Oriental medicine, which is to regard physical problems as imbalances in energy circulation, applies even in the case of excess weight. Restoring the energy balance is always the solution. The causes for becoming overweight as identified by modern medicine include an imbalance in the intake and expenditure of calories, organic dysfunctions, hormonal imbalances, and psychological conditions. Although the validity of such rational conclusions cannot be refuted, when it comes down to the practical problem of reducing weight, since these various factors are present in differing combinations, it is difficult to decide just where to begin.

In Oriental medicine, instead of a scientific analysis, the type of imbalance is ascertained from a holistic perspective and all physical and psychological conditions are categorized according to the meridians. Reducing weight is not distinguished from curing an illness, and diet is not separated from psychological factors. Six basic overweight types associated with the six Yin-Yang pairs of meridian are introduced below to enable people to set an idea of which meridians are involved and to find the way to greater physical and mental well-being.

Type A (Lung and Large Intestine Meridians)
This type of overweight person is characterized by a lack of vigorous respiratory activity. People of this type often have had tonsillitis or recurrent respiratory infections in their younger years, and their weak respiratory system often has caused them to refrain from vigorous physical activity. In other cases such people dislike sports or lose interest in sports early in life. In any case, they have very little oppor-

tunity to exercise and rarely do they get the chance to breathe deeply. Such people are usually quiet types with a pale complexion and they have fine skin which sweats very little. They do not like to undertake any physically demanding work.

The muscles in people of this type are not that well-developed and they appear chubby. Their body has an overall rounded appearance and fat accumulates in places which usually stay thin to enable movement. Those parts where fat should be burned up during exercise instead become repositories for the accumulation of fat.

The most important exercises for people of this type are those stimulating the Lung and Large Intestine Meridians. This will improve the respiratory function and increase the desire to exercise. Along with meridian exercises, brisk walks gradually leading up to jogging are recommended.

Type B (Spleen and Stomach Meridians)

The characteristics of a person belonging to this overweight type are worrying too much about details, craving food without really being hungry and never feeling satiated. Generally such people are nervous types who eat too fast, and they get little exercise in relation to the quantity of food they consume. They usually prefer sweet foods and foods high in liquid content. These people tend to belch and release gas often and they often complain of shoulder tension as well as pain in the knee joint. The chest, stomach, and legs of such people tend to accumulate fat, but despite this the skin on their arms and legs tends to be dry and rough.

People of this type often become diabetic, but since it is seldom a case of diabetes mellitus,* insulin injections and dietary restrictions only seem to sap their energy. Since this type of person tends to be a worrier anyway, finding out that they are diabetic only compounds the problem. Therefore, for these people, rather than imposing strict restrictions on their diet, it is better to ask them to reduce the amount they eat and to chew their food well. Their recovery is much faster when the above practice is coupled with a healthy amount of exercise, especially that which stimulates the Spleen and Stomach Meridians.

Type C (Heart and Small Intestine Meridians)

Those who belong to this overweight type have a little too much self-control and are long-suffering. They tend to be tense and have a formal manner. People of this type always seem to be busily running around. They often feel a little feverish in the head and sweaty in the palms, while the lower half of their body easily becomes chilled. They also tend to have low back pain or a feeling of heaviness in their legs. There are many people like this, especially among women, and such women often have some gynecological problems. Women of this type who have menstrual irregularities and a tendency to get chilled tend to put on weight while they are still young. Women of this type without such problems usually begin gaining weight after menopause. People of this type have to be careful because they are predisposed toward heart problems. The waist becomes large and flabby in people of this type, and the distinction between

---

* Diabetes mellitus is a metabolic disorder caused by insufficient secretion of insulin. Its main symptoms are excessive thirst, hunger, and urination together with the appearance of sugar in the blood and urine.

the thighs and the torso is unclear because their hips and legs are quite large. These people also have great tension and rigidity between their neck and shoulders and often complain of headaches or dizziness. The problem is not so apparent while they are young, but in their later years all manner of physical problems begin to appear. This is associated with the "stagnation of blood" as spoken of in Oriental medicine. People belonging to this type should reduce their intake of fruits and do exercises which improve the function of the Heart and Small Intestine Meridians.

Type D (Kidney and Bladder Meridians)

People of this overweight type tend to be emotionally unstable and become tense and excited over the slightest thing. Often such people are irritable and experience symptoms associated with dysfunctions in the autonomic nervous system such as insomnia and headaches. Among people of this type the lower back and limbs easily become chilled and urination tends to become more frequent. Their arms and legs sometimes appear swollen although there may not be any actual swelling. Also their skin tends to be dark and lacking in resiliency. People like this must be careful to avoid getting renal hypertension.*

This type of overweight person usually has a bloated appearance. People like this worry about every little thing, and since they lack motivation, they easily become fatigued and lethargic. Also they sweat mostly from their face and hands, and there is a tendency of fluid retention in their bodies. If they catch a cold it often gets drawn out, and nasal congestion and coughing persists for a long time. In times like this, swelling becomes more serious. People of this type generally suffer from poor nutrition because of an unbalanced diet. Instead of eating a square meal, they tend to be constantly nibbling. The best thing for people like this is not to eat anything between meals and to reduce their intake of fluids. The most beneficial exercises for this type of person are those which stimulate the Kidney and Bladder Meridians.

Type E (Heart Constrictor and Triple Heater Meridians)

People of this overweight type have poor circulation and they have sensitive skin which is prone to problems. They have a tendency to allergies and often get pimples or skin rashes. Also they tend to be ticklish and are adverse to humid weather. These people easily catch colds and get sore throats. Other common symptoms experienced by this group include a feeling of hotness in the head along with chilling of the extremities, heaviness of the head, shortness of breath, palpitations, and fluctuating blood pressure.

People of this type become fat mostly in the upper part of their body, and thus their neck, shoulders, and arms seem to bulge. The actual increase in their weight, however, is seldom large. Often their stomach is more distended from gas than it is from fat. They generally have a feeling of oppression in the chest and lack stamina and perseverance. Their whole body seems tense and swollen, and they are lacking in resistance and often have many complaints all over their body. The best thing for people like this is to expel fluids from their body by sweating them out at least once a day. They will gradually become lighter and trimmer after they rid their body of

* Renal hypertension is high blood pressure caused by kidney disorders in which increased fluid retention leads to an increase in blood volume and a rise in blood pressure.

excess materials. It is important that they avoid sudden and strenuous exercises and not go on crash diets. Exercises to stimulate the Heart Constrictor and Triple Heater Meridians are the most beneficial for this type of overweight person.

Type F (Liver and Gallbladder Meridians)

A common tendency for this type of overweight person is to work very energetically and also to eat and drink a lot. This type of person is able to nap easily and get rest in almost any situation. This type of person also tends to have high blood pressure. Once people like this become middle-aged, they do less work requiring physical effort or they quit doing sports so they get less chance to exercise, but opportunities to go out eating and drinking only increase. This eventually causes their stomach to bulge, and in some cases their waist size keeps on increasing until it gets to a point where their pants slip down easily. Many people like this are in positions of responsibility and have begun to feel the effects of aging. This overweight type is common among men, but many professional women are included in this group. These individuals tend to have a thick neck and their overactivity is often associated with enlargement of the prostate or thyroid glands.

The abdomen and chest become very big in people of this overweight type, and dieting not only often fails to reduce their size but makes them feel less energetic. These people usually have to contend with more than the normal amount of stress and they often get eyestrain. People like this rarely lose much weight with a moderate amount of exercise, so many of them just resign themselves to being overweight. Nevertheless, regular exercise is an absolute necessity for people of this type in order to lose weight. People like this should cut down on their consumption of meat and dairy products and do those exercises which stimulate the function of the Liver and Gallbladder Meridians.

Everyone wishes to become or stay attractively trim, and countless people are constantly making efforts to lose weight or to stay slim. There are a large variety of weight loss programs advertised to meet this demand. Each the various methods for weight loss has its merits and shortcomings. Viewed from different perspective this variation means that it is not so easy to stay trim and that many people are unsuccessful. For this reason it is important that you keep your goal firmly in mind and make consistent efforts and keep yourself from getting too impatient for results. Imagery Exercises, aside from having real benefits in terms of staying trim, are a holistic approach enhancing your body's overall functional ability. So you can be assured that regular practice coupled with the recommendations for your type will yield the best overall results.

Chapter 10

Reclining Exercises

One of the basic problems with most weight loss programs is that the only aim is to lose weight and little if any attention is given to the meaning behind losing weight. Thus these methods overlook the cause of the problem and ignore the fact that losing weight can sometimes even be detrimental to a person's health and well-being. Exercises for the purpose of losing weight must also be done from a holistic standpoint with movements designed to bring the whole body into balance. In Zen Imagery Exercises, the exercises requiring special emphasis can be decided by each person with a view to improving one's overall physical balance. Doing exercises tailored to personal needs is of particular importance when working on losing weight and improving one's appearance. You should learn each series of meridian exercises throughly and then regularly practice a combination which best suits your physical make-up. The next series of exercises were designed particularly for those interested in exercises for improving their appearance, especially in terms of becoming more slim.

One of the basic aims in these exercises is to determine what meridian type you belong to in order to better understand the reason for your present physical condition. The six overweight types are general categories indicating which one of the six essential life functions is the basic cause. These six functions used to distinguish the six overweight types can be divided further into Yin and Yang aspects which correspond to the twelve meridians. The Reclining Exercises, in the same manner as the Type Exercises, are related to one of the twelve meridians.

As explained before, the Kyo-Jitsu combination of twelve meridians creates 120 possible types of meridian imbalances. Exercising for better appearance or weight loss, just as when exercising for health, is most effective when one's meridian imbalance is determined beforehand and the most suitable exercises are performed regularly. Doing the full sequence of Reclining Exercises is beneficial in all cases, but it is best to identify one's "type," or meridian imbalance to place emphasis on the most suitable exercises. You may continue to do the full sequence of Reclining Exercises after deciding what "type" you are; just reduce the number of repetitions for the exercises which are not as useful to you. There is no need to improve your performance or to work specially hard on those exercises you have difficulty with. Instead place your emphasis on doing the exercises you like in the most relaxed and enjoyable manner. If you continue practicing all of these exercises in a relaxed way, you will begin to notice that those exercises which were difficult become easier and easier without special effort.

Doing only the exercises you like, however, seldom gives good results. For the best results, you should do the entire sequence of either the Type Exercises or the Reclining Exercises to find out which meridian imbalance you have and to bring about an overall improvement in the circulation of Ki. First you have to find the superficial and more obvious Jitsu condition, which is tension, discomfort in movement, or lack of flexibility. Then you should look for the opposite of the Jitsu condition, or the Kyo aspect, which is hidden beneath the surface and is the underlying cause of the Jitsu condition.

Once you find out which overweight type you are, or decide what kind of meridian imbalance you have, you should concentrate on the meridian exercises most suited to your "type." This is a very simple and effective approach for restoring an overall balance and increasing health and well-being. When we do exercises focusing only on the movement of individual parts, this tends to increase our imbalance and does not benefit our health. This principle also applies to our diet, for even so-called health foods can be unhealthy when eaten at the expense of a balanced diet. A strict vegetarian diet with brown rice may be good for a person in some cases, but this kind of diet can also cause an imbalance if adhered to too rigidly. This is because those things truly beneficial to health are generally enjoyable, comfortable, and keep a wholesome balance.

The Reclining Exercises are designed so that they can be done quickly and easily in bed or on the floor. Since they can be done even in bed, they require no preparation and minimum effort. The effects of each exercise in terms of improving appearance are listed after the explanation of the exercise so that those who wish to work on certain features can practice more for specific effects. Doing this sequence of exercises before getting out of bed in the morning will enable you to start the day wide awake and full of energy. Also these exercises can be performed in reverse order at night just before going to bed to promote deep and restful sleep.

Imagining becoming more healthy and attractive in a dream-like state early in the morning, before you are fully awake, will enhance the effect of these exercises. One of the best times of the day to exercise is early in the morning because it gets us off to a good start. It is ideal to exercise before we begin our regular daytime activities. This way we can find out where tension still resides by seeing which movements are difficult, and we can relax and stretch those parts to start the day off right with a balanced and free flow of energy.

For this series of exercises, it is best if you could altogether discard the idea that you are doing exercises. The ideal thing when exercising early in the morning would be to let yourself be slowly aroused by the awakening of energy from within. This comes with moving and stretching your body in every direction. The ideal way to do these exercises before going to sleep would be to gradually let go of all the stresses and tension of the day with the intent of checking in with your body to see how it is doing. A good mental picture is one of using all movements to draw your consciousness from the external world back into yourself. Thus you will become in touch with each and every part of your body, and after relaxing and releasing tension from every part, you will fall off into deep and restful sleep.

Exercise "j" (Large Intestine Meridian)

As you begin to awaken, imagine that it is early in spring when everything in nature begins to come alive and animals come out of hibernation. Exercise "j" gives you a chance to express this incipient movement of life with a squirming and wriggling

Fig. 125

Fig. 126

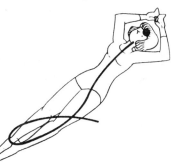

motion of your whole body. Start by pressing your heels and shoulders against the bed or floor and shake your body loosely (Figs. 125 and 126). Keep your waist relaxed and allow it to bend from side to side.

Once you become used to this movement, you will be able to increase the movement of your waist, and the rest of your body will move in synchronization just like a little animal trying to work its way out of the ground. Start with slow movements from side to side and allow the energy from inside of you to build up the movement. You will be able to feel the dormant energy within you stirring to meet the day. While you are asleep the energy in your body is evenly distributed, but once you begin to wake up this energy is collected in certain areas to initiate activity. Think of this exercise as a movement to awaken the energy lying latent in your body.

Exercise "i" (Spleen Meridian)

As you pass the threshold of wakefulness, bring your attention to your body and become aware of your feet. Straighten your body out and slowly draw your toes upward so that the stretch extends up the back of your legs and body (Figs. 127–129). Then slowly extend your feet and point your toes down so the front of your body is stretched. Keep the image that your feet are pulling on all the rest of your body and

Fig. 127

Fig. 128
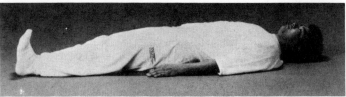

Fig. 129

then turn your feet in big circles so that the movement reaches all parts of the body. It is important not to use much strength at first. Begin slowly and allow your energy to build up gradually.

Exercise "h" (Lung Meridian)

After you are almost fully awake from the last exercise, you may notice that Ki has still not reached the ends of your toes. To send Ki into the tips of your toes, bend one knee up and then straighten your leg out quickly with a kicking action (Figs. 130–132). This exercise is not merely intended for bending and extending the legs so do not bend and straighten your knees mechanically. The point is to throw your leg back into the straightened position while keeping your legs loose so that the vibrations can be felt through the whole limb. When the leg is extended mostly with muscular force, although a stretch in those muscles may be felt, the vibration sensation through the leg cannot be felt. It is important to pause and feel the energy coursing throughout your leg before bending and stretching the other leg.

After alternating four to five times between each leg, raise both knees up together and throw the legs straight out together. This should be done so that you straighten out from head to toe like a whip. This will fill your legs up with energy to the tips of your toes. Do not bend your knee too far up in the beginning. About a ninety degree angle is good to start with, and then as you repeat this motion, gradually bring your knees up more and more. This will serve to prevent cramping in the calf muscles.

Fig. 130

Fig. 131

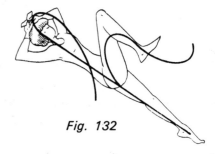

Fig. 132

The Effects of Exercises "j," "i," and "h"
The main effect of Exercises "j," "i," and "h" is to firm up the lower limbs and make

them slimmer. These exercises also make the ankles more flexible. The Lung and Large Intestine Meridians are related to bending and stretching the legs and the Spleen Meridian is related to the working of the knee joints.

Women who have gynecological problems and other complaints tend to have unshapely legs which lack muscle tone and sometimes their legs seem to be the same thickness from top to bottom. Their legs appear heavy and their step is unnaturally heavy when they walk. Exercising the legs is of particular importance for these women, and exercises according to your own condition are the shortest route to healthy and good looking legs.

Exercise "z" (Stomach Meridian)

After alternately flexing and straightening your knees in Exercise "h," bring both knees up to your chest together and hold them below the knees (Figs. 133 and 136). Curl your body up and bring your knees up to your chest naturally rather than just using your strength to bend your knees up. Holding the knees comes as a natural act when you curl up. Do not try to draw your knees closer to your chest with your arms. Simply hold your knees in this position in a relaxed way for a while and then let go of them (Figs. 134 and 135). Your legs will go back naturally to the original position so that your feet are on the floor with the knees bent. Do not straighten your knees.

Exercise "k" is begun from this position. Exercise "z" should be done once again after finishing Exercise "k." When Exercise "k" is done properly, one should notice a definite improvement in flexibility upon repeating Exercise "z." Always do Exercise "z" both before and after exercise "k" so that you can compare the difference.

Fig. 133

Fig. 134

Fig. 135

Fig. 136

Exercise "k" (Triple Heater Meridian)

Raise your knees up to your chest and place both hands behind your head and relax your elbows so they lie on the floor. Relax briefly in this position and then let your knees go down together to the side in whichever direction you are inclined (Figs. 137–139). Your knees should reach the floor without effort. Once you turn your knees down to one side, slowly raise them back up again and let them down in the other direction. The stretching action on the waist should be stronger moving to this side so refrain from the impulse to bring your knees down to the floor forcefully. It matters very little whether your knees touch the floor on this side.

Fig. 137

Fig. 138

Fig. 139

When this twisting movement is repeated about three times in the easier direction, the knees will go down to the harder side and reach the floor with greater ease. The twisting action on the waist should increase with each repetition so that the stretch extends all the way up to the shoulders and arms. The aim of this exercise has been reached when the twisting movement can be felt to extend all the way up to your elbows. The effects of this exercise can be checked by doing Exercise "z" once more. You will see that your waist has become much more flexible and that your knees come up much farther without effort.

The Effects of Exercises "z" and "k"

Exercises "z" and "k" not only work the waist but improve the circulation of Ki along the Stomach Meridian, which runs down the front of the body, as well as along the Triple Heater Meridian, which runs down the side of the body. Stimulating the Stomach Meridian serves to reduce excess fat and facilitates the proper development of muscles. Stimulating the Triple Heater Meridian removes excess accumulation of fluids under the skin to create a sharper body contour. These exercises thus are effective in slimming the body and bringing out the natural contours.

These exercises are also useful as prevention against low back pain, which is common in people past middle age since they seldom get good exercise in the waist and lumbar area. When movement of the waist is not smooth, all movements become awkward and a sudden load or strain can cause a "slipped disk," or a sprain in the lumbar area. If one has low back pain, these exercises should be done slowly and cautiously. Sudden and forceful movements can aggravate the condition. The key point in finding relief is to first move in the direction which comes easily and then to try the other direction without forcing.

Exercise "n" (Heart Meridian)

Keep both knees bent together after doing Exercise "k" and place both feet together on the floor close to your hips (Fig. 140). Next place your hands behind your waist and lift your hips up by supporting them with your arms (Figs. 141 and 142). Instead of just trying to raise your hips up, it is best to have the image of moving the knees forward to create a stretch from the knees to the shoulders so that the abdomen extends and the hips rise automatically. Support your waist by propping it up with your elbows and hands.

Fig. 140

Fig. 141

Breathe and extend in this arched position for a moment, and then relax and let your hips back down on the floor as you exhale. Do not let your hips fall abruptly back to the floor. Try to support the weight of your hips on your upright lower legs and this will make your descent smoother. Then just lie on your back and place your arms out to

Fig. 142

the side and relax every muscle in your body. After this, stretch once more in the same way from your knees to your shoulders by raising your hips off the floor and forming an arch. Inhale deeply and hold the tension of.the stretch for a moment while supporting your waist from underneath with your arms. Right after this, exhale and sink back down to the floor. Relax your whole body and let it feel warm and light. This stretch should be repeated four or five times.

Exercise "g" (Heart Constrictor Meridian)

Let the legs that were held in a vertical position during Exercise "n" fall out to both sides but keep both feet together. Clasp your hands together over your head so that both palms face the top of your head (Figs. 143 and 145). Keep your elbows on the floor. Then visualize energy pouring in from the back of your *hara* (the low back region) and coursing in either direction up and down your body to reach the tips of your fingers and toes. As you feel this energy fill you, extend your body fully and stretch your arms and legs completely (Fig. 144). This exercise is most effective when the toes are stretched out as far as they will go so they reach for the floor. It is important, however, that you do not try too hard to touch the floor with your toes because this could cause your calf muscles to cramp. It is best to do this stretch two or three times and to increase the stretch gradually.

After stretching completely and feeling your body brimming with energy, let out a long breath and relax all the tension in your body as you bring your arms and legs back to their original position. The mental image to hold here is that of relaxation causing your arms and legs to come back into position naturally. Try not to make this an intentional

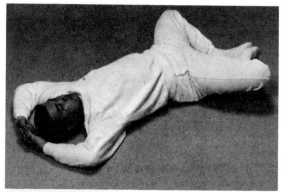

Fig. 143

Fig. 144

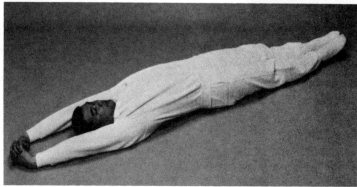

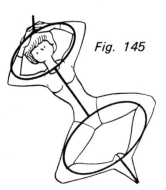

Fig. 145

movement. When done right, your whole body will feel light and expanded. Be aware of the inside of your body and check for any sign of lingering tension. Then once more feel the energy pouring in from behind your *hara* as you inhale, and do another full stretch as the energy fills your whole body up from your fingers to the tip of your toes. Repeat this stretch five or six times for the best results.

The Effects of Exercises "n" and "g"

Exercises "n" and "g" in particular have the effect of improving the shape of breasts in women. The breasts do not become shapelier or firmer just by exercising the chest area. The Heart and Heart Constrictor Meridians travel over the breasts and the functional state of these meridians is related to the shape of the breasts. Activating the function of these meridians causes a woman's breasts to become more shapely and in balance with her overall figure.

Poor or insufficient breast milk is also associated with problems with the Heart or

Heart Constrictor Meridian. Often mothers with poor lactation who are prone to anxiety have some distortion in their upper thoracic vertebrae. Naturally correcting such problems requires some spinal adjustment in addition to exercises which directly affect the meridians in the chest area.

Exercise "I" (Conception and Governor Vessels)

Keep your legs extended after stretching in Exercise "g." Take your clasped hands and place them on the back of your head and let your elbows rest on the floor. If you are in bed when doing this exercise, place some covers on yourself below your waist. The extra weight on the lower half of your body will make this exercise easier. Normally when people do sit-ups, for developing the abdominal muscles, somebody else has to hold the feet. Otherwise sit-ups are difficult to do for most people because the feet tend to lift off the floor. Many people would like to do sit-ups regularly, but give up on the idea because someone is not always available to hold their feet while they do sit-ups and they do not know of a good way to keep their legs on the floor by themselves. There is no need for a special contraption to hold your feet down. All you really need to do is to place a quilt or blanket over your legs. Keeping the legs on the floor is much less of a problem with a little extra weight on them. If you make a sudden effort to raise the upper half of your body when doing a sit-up, the lower limbs become tense and tend to lift up off the floor. On the other hand, it takes just a little extra weight on your legs to keep them on the floor when you raise your upper body smoothly with the mental image of using your arms to slowly pull yourself up (Figs. 146 and 147). Therefore, instead of using the force of the rebound to do more sit-ups, raise your body up each time as if you were drawing your head forward and up. This way the level of tension is kept fairly even throughout your body. The abdominal area thus receives an even load and becomes firm.

The important thing in this exercise is to pull your head up only as far as it will go. There is nothing to gain whatsoever in straining yourself. Repeat this sit-up exercise at least five or six times.

Fig. 146

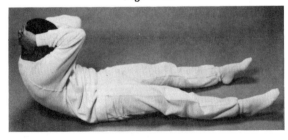

Fig. 147

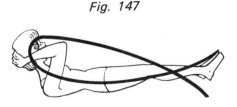

Exercise "H" (Kidney Meridian)

Remove any bed covers completely for this exercise. Lie on your back with your arms spread out to the side and your legs apart. Next lift one leg straight up into the vertical position. Then lower this leg out to the side, extending it straight out to the

Fig. 148

Fig. 149

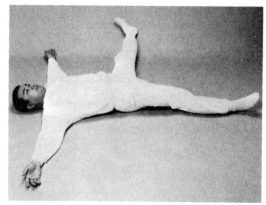
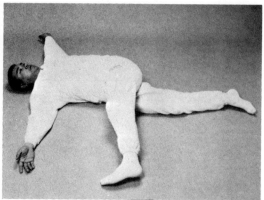

Fig. 150

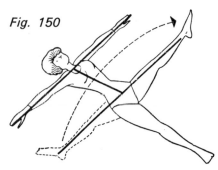

side if possible (Figs. 148 and 150). Bring the leg back to the original position and try this same movement with the other leg to see which side is more flexible. Begin with the more flexible leg and lift it straight up. Lower it down to the opposite side at a right angle so that your waist is twisted (Fig. 149). Your arms should be outstretched so that your upper body does not move much. Then raise the leg back to the vertical position and down to the other side. Repeat this same movement back and forth three or four times on the flexible side. After this do these same movements with the other leg. You should notice an improvement in the range of movement of this leg.

The Effects of Exercise "I" and "H"

Exercise "H" stimulates the Kidney Meridian and serves to improve muscle tone in the waist and hips. Since exercises which work just the waist and hips are not so beneficial by themselves, Exercise "H" is paired with Exercise "I," which stretches the Conception and Governor Vessels, to activate the Ki on both the Yin (back) and Yang (front) sides of the body. Exercise "I" works the abdominal muscles to trim the waist, but its effects are not limited to the waist and hips. In the Orient the waist or pelvic region is regarded as a vital part of the body where Ki is concentrated to balance and integrate the upper and lower halves of the body. Doing Exercise "H" while keeping your attention on breathing through your *hara* will greatly enhance the effect of making the waist firm and trim.

Exercise "x" (Liver and Gallbladder Meridians)

Lie on your stomach and lift your head up, placing one arm under your upper chest for support. Stretch the other arm straight out at an angle. Lift and stretch out the leg on the opposite side of the outstretched arm and support this by bending the other leg slightly (Figs. 151–153). Thus when the right arm is stretched out, the left arm is bent to support the upper body, the left leg is stretched up and slightly out and the right leg is kept on the floor to support this lift. This posture somewhat resembles the letter "x" in cursive writing. The best image for this exercise is that of a surf board riding on a wave—straight, rigid, and floating out of the water.

Fig. 151

Fig. 152

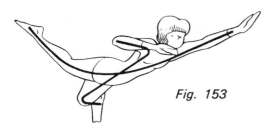

Fig. 153

Once you "ride the wave" with the right arm and left foot stretched out, switch to the other arm and leg and straighten them up and out to catch between stretches and lie on the floor totally limp, and just breathe deeply for a moment. Alternately stretch your arms and legs three or four times on each side and extend the energy within your body out to the tips of your fingers and toes.

Exercise "o" (Bladder Meridian)

After finishing Exercise "x" remain on your stomach and rest your head on the floor. Bend one of your knees and slap your buttock with your foot (Figs. 154 and 155). Your heel is not likely to reach the buttock that easily so you should bring your foot back with some force. This should make the heel reach the buttock. Even if this is difficult at first, it should become easier with practice. After doing this on one side, straighten your leg and relax it completely before switching to the other leg and kicking your heel up to your other buttock. After doing this on each side about three times, do this on both sides at once.

Fig. 154

Fig. 155

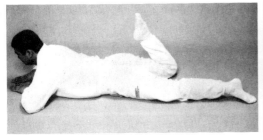

Fig. 156

Fig. 157

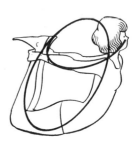

Then bend both feet back up to the buttocks and reach your hands behind you in this position to grasp the ankles from the outside. Then pull on both of your legs so that your upper body is drawn back and your body forms a loop (Figs. 156 and 157). In this part of Exercise "o," not only must you pull on your legs with your hands, but you must keep the tension exerted across the hips and chest in an even manner so that your body forms a circle. This exercise could be just a matter of holding your legs and arching your back, but you really need to do more than just arch your back in this exercise. It is important to let the force of the stretch extend to your hands and feet so that they rise as far above the hips as possible.

After inhaling deeply and holding your breath in this position, allow your body to relax with a slow exhalation and let the circle deflate. Just keep your hands behind you on your legs and exhale completely. Then as you slowly draw in another breath, imagine that you are filling up and expanding in your chest, hips, arms, and legs. In this way you should form something like the letter "o" once more. Repeat this up to five times. The mental picture of a sled shooting down a snowy slope may be helpful in this exercise.

The Effects of Exercises "x" and "o"
Exercise "x" stimulates the Liver and Gallbladder Meridians, which control the tone of muscles and tendons as well as the condition of joints. Exercise "x" also works the muscles of the hips along with those of the arms and legs to produce a good overall effect in firming up the hips. Exercise "o," aside from stimulating the Bladder Meridian on the back, corrects the postural tendency to stoop forward.

The tone of the hip muscles in women is associated with the function of the ovaries and the reproductive system in general. By this association Exercises "x" and "o" also improve the function of the sex glands in women and increase sexual response. This effect, needless to say, is a natural result of attaining good health in general.

Exercise "m" (Small Intestine Meridian)

If you are doing these exercises in bed, by the time you get to Exercise "m" you are almost ready to get up and start the day. For this exercise it is best if you imagine a cat stretching its back in a relaxed and leisurely way after waking up. From the position of lying face down, draw your knees up under you and come up onto your knees. Place your palms down flat on the floor and also let your elbows touch the floor as you begin to raise your hips to the back and lower your head and shoulders (Figs. 158 and 159). You must keep your forearms on the floor and try to stretch your back fully in a reversed arch, otherwise the stretch will not be as good as that of a yawning cat. Therefore after raising your buttocks most of the way, you should try to move your buttocks toward the rear rather than just moving them up. Sink your shoulders down and keep your chin on the floor while you arch your back, and this will make the stretch more complete. When you allow your belly to drop down and bring the full weight of your abdomen over your knees, this will make your hips go up farther naturally. After breathing deeply and relaxing for a moment in this position, go on to the next exercise as you exhale slowly.

Fig. 158

Fig. 159

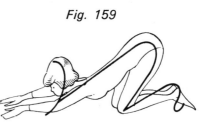

Exercise "v" (Small Intestine Meridian)

In Exercise "v," you must assume the opposite posture from Exercise "m." Raise your head up and then back as you bring your hips forward and rest the weight of your upper body on your upright arms (Figs. 160 and 161). Keep your lower abdomen and legs flat against the floor. Since your body from your legs up is going to be arched backward, it is important that you try to keep your lower abdomen on the floor. Cats also do a stretch similar to this with their hind legs stretched out to the back. Look as far back on the ceiling as you can to get the maximum stretch.

Exercise "v" is very similar to the cobra posture in yoga. The special thing about this exercise is that it is paired with Exercise "m" so as to mimic the stretching movements of a cat right after waking up from a nap.

Fig. 160

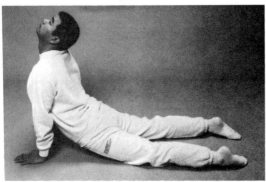

Fig. 161

After inhaling deeply in Exercise "v," go back to the position of Exercise "m" as you slowly exhale. Relax as much as you can in this position. Do not move back and forth from one position to another quickly or with force. Moving briskly from one position to another will not give you the best stretch, and it is against the principles of Imagery Exercise to use force in stretching. Slow movement in tune with breathing is essential for sensing the flow of Ki. The objective in these exercises is to guide the basic functions of our body toward health and beauty by attuning ourselves with the movement of Ki within our body. Thus, the movement of Ki caused by Exercise "m" is reversed in Exercise "v" and then the Ki is once more "rocked" back into the movement of Exercise "m." Do these two exercises four or five times alternately and this series of meridian exercises in the reclined position is complete.

The Effects of Exercises "m" and "v"

Both Exercises "m" and "v" stimulate the function of the Small Intestine Meridian. These exercises also have a strong effect on the Governor and Conception Vessels, and make one's body more relaxed and supple. In addition, these exercises work the abdominal muscles to remove excess fat.

It may sound strange to say that many people with excess fat have poor absorption of food in their intestines, but this is often the case. The tendency to overeat is often related to incomplete absorption in the small intestine. This makes a person crave more food. Also since absorption is incomplete, there is less energy and a person is not able to fully metabolize the nutrition that is absorbed. Performing Exercises "m" and "v" together regularly with special emphasis on centering yourself in the lower abdomen (being aware of breathing through the *hara*) will give better circulation of Ki through the lower abdomen, and the function of the small intestine will improve along with this.

Chapter 11

Finishing Exercises

Exercise "M" (Neck and Shoulder Adjustment)

Exercise "M" is for general adjustment of the neck and shoulders. It may be done before or after the other exercises, or otherwise any time during the day. The focus of exercise "M" is on the neck, and since all twelve meridians pass through the neck, this exercise has an overall relaxing effect on the body.

Fig. 162

Exercise "M" is done in the seated position. To do exercise "M," slowly raise or shrug both shoulders as high as you can while inhaling (Figs. 162 and 163). Your upper body thus forms an "M" of sorts. After raising both shoulders as high as they will go, drop your shoulders all at once just as you begin to exhale. This is a good way to release tension in the neck and shoulders. Repeat this movement along with the breathing about three times.

Fig. 163

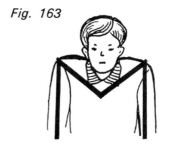

Next alternately raise each shoulder up to your ears. Allow your head to bend toward the lifted shoulder by relaxing your neck and letting it incline toward the raised shoulder (Fig. 164). After doing this on both

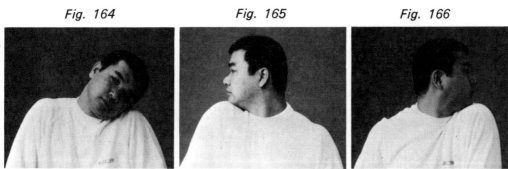

Fig. 164   *Fig. 165*   *Fig. 166*

sides and finding out which side is easier, repeat this same movement four or five times on the easier side, dropping the shoulder to the normal position each time as you begin to exhale. Then repeat the same movement on the harder side for another two or three times.

After this, alternately turn your head to look back over your shoulder on each side, and each time bring the shoulder on that side up to touch your chin (Fig. 165). Keep your arms relaxed and drop your shoulder as soon as you begin to exhale. Do this movement about five times on the easy side and three times on the hard side. Then repeat these same movements once more but this time as you touch one shoulder to your chin, draw the other shoulder up and back in the opposite direction (Fig. 166). Relax both your shoulders and neck all at once just as you begin to exhale. Do this up to five times on the easy side and three times on the hard side.

As the last movement in this general adjustment exercise, exhale as you roll your head around to the right and then do the same thing to the left. Decide which direction is easier for you and rotate your neck in the easier direction, keeping it relaxed and just letting it roll around on your shoulders with a long exhalation. After going in the easy direction up to four times, roll your head around in the harder direction about three times.

Exercise "N" (Headstand)

Exercise "N" is a headstand. Many people find headstands difficult, no matter how it is done. It would be much easier, however, if you could picture that you are able to hang with your feet in the air as if you were hanging upside down from your feet. Being upside down is the natural position for a fetus, and most children love to hang upside down. Therefore it is not difficult to understand how assuming the upside down position from time to time has a healthy effect. The headstand of Exercise "N" is meant to be easy and natural in the same way that monkeys and children enjoy being upside down.

Kneel down and place both hands on the floor and put the top of your head on the floor just in front so the three points of contact form an equilateral triangle.

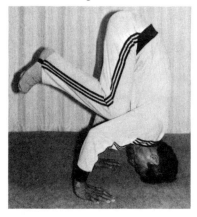

Fig. 167

Raise your hips up slowly by walking toward your head until your torso is in the upside down vertical position (Fig. 167). Now try to imagine that your body is a rocket. Picture your body being filled up with rocket fuel through your *hara* and that this fuel is beginning to fill up your body from your head. When the fuel reaches up to your shoulders, your feet will become lighter. Then gently raise your knees so they come up to waist level (Fig. 168). Rather than jumping up into position, raise your legs slowly and surely while maintaining your balance. As you continue imagining your body filling up with fuel, your legs will begin to feel lighter and ligher, so you will be able to straighten

Fig. 169

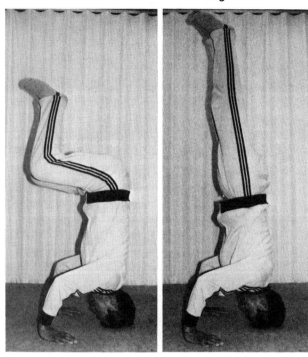

Fig. 170

them into the vertical position with ease (Figs. 169 and 170). Once your body forms a straight line, with your toes pointing straight up, imagine that the rocket from the very top of your head is being fired and that you are blasting off into space. Hold this position as long as it is comfortable and come back down slowly.

Exercise "V" (Completion)

Letters of the alphabet have been assigned for each one of the Imagery Exercises. These are mostly meant to serve as a device to aid memory, and also they provide a basic mental picture for each exercise. Although the use of these letters has been stretched almost to the limit, I have not yet exhausted all the possibilities. I used most of the capital letters for the Basic, Complementary, and Work Exercises. However, one important letter with a deep significance was left over. One day it dawned on me that it had been reserved for this special moment. The letter is "V," which stands for victory. It was waiting to be used for the last exercise, which is a celebration of the completion of Imagery Exercises.

One exercise presented itself as the natural choice for the letter "V." I drew a hint from a floor exercise in gymnastics which is a demonstration of strength in the abdominal muscles. The purpose of Exercise "V," however, is just to quietly hold your balance. From the seated position on the floor, lift both legs up with the knees straight and lean your torso backward to counterbalance your legs (Fig. 172).

Quietly savor the taste of victory and a sense of accomplishment as you do this last exercise. The purpose of this exercise is not for strengthening abdominal muscles.

Fig. 171

Fig. 172

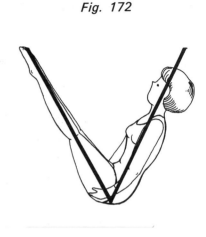

Therefore it is permissible to raise your legs by holding the back of your legs (Fig. 171). This should help in keeping your balance. Ideally the hands holding the legs should be there more for the sake of balance rather than to hold the legs up. The main point is that you quietly hold this position and breathe slowly and deeply. It is important to relax as much as possible. Breathe deeply for three times after reaching a stable position and Exercise "V" is complete.

It is best to assume the corpse posture of Exercise "Z" after finishing this exercise. As I have said before, "Z" is the last letter in the alphabet and Exercise "Z" is the most appropriate way to end any kind of exercise. Lie flat on your back and lightly shake your body back and forth to loosen it up and relax totally. Total relaxation, like sleep and even death, is the first step to a new beginning. To wake up renewed and refreshed, you must practice the art of letting go daily and learn to feel the emptiness within yourself and exercise in a way which fills this void.

Chapter 12

Family Exercises

Exercise and Shiatsu

Interest has grown in recent years concerning the relationship between postural alignment and health. Many health practitioners (notably chiropractors) claim that misalignment of the spine is the cause of disease and some even recommend devices for hanging upside down to straighten the spine. The skeletal and muscular structures are viewed as primary factors determining posture, and the condition of the spinal nerves, which is affected by posture, is said to influence the function of internal organs. The growth of interest in structural alignment is most likely a consequence of the bias of modern medicine which ignores the general issue of posture and the structural balance of the entire body and concentrates on the pathology of specific organs and localized tissues.

Nevertheless, identifying supposed imbalances in the musculoskeletal structure and trying to "correct" these structural imbalances means that a certain amount of force must be applied to the "distorted" part of the body in an attempt to bring that part of the body back into alignment. Viewing posture from the standpoint of structural alignment and seeking external signs of imbalances may be one way to understand health and disease, but it falls short of perceiving the life process of an organism as an integrated whole. Abnormalities of the body may appear as imbalances in the musculoskeletal system, but these are usually the result and not the cause. That is to say, posture is not solely the function of external physical forces, and even if force is applied to "correct" an imbalance, certainly the body would react to this as a whole, and the structure of the body would be affected in more ways than intended.

In Oriental medicine the body is viewed as an integrated whole rather than an assembly of separate parts. Ki exists in all living things as the basic life-force which sustains every part of the body and holds all these parts together as a whole. Obviously the skeleton and internal organs cannot exist without each other, and in the same way one muscle cannot move independent of the rest of the body. Since the circulation of Ki controls all the movements of the body, all imbalances in posture can be viewed as imbalances or distortions in Ki. Therefore one of the important aspects of diagnosis in Oriental medicine is to determine what imbalances exist in Ki by observing postural imbalances.

It is very difficult to recognize your own imbalances, but with Imagery Exercises the lines of tension along the meridians can be felt and the areas with tension, or obstructions in the flow of Ki, become evident. Be that as it may, overall postural imbalance is much easier to detect in another person than it is to find in yourself. Another person is more able to examine us objectively as a whole to detect apparent imbalances. Therefore it is a good idea to get someone to help you in identifying the places where you are physically out of balance. Receiving a massage or shiatsu is an ideal way to identify functional imbalances such as the presence of excessive tension or lack of muscle tone. A simplified form of shiatsu is presented here as Family Exercises in the hope that more people will learn and apply this valuable technique for mutual benefit among their family and friends.

The person giving shiatsu is able to observe the subject's body as a whole. By pressing and moving the subject in various ways, the person giving shiatsu can feel the lines of tension which are directly related to imbalances. The subject can also feel where there is tension with the pressure and passive movements. The main purpose of shiatsu (Family Exercises) is for the subject to become aware of his pattern of tension and physical imbalances in order to learn what is keeping him from good postural alignment.

In most types of exercise and manipulation, including some methods of shiatsu, those parts that are lacking in flexibility are bent or stretched by force, but such approaches go against the holistic perspective of Oriental medicine. When an attempt is made to "correct" the perceived imbalances by force, not only is there a physical reaction against the force, but the subject will experience pain and discomfort. Inflexibility and lines of tension which inhibit free movement exist because the flow of Ki is obstructed. When the parts where Ki circulation is hindered are cleared, the tense parts will soften up naturally. If your aim is to restore a balance, you should work on stimulating the action of Ki to get it flowing smoothly instead of trying to correct physical structure. You can experience the effectiveness of this approach for yourself by practicing Family Exercises.

Through the practice of Imagery Exercises you can experience the movement or tension created by Ki in your own body, and you can apply this experience directly in Family Exercises. Unlike factual knowledge, however, the things you learn about Ki in this book will not necessarily work to your satisfaction right away. Just as it takes daily practice to learn some new skill, it takes regular practice before what you have learned about Imagery Exercises really becomes part of you. Practicing Family Exercises along with Imagery Exercises will reinforce what you learn about Ki.

In this way you can realize for yourself how the miracle of life is at work in every one of us and how the greater order of life is held in common among all living things including our environment. The same principle which nurtures the life within each individual also serves the whole community of life. We can feel a deep empathy with other living beings when we personally experience the nature of life in which all individuals are connected through a greater order of life. This nature of life can be experienced most readily when two sentient beings work together as one.

The basic framework for understanding the essential nature of life is a knowledge of its basic functions, or the meridians. Your working knowledge of the meridians will increase dramatically through the practice of shiatsu. An important feature of shiatsu is the pairing of an active person who gives treatment and a passive person who receives, so that two individuals can work together as one. In exercising we move our body to benefit ourselves, but in shiatsu we move our body for the benefit of others. This makes it easier to observe the basic functions of life, or the meridians. Becoming aware of something about yourself through others conforms more closely to the true nature of life than becoming aware of something on your own.

This is probably the reason Do-In and Ankyo were treated as a pair in ancient

China. Do-In, which was exercise for health, and Ankyo, which was a form of massage similar to shiatsu, complemented each other perfectly. In a similar way, in Zen Imagery Exercises the practice of Family Exercise is indispensable for acquiring the sensitivity and awareness to make the Imagery Exercises meaningful to each individual. Just becoming healthy or beautiful are not lasting goals in themselves. Instead they are the natural result of pursuing a path of learning to experience life more fully. The ultimate aim of shiatsu and of Imagery Exercises are the same—to attain a greater awareness of the true nature of life.

Tips on Practicing Family Exercises

Imagery Exercises are exercises for health which can be done at one's own pace with a minimum of effort, and they can be practiced anytime and anywhere. The principle is quite simple so anyone can learn to do these exercises given a little practice. When these exercises are done properly, the benefits should become evident right away. Nevertheless, some people may very well grow tired of them before they learn the proper timing and rhythm. Imagery Exercises are quite easy to do, but they can be given up just as easily. Therefore, if at all possible, it is a good idea to practice these exercises regularly with another person so that you can encourage each other. Not only will this make the exercises more enjoyable, but there is a greater chance that you will keep practicing regularly until you come to appreciate their benefits.

If you can exercise with another person, there are greater possibilities in terms of exercise methods available for achieving better balance and health. Perhaps in the past you may have done some exercises in pairs at school or elsewhere. Family Exercises introduced in this chapter are similar to paired exercises in a few ways, but there is an essential difference. When exercising in pairs, it is usual for one person to perform the main action while the second person assists in some manner. In the case of Family Exercises, one person assists and the other person does not move at all. In fact, it works best if the receiver relaxes completely and makes no effort at all. The person assisting assumes an active role and moves the receiving person's body so that the person is passively exercised.

The pairing of a passive subject with another person who moves the subject in various ways may give one the impression that Family Exercises are manipulative techniques to be performed on a person by another person. When these manipulations are viewed as an exercise, however, the focus of stretching and balancing all parts of the body to increase health and well-being is the passive subject and not the active assistant. Therefore the receiver, or the subject, is the important person who is the focus of attention in Family Exercises. In medicine the physician is generally regarded as playing the main role in health care. In reality, however, since healing can only take place with the recuperative powers of the patient, the proper role of a physician is just to assist the patient in the process of recovery. In Oriental medicine, ideally, the patient assumes the leading role and the therapist is just there to assist. In any therapeutic situation the person who relinquishes control of his body should be the main focus. This therapeutic relationship applies to the two individuals doing Family Exercises together. Therefore, the person who is the focus of attention will be called the subject, and the individual assisting this person will be called the helper.

The majority of instructions for Family Exercises is directed to the helper because the helper is the one who performs the various procedures. The helper must perform all procedures and movements as explained, but should also pay close attention to the condition and physical response of the subject in order to follow the indications of the subject's body and guide the subject toward better balance and health. Anyone can be the subject in Family Exercises since the subject just gives over control to the helper, and there is no need to think or to make any effort. The key point in Family Exercises is that the subject, who is the one being exercised, does not move his body of his own accord. This is similar in many ways to Imagery Exercises, in which instead of willing the body to move in a certain way, the body is given an opportunity to assume a pose or posture created by a mental picture. In Family Exercises the subject has an ideal opportunity to experience his body and to observe the various changes which come about while being moved by the helper.

In other kinds of stretching exercises done in pairs one person helps another person stretch more than he can by himself. The difference in Family Exercises is that the subject leaves everything up to the helper while stretching and relaxing. This is similar in some ways to "automatic movement" where one begins moving involuntarily by letting go of conscious control of one's own body. This type of movement is initiated not by one's mind, but by one's subconscious needs. However people often find it very difficult to totally let go of themselves in this way.

One aim of Family Exercises is for the helper to induce unconscious or unintentional movements in the subject. This is why it is important that the subject does not try to stretch or become active in any way. The helper should also refrain from thinking about how he wants to move or stretch the subject. The helper and the subject should work together silently as one and keep from becoming engaged in extraneous thoughts. Such a state of selflessness, difficult to attain on one's own, can be achieved with relative ease when one learns to give complete trust and to rely on another. The movements which are made in mutual trust will be as original and unique as the relationship. All the helper has to do is to observe how far the subject can move with comfort and then give the subject assistance in relaxing more completely in that position. It should never become a matter of forcing something or having to endure pain.

The idea held by Professor Noguchi about helping each other when exercising in pairs is that, rather than trying to make up for the shortcomings of the other, each person should be there to establish a unique relationship in which something entirely new emerges. According to Professor Noguchi such a relationship is neither fixed nor one-way, and two persons join together as two human beings to find some common ground through exercising. The active and passive roles are incidental to forming such a relationship.

Naturally assuming the passive role of the subject in Family Exercises will make it easier to experience the various exercises. The most important aim in Family Exercises is for the subject to learn to give himself completely to the movements induced by the helper. When the subject thinks that he must move deliberately or achieve some objective in these exercises, this gets in the way of automatic or involuntary movements. Once the subject gets accustomed to leaving everything up to the helper, he will easily come to the realization that what the body wants most is to move freely with joy and ease.

When assuming the active role of the helper, instead of thinking only of how you want to move the subject, pay close attention to which way and to what extent the subject's body is inclined to move so as to work with these tendencies. The helper must always remain open to movements which are outside the bounds of he originally had in mind.

Therefore exercising in pairs, in the case of Family Exercises, is not solely for the purpose of improving performance in individual exercise or for assisting those who are still unable to do certain exercises by themselves. Family Exercises are a chance to learn about movements which are not dictated by one's mind and which come about as a result of a cooperative effort of two people offering themselves to each other in a relationship of trust. This is an excellent way to experience and understand the real meaning behind Zen Imagery Exercises which is to draw forth movements which are beyond the constraints of our conscious mind.

There can never be such a thing as a one-way relationship in Family Exercises. If both parties are healthy, variously exchanging the roles of subject and helper allows both parties to further increase their health and fitness. Even when the subject is unable to switch roles with the helper, the helper can benefit by experiencing the nature of life through close personal contact, and he can also learn more about the workings of the body to apply this in his own fitness program. Imagery Exercises, yoga and Tai Chi are done for one's own benefit, but Family Exercises are done for the benefit of others. On the other hand, the essential points of Imagery Exercise, yoga, and Tai Chi can be learned through helping others to relax and move with greater ease. In other words, as a helper you can learn how to move your own body with greater ease and effectiveness by working together with the subject.

When assuming the role of the subject, you must learn to become more receptive and accept the movement initiated by the helper. In this way you can develop sensitivity to changes caused by the stretching or pressure whether they are internal changes or external changes such as posture and body alignment. When we exercise by ourselves, our conscious mind, which wants to do the exercise right, tends to interfere with the mental image we are trying to hold. This makes it difficult to experience the dynamics of Ki which actually bring about the movement. When working in pairs, the helper initiates all movements so there is no need for the subject to think or make any effort at all. The subject's body moves and undergoes changes without his conscious intention by accepting the manipulations of the helper.

The only thing a subject has to do is to learn to receive the movements as a whole. The subject's body must receive and integrate the manipulation as a complete whole. The body never moves or changes in one part only. When we receive an injury, no matter how slight it is, our body always responds as a whole. This does not mean that all stimulation spreads in an even manner across our body. You must learn to feel how physical changes are transmitted through various interconnected physical systems to maintain an overall balance. This transmission system forms the pathways which are the twelve meridians. Receiving the Family Exercises as a whole allows you to experience the meridians.

In this sense, it is better for the subject to keep the eyes closed. When our eyes are open, we tend to pay more attention to the part that is being pressed or moved. The helper, in turn, must work in such a way that his movements can be received as a whole. That is to say, he must avoid bringing too much strength to bear on one part and keep from becoming preoccupied with the hand doing the manipulation. When the helper's body moves as a whole, it is able to conform exactly to the subject's needs. Thus it is possible for the two people doing the Family Exercises to experience going beyond their individual selves to exercise as one whole.

Note: In the following instructions for Family Exercises, for the sake of convenience and in conformance with the photographs, the subject is referred to in the feminine gender and the helper, in the masculine.

Seated Position

The subject should sit in a comfortable position on the floor. The subject may sit in the cross-legged position, seiza position, or in any other way. The only requirement is that the subject be able to relax and leave everything up to the helper. The helper sits behind the subject at a little less than arms length where he can place his palm on the subject's back with his arm comfortably bent. The helper can also assume any sitting or kneeling posture so long as he is stable and can lean slightly onto the subject as he works.

Attunement

Fig. 173

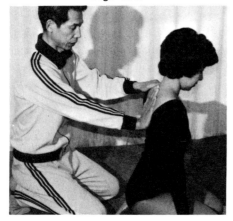

The initial laying on of hands by the helper has a deep significance because it sets the tone for complete trust and cooperation in the work which follows. There is a common bond of life which we all share regardless of whether we are good friends or first acquaintances. It is important that we experience this essential oneness of all beings by taking a minute to attune ourselves to the life energy of our partner in Family Exercises.

To do this, the helper places his favored hand over the subjects' spine between the shoulder blades (Fig. 173). Instead of pressing the subject's back with his hand, the helper supports and holds the subject up by leaning into her slightly. The subject feels the helper's gentle but firm supporting hand on her back and lets herself relax and lean backward. In effect, the helper and subject both lean each other. When the helper and subject feel the warmth in each other's touch this way, they open up to each other and become ready to work together as one.

Back Extension

The helper places his left hand over the subject's left shoulder as if to cover it, and keeping his right hand on the subject's spine, leans onto it to apply firm pressure. The left hand supports the pressure of the right hand so the subject does not move. After one breath, the helper relaxes his right hand and moves it down a little on the spine and leans onto it once more. The subject does not move because she is supported at the shoulder, but her spine is arched forward slightly because it gives somewhat under the pressure. The arching motion of the spine is greatest toward the middle of the back. The helper must not use force with his arms to make the subject's back arch. Instead the weight of the helper leaning on the subject should cause a relaxed stretch without resistance. The helper moves his hand down the subject's back in six or seven steps, gently pressing over the spine. This procedure is repeated three times, starting out gently and increasing pressure each time.

Relaxing Back

Fig. 174

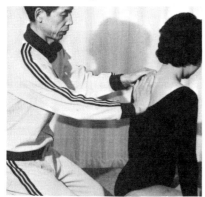

Fig. 175

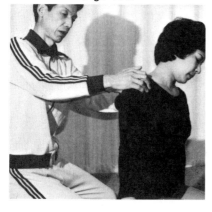

Continuing on from the same position and hand placement of the Back Extension exercise, the helper places his right hand on the upper part of the subject's back to the left of her spine (Fig. 174). Directing most of the pressure to the inside of the shoulder blade, the helper pulls the subject's left shoulder back with his left hand. Since there is pressure against the right hand, this will cause the left side of the subject's back to expand and relax. After pressing this way for the duration of one breath, the helper slides his right hand down about half its length and applies pressure again by pulling his left hand back. The pressure is held for one breath and then the right hand is moved down to the next position to successively press down the back. After reaching the waist area, the helper begins from the top again to press along the spine, this time pulling the subject's shoulder back a little farther.

After this the helper applies pressure on the right side of the spine by switching his supporting and pressing hands (Fig. 175). The right side of the subject's back is pressed in the same manner to successively expand and relax the back from the top to the bottom. The helper must pay attention in this exercise so that the emphasis goes to the hand drawing the shoulder back and not to the pressing hand. It is best to press only up to a certain point and then pause and allow the subject to relax by herself.

Fig. 176

Relaxing Shoulders

This exercise is performed with just about the same hand placement as the previous exercise. The helper places his right hand over the left shoulder blade of the subject with his little finger over the inside edge (Fig. 176). Then the helper draws the subject's shoulder back with his left hand. This exercise is repeated three times by shifting the right hand from the top of the shoulder blade to the middle and then to the bottom. The subject's right shoulder is relaxed in just the same way by reversing hand placement.

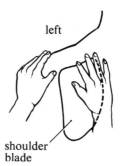

left

shoulder
blade

Relaxing Arms

To relax the left arm of the subject, the helper places his right hand over the left shoulder of the subject and uses his left hand to squeeze the arm on the outside from the end of the shoulder down to the wrist (Fig. 177). After each squeeze the helper moves his hand right below the place just squeezed so that the entire arm is covered from top to bottom to relax the arm on the outside. The squeezing motion, instead of being a forceful grasp, should be more like a firm hold, and the pressure should come from the helper's body as a whole rather than just his hands.

Fig. 177

Fig. 178

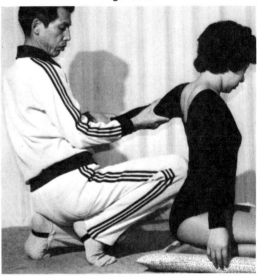

Fig. 179

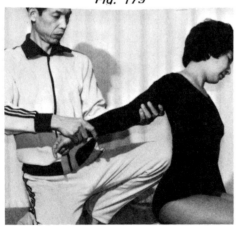

After the helper squeezes the subject's arm on the outside down to the wrist, he takes hold of her wrist with his left hand and moves her arm out away from her body a little, after which he moves his right hand just under her armpit. Then the helper squeezes down the inside of the arm with his right hand with a gentle but firm squeezing action (Fig. 178). While doing this the helper can use his right knee to support the lower back of the subject on her left side. This will provide good support and hold the subject steady while her arm is being drawn back. Supporting the subject by placing one knee against the lower back is particularly important for the next arm rotation exercise which requires greater support. Relax the subject's right arm on the outside and inside in exactly the same way by switching the placement of the arms and supporting knee (Fig. 179).

Arm Rotation

(A) The helper holds the left shoulder of the subject with his right hand and holds the subject's left wrist with his left hand to rotate her arm forward and up. After bringing the arm up to the raised position, the helper stretches the arm out to the side while continuing to draw the arm backward so that the arm is outstretched about 45 degrees from vertical (Figs. 180–182). Resistance will be felt as the arm is drawn back into this position to the limit in the range of motion of the subject's shoulder. At this point the helper applies an even force with both hands (right hand pushing forward and left hand pulling back) to stretch the subject's arm a little farther beyond its initial limit.

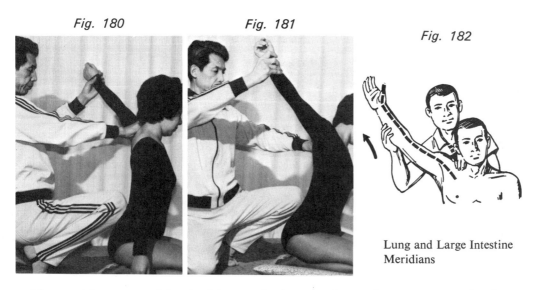

Fig. 180   Fig. 181

Fig. 182

Lung and Large Intestine
Meridians

The most important thing in this exercise is to apply steady pressure to take the arm just beyond the normal range of motion. Even though moving a joint beyond its normal range with a jerking motion may work to increase flexibility by forcing a stretch in the muscles and tendons, it seldom works to release the blockage of Ki which is the primary cause of inflexibility. When the arm is drawn back to its limit in the Arm Rotation exercise, one will naturally encounter resistance from the muscles and tendons. The best way to stretch the arm farther is to have the subject relax with an exhalation and to stretch the whole arm by applying a steady and even force with both hands.

After the helper stretches the subject's arm in the above position, he lets her arm down, bending it at the elbow so that her hand comes next to her shoulder. The helper continues the movement by bringing the subject's arm forward and up again to the outstretched position to repeat the same stretch once more.

(B) Finishing the first procedure of the Arm Rotation exercise, the helper lets the subject's arm back down as before and raises it forward to bring it straight up so that it comes next to the subject's ear (Figs. 183–185). Next the helper draws the arm back as far as its limit without undue force and stretches the arm straight up and

Fig. 183

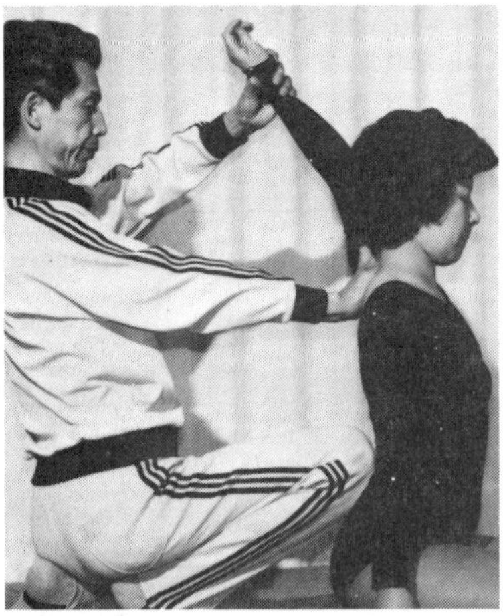

Fig. 184

Fig. 185

Heart Constrictor
and Triple Heater
Meridians

back. When the helper feels resistance to this movement, he uses his weight and applies steady pressure with both hands to take the subject's arm just beyond its normal range of motion. The subject relaxes with the stretch by breathing deeply. After holding the stretch for one breath, the helper lets the arm relax and rotates it backward and circles it down and around to the front. The helper rotates the arm back up into the same position again to repeat the same stretch once more.

(C)   The helper places his right hand on the subject's right shoulder at the base of her neck and holds her left arm just above her elbow with his left hand (Figs. 186–188). Then the helper rotates the subject's arm forward and raises it up so it touches her ear, bending her arm at the elbow so that the forearm comes behind her head. Next the helper presses the elbow toward the other shoulder, and when he encounters resistance, he holds steady pressure for one breath. Once the subject completes a long exhalation and Ki is released to bring relaxation and a greater stretch, the helper brings the arm back down to her side. The same stretch can be repeated by rotating the arm back into the original position.

Fig. 186

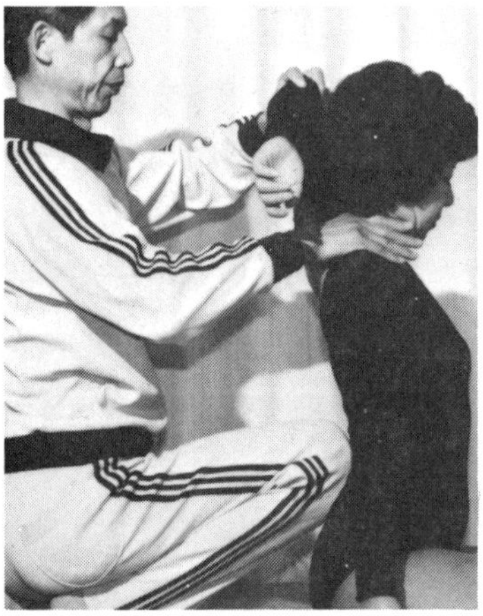

Fig. 187

Fig. 188

Heart and Small Intestine
Meridians

The sequence of procedures (A), (B), and (C) are performed next on the right arm by switching the hand placement and the supporting knee on the subject's back. It is best to perform the Relaxing Arm and Arm Rotation exercises in succession on the same arm and then switch to the other arm.

Relaxing Neck

Fig. 189

The helper supports the left shoulder of the subject with his left hand and grasps the back of her neck and applies pressure with his right hand (Fig. 189). The squeezing action must be steady and even just as in the Relaxing Arms exercise. The neck is grasped in three places, beginning just under the back of the skull, then moving to the center of the neck, and ending at the base of the neck. This procedure is done twice in a row and then the helper switches his hands to give grasping pressure on the neck with his left hand. Each squeezing movement should last about half a breath. Instead of using the strength in his fingertips only, the helper presses his palms up against the subject's neck as he squeezes so the pressure feels softer.

Neck Rotation

(A) The helper holds the back of the subject's neck with his right hand and puts his left hand on her forehead from behind. He then tilts her head back and stretches her neck. The bottom side of the helper's right wrist (on the side of the little finger) should rest on the seventh cervical vertebra.*

Fig. 190   *Fig. 191*

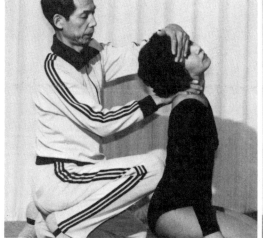   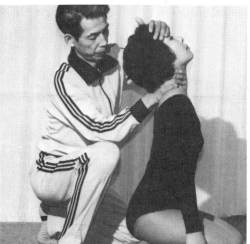

* The spine of the seventh cervical vertebra can be felt at the back of the neck. It is the only vertebra of the neck that can be easily located on the back of the neck because it protrudes backward.

(B) The helper rotates the subject's head around to the right so that it rolls over the top of the supporting hand on the neck as it comes back around (Fig. 190). After two rotations, the helper reverses the direction to rotate the head twice around to the left.

(C) The helper bends his right knee up and places his right elbow on this knee. Since his right hand is holding the subject's neck, this should put pressure right under the back of her skull (Fig. 191). If the subject is very tall, draw the subject's head farther back so as to lean her back on the supporting hand. Then the helper can raise the heel of his right foot to farther lift the subject's head and extend the cervical vertebrae. After holding this stretch for one breath, the helper lowers his heel and gently releases his hold of the subject.

Fig. 192

Shoulder Press

The helper stands up and places his right knee against the subject's back while keeping his left foot back (Fig. 192). The helper's thumbs are placed on the shoulders just on either side of the subject's neck and his other fingers go over the shoulders to rest over the collarbone (clavicle). Once the subject's body is stable, the helper puts his weight over his arms. The helper may even go up onto his toes so long as he is able to keep the pressure steady. After pressing on the subject's shoulders for the length of one full breath, the helper moves his thumbs to the middle of the subject's shoulders and presses again in the same way. This same thumb pressure is applied once again toward the end of the subject's shoulders.

Shoulder Rotation

In the same position as the Shoulder Press exercise, the helper grasps both shoulders of the subject. He rotates the shoulders backward while pushing the subject's back gently forward with his knees to expand her chest. The helper continues to circle the shoulders back and down and then forward and up. This rotation of the shoulders is performed about three times to open up the chest area.

Torso Extension

Continuing from the previous exercise, the helper slips his hands down from the shoulders to grasp the subject's forearms and lifts them forward. As he raises the arms, the helper moves his hands farther up to hold the subject by her wrists and pulls the arms straight up (Fig. 193). Then the helper bends the knee that is supporting the subject from behind and draws her arms far back to stretch her whole body backward (Fig. 194). He holds this position at the limit of the stretch for one full

Fig. 193

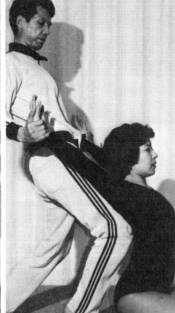
Fig. 194

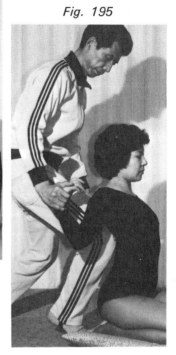
Fig. 195

breath and then lets the subject's arms down slowly.
The subject should exhale fully after getting into
the stretched position to release Ki and remain as
relaxed as possible.

Two-Arm Rotation

After the Torso Extension exercise, both the subject's elbows are bent out to the side.
The helper, while still holding the wrists, draws both arms backward with the elbows
bent (Fig. 195). In order to stretch the chest muscles fully, the helper spreads the
subject's arms out to the side and draws her elbows as far back as they will go.
The forearms of the subject are held vertical. Both elbows should be drawn back
behind the subject to effect a full stretch. The helper holds the subject in this position
long enough for her to inhale and feel the tension build up in her chest. Then the
helper relaxes the stretch and the subject exhales completely to release the Ki
which had been held in. The helper rotates the arms forward with the elbows bent
and then once more draws the arms slowly up and back into the same stretch to
expand the chest again.

There is a ritual in Sumo Wrestling in which Sumo wrestlers about to enter the
ring squat down and clap their hands at the edge of the ring. They must squat down
with both legs out to their sides and bend their arms so that the forearms are vertical,
the elbows are over the knees, and the palms face out. There is a momentary tension,
or a holding of Ki, and then the tension is released with one loud clap of the hands.
Very effective practices for releasing Ki like this are stylized in many traditional arts.
The special significance in the Two-Arm Rotation exercise is that people ordinarily
just use their arms in front of themselves and seldom move their arms back to stretch

their chest muscles. This exercise compensates for the tendency for our chest to become compressed. Thus, this exercise facilitates deeper respiration. Repeating the above stretch about three times serves to open up the chest and any obstruction in Ki should be quickly cleared up.

Spine Extension

The subject assumes the Seiza position after the Two-Arm Rotation exercise and the helper takes a hold of the front of the subject's shoulders from behind by getting his forearms in under the subject's arms. Next the helper gets into a half-squat and goes up onto his toes to place his knees in the small of the subject's back. He then begins to lean backward slowly while pulling the subject's shoulders from behind. The helper lets his heels back down to the floor and squats all the way down as he pulls the subject's back over his knees (Fig. 196). He continues to lean back and extends the spine and stretches the subject's whole body by leaning back to the floor. After holding this position for one breath, the helper slowly comes back up and lets the subject's hips down so she can return to the original position.

Fig. 196

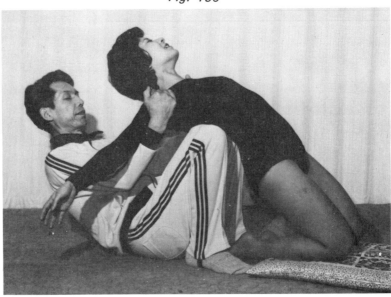

This is an advanced technique and practice is recommended with children or limber subjects because it can be very stressful for people in poor condition. Once you learn to keep your balance with the younger and smaller subjects, you can attempt larger and less flexible subjects. Remember not to stretch people much beyond their limit as this can do more harm than good. One important rule in this exercise is to make sure that both you and your subject are able to breathe deeply and rythmically while moving. This way you can be sure that you are not straining yourself or the subject. Straining and holding your breath is counterproductive to our aims. When done properly, this Spine Extension exercise is a fine example of harmony in breathing, timing, and balance.

Side Position

Lying on your side is a nice comfortable way to take a brief rest. The side position is also a convenient position in which to work out tension with Family Exercises. The only problem with the side position is that a person is rather unsteady. Applying pressure or moving people in the side position often makes their body tense up to keep from falling forward or backward. This point must be taken into account when and the helper must be sure to provide firm support. Otherwise the subject will not be able to relax. The advantage of the side position is that the limbs on the top side can be moved freely through their entire range of movement. Thus the side position is ideal for stretching the subject fully to work out tension.

When doing Family Exercises in the side position, it is usually best to begin with the left side up since most people are right-handed. The side of the favored hand is most often more tense, and the opposite side should be exercised first. All exercises and stretching should be started on the side with less tension and greater flexibility.

Shoulder Rotation

The subject lies in the side position, and the helper sits behind the subject, facing the back of her head. The helper firmly holds the subject's shoulder on top in the front and the back between both hands. (Fig. 197). Holding her shoulder firmly, the helper rotates it clockwise two or three times in as large a circle as possible. Next the helper rotates the shoulder counterclockwise two or three times. Then he moves the shoulder up and down (up toward head and down toward feet) two or three times. These movements are made slowly and deliberately so as to cover the full range of the subject's shoulder movement.

Fig. 197

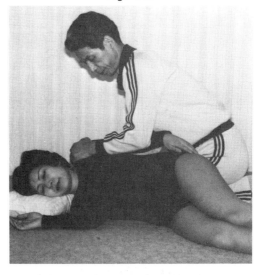

The Shoulder Rotation exercise is done as a preparation for the Arm Rotation exercise which follows. Also it is performed again after the Arm Rotation exercise to adjust the shoulder joint. When performed as a preparation for the exercise to follow, Shoulder Rotation must be done gently to check the range of movement in the shoulder joint, to locate problem areas if any, and to prepare the joint and muscles for further movement. When doing Shoulder Rotation after the Arm Rotation exercise, the aim is to rotate the shoulder to its fullest limit of movement. Instead of using his hands only, the helper uses his arms and shoulders to make the movements. In this way a full and even force is brought to bear on the subject's shoulder at the limit of its movement.

Arm Rotation

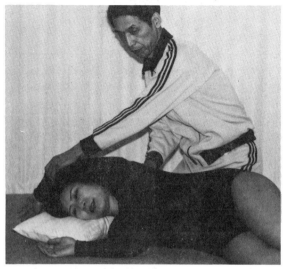

Fig. 198

A similar Arm Rotation exercise is performed in the seated position, but doing the same rotation in a different position allows the shoulder to be adjusted more easily. With the subject lying on her right side, the helper holds her left arm just below the wrist with his left hand. His right hand supports the subject's back just over the shoulder blade (the four fingers point toward the subject's head and the thumb goes to the armpit). Then the helper moves the subject's left arm out in front and then over her head parallel to the floor (Fig. 198). Since there is no resistance to the forward rotation, the helper should use minimum force and keep the arm relaxed for the stretch that will come when the subject's arm is brought behind her head. When the subject's arm is rotated over her head, it should brush against her ear. Just beyond this point should be the limit of movement. This limit varies according to each individual, depending on flexibility and the presence of shoulder problems. The stretching of the arm in this way is made easier by the helper pushing the subject's body forward with his supporting hand and applying a gentle pull with his other hand to draw the subject's arm back to its farthest extent of movement.

When the arm is held briefly in the fully stretched position, the resistance which caused movement in that direction to come to a stop will relax slightly so that the arm stretches a bit farther. It is not usual for a person to move their arm back this far, but taking the shoulder joint to its limit serves to release the blocked Ki. Even this new limit can be extended slightly farther by repeating this same procedure two or three times. The subject's shoulders should feel much lighter after doing this exercise.

In the last Arm Rotation the subject's arm is brought over behind her ear to stretch it toward the back of her head. Once the arm is in this stretched position, the helper holds the subject's arm with his left hand and uses his right hand to press down gently on the inside of her upper arm to extend the limit of motion and expand the armpit area. Rather than pressing down forcefully, the helper just allows his weight to stretch the subject's arm naturally and effortlessly. Before going on to the next exercise, the arm is returned to the subject's side and the previous Shoulder Rotation exercise is performed a few times to adjust the shoulder joint. Then with his hands still covering both sides of the subject's shoulder, the helper uses his weight to pull the subject's shoulder down toward her feet.

Thigh Stretch

The helper places his right hand on the top
of the subject's hip and puts his left hand
over the kneecap on the leg on top. Then
the helper places his left knee against the
back of the subject's buttock and draws her
leg back to extend her hip joint. Next the
helper moves his knee over to the crease of
the same buttock and pulls back with both
arms to effect another stretch. The helper
moves the position of his knee three more
times to press down the back of the subject's
thigh to her knee (Fig. 199). In order to
facilitate the stretch, the helper's hold on
the top of the subject's hip and on the front

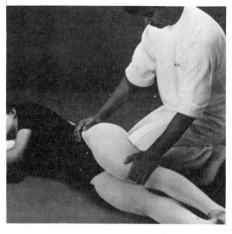

Fig. 199

of her knee is adjusted as he goes along. Getting up on the toes of his left leg enables
the helper to have better control of the pressure exerted by his knee. For the other
foot, it does not matter whether he is on his toes or not, as long as the subject receives
steady support.

Back Stretch

The helper pushes the subject forward with his hand on her hip to tilt her forward
and then he places his left knee against her top buttock. He then pulls back on the
subject's kneecap with his left hand to apply some pressure with his left knee and
stabilize its position on the subject's buttock. Next the helper moves his right hand
over to the left (top) shoulder of the subject and places his right knee against the
subject's back just below her left shoulder blade (Fig. 200). The helper must tilt the
subject's body forward to almost face down when placing his knees on her buttock.

Fig. 200

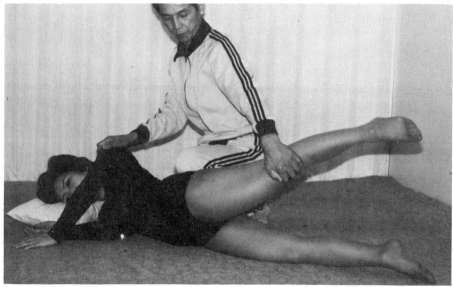

If the helper starts out by pulling the subject back toward himself with both arms so that the stretching is begun with the subject already in an upright position on her side, the Back Stretch is not as complete. The stretch is most effective when the subject is almost facing down before the stretching is started. This way the full weight of the helper's knees comes to bear on the subject's back and hip.

In the last part of the Back Stretch exercise, the helper pulls back with both arms to stretch the subject's back. It is best if the helper, rather than using the strength of his arms, just leans backward with his whole body. This will make the back stretch gradually and completely. If the helper places his emphasis on pulling back with his arms, this creates tension and resistance in the subject and a full stretch is not possible. In such a case there is less release of Ki and relaxation is incomplete. For the helper to lean back fully means that he is part of the stretching and relaxation. The best stretch comes from the subject receiving steady support at the position of maximum stretch by the body weight (counterbalance) of the helper. The helper holds this stretched position for a few breaths to increase the stretch of the subject.

Fig. 201

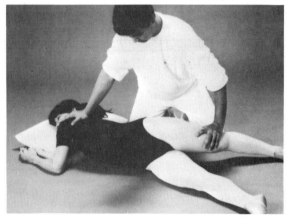

Side Stretch

After finishing the Back Stretch exercise the helper, while keeping his left knee and left hand in the same place, puts his right knee back down on the floor and moves his right hand to the back of the subject's left shoulder. The helper pushes the subject's shoulder toward her head while continuing to hold her thigh to effect a full stretch along the side of her body (Fig. 201). After getting a complete stretch, the helper pushes the subject's shoulder forward toward the floor so that her upper body is almost face down. The subject's body is twisted since the lower half of her body is kept in a side position by the top leg being pulled toward the back. In this stretching exercise the Gallbladder Meridian is fully extended. When the subject exhales after getting into this stretched position, the stretch along her side should increase slightly. This means that the obstructed Ki or tension in the Gallbladder Meridian has been released.

Spine Twist

After doing the Side Stretch exercise, the helper takes the left leg of the subject and puts it back down on the floor. Next he places his left hand on top of the subject's hip and pushes it forward while pulling the subject's shoulder backward with his right hand (Fig. 202). This exercise twists the patient in the opposite direction from the last exercise. The helper, after twisting the subject to her natural limit, relaxes the pressure momentarily and then pulls back on one hand and pushes with the other for a final full twist. When the helper uses his arms to forcefully twist the

Fig. 202

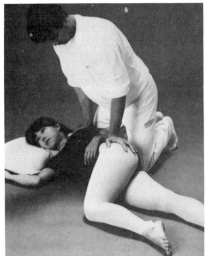

subject, unnecessary tension and resistance is created in the subject. The Spine Twist exercise is much easier when the helper produces the twisting action by using his whole body.

Fig. 203

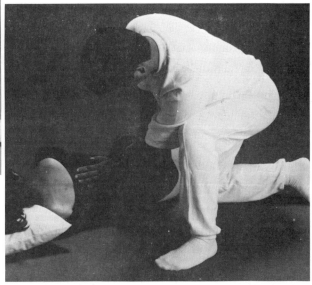

Back Press

The Spine Twist is actually the last exercise in the side position. The Back Press is repeated after the last exercise in the side position to bring this sequence of exercises to a smooth finish. The helper supports the subject's side with his right hand just below her waist and presses over the spine with his left hand from her upper back down to her hips twice in a row (Fig. 203).

After completing the entire sequence of exercises on one side, the same sequence is repeated with the subject lying on her other side. Every exercise is performed in exactly the same way except the placement of the arms and legs is reversed.

Face-down Position

For some people, lying on the stomach is a natural and comfortable way to sleep. But it is not so easy to relax completely in this position for most people. The face-down position, however, is the position most preferred in massage and shiatsu treatments because the subject feels more safe and secure. Be that as it may, the helper can cause pain and discomfort if he uses excessive force, particularly with those subjects who find it difficult to fully relax in this position. Problems are most likely to occur when the helper applies pressure in a tense and forceful manner which causes the subject to react and become tense. The combination of a tense subject and the use of excessive force can even cause injuries in the ribs and muscles in the chest.

When this happens, usually the pain is mild in the beginning, but it increases later on to be felt strongly with deep breathing and movement of the arm.

It is therefore very important to refrain from applying a concentrated force on a small area. The helper should always first check the subject's condition to assess the amount of tension and physical idiosyncrasies. The injuries which sometimes result from various manipulations, including shiatsu and chiropractic treatments, most often occur when the subject is not completely relaxed. It is much safer to work on subjects who have already received work in the sitting and/or side positions since most of their tension has been worked out and they are able to relax completely while being worked on in the face-down position. The best assurance against possible injury is to have the subject lie down totally relaxed and to work slowly and deliberately. Another way to reduce the risk of injury is to have the subject lie on a *futon* or a thin mat, rather than directly on the floor.

Needless to say, the helper and subject must have a trusting relationship. In this sense, the helper must refrain from making any sudden or forceful movements. When the helper moves in a relaxed and natural manner to help facilitate the circulation of Ki in the subject's body, the physical distortions in the subject's body will tend to adjust themselves. When the subject is not completely relaxed, the natural and even pressure of the helper will make the subject aware of where tension is being held. The face-down position is ideal for the helper because it is the easiest position to use body weight instead of muscle power to press and stretch the subject. When the helper uses his hands as if they were his feet to "walk" over the subject's backside, the subject will feel the point of pressure much less. This way the subject feels the pressure more as a weight borne by the whole body and the helper can get a better sense of the movement of Ki. The helper must learn to move and work from his *hara* and to bring his body weight over his hands.

Spine Press

The spine and its supportive structures are especially prone to trouble in man because of his unique evolutionary development. By assuming an erect posture the main axis of physical movement became perpendicular to the pull of gravity, and while this was better for holding up the head, it increased the burden on the spinal column. This makes man especially susceptible to strain and distortions in the spine. Distortions usually result from chronic fatigue or poor postural alignment which must be corrected in order to improve a person's physical condition. People sometimes complain that their back feels stiff or rigid. This generally means that they are having difficulty in bending at their waist. This condition is caused by the obstruction of Ki in the various supportive structures in and around the vertebrae, which usually precedes real structural abnormalities. Relieving this energetic disturbance along the spine is the key to restoring healthy alignment and flexibility.

To do the Spine Press exercise, the subject lies down on her stomach and the helper kneels on the left side of the subject, facing her head. Then the helper gently places both of his hands on the subject's back (the left hand over the right) so that the left palm covers the second and third thoracic vertebrae, and the right palm covers the seventh and eighth thoracic vertebrae (Fig. 204). The helper then slowly leans onto the subject to place his weight over his hands. The helper should not press down with

Fig. 204

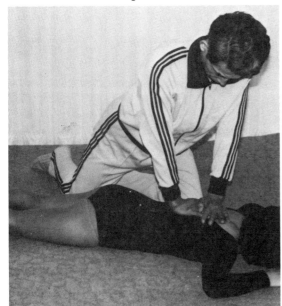

Fig. 205   Spinal Column

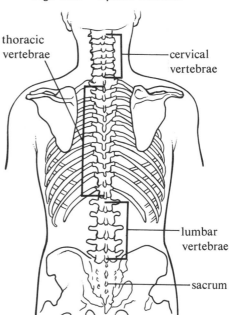

force from just the upper part of his body. Instead he should move his waist forward to bring his weight over his hands, which are firmly placed on the subject's back, so that he is just leaning over the subject effortlessly. After pressing down on the spine in this way for the length of one breath, the helper shifts most of his weight back on his knees to lift his hands and slide them down a little without taking them off the back entirely. Next, the helper places his weight over the subject's spine with the top palm over the fourth and fifth thoracic vertebrae and the bottom palm over the ninth and tenth thoracic vertebrae.

The helper applies pressure successively down the spine in the manner described so that the left palm and right palm respectively come over the sixth and seventh thoracic and the eleventh and twelfth thoracic vertebrae; eighth and ninth thoracic and the first and second lumbar vertebrae; eleventh and twelfth thoracic and the fourth and fifth lumbar vertebrae; and finally the lumbar vertebrae and the sacrum (see Fig. 205). The palm of each hand should cover the spinous processes* of the vertebrae mentioned although there is no need for total accuracy. Both hands should slide together into position, and steady and even pressure must be brought over the whole spine. Repeat the Spine Press exercise two or three times from top to bottom.

The helper should not move back and forth while pressing down on the spine. Also, the helper must avoid the use of quick rhythmical movements to press the spine. Each press should be done slowly and deliberately as if the helper's hands were feet walking on sand. With each press the helper must examine the shape of the spine underneath and feel the condition of the subject's back. Before moving his hands to the

* The vertebrae of the spinal column have several bony protuberances called processes and one of the largest, the spinous process, extends backward. These can be felt as small bumps in the middle of the back and indicate the position and orientation of the vertebrae.

next position by sliding them downward, the helper should move on his knees slightly toward the subject's feet so as to use his weight fully in the next position. In other words, the emphasis must be on the helper's position and movement in the lower half of his body, and the hand placement is decided after the helper shifts his weight forward. This will make the transfer of weight onto the subject much smoother.

This principle of the natural transfer of body weight is seen in walking, where our pelvis (center of gravity) first shifts forward and then a foot comes out to catch the forward momentum. Very rarely do we place our foot out first and then shift our weight forward. This principle is important for all movements involving the transfer of body weight or a change in the direction of movement. You should notice that trying to walk by placing your foot down first and shifting your weight after this requires more muscular strength and control. Shifting your weight first and catching this afterward with a step takes less effort because you are working with gravity and the natural principle of motion.

Back Press

In the Back Press exercise, in order to improve the tone of the muscles on either side of the spine, pressure is placed down the side of the spine in a similar manner to the Spinal Press exercise. The helper begins on the left side of the spine and places his hands side by side on the subject's back at a right angle to the spine and holds the palm pressure for one full breath (Fig. 206). It is important that the helper lean over the subject so that all the muscles of his body are tensed equally. This serves to relax the muscles next to the spine evenly, especially in places where the spine is out of line.

Fig. 206   *Fig. 207*

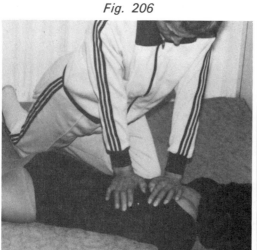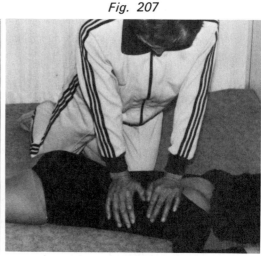

After pressing from the base of the neck down to the hip two or three times, the helper moves his palms over to the right side of the spine to repeat the same procedure (Fig. 207). Most people are right-handed and have a tendency to overuse their right arm. This often creates an excessive concentration of Ki on the right side. Therefore treating the left side first helps to restore the balance of Ki on both sides of the body. It naturally follows that when a person is left-handed, it is better to treat the right side first.

Fig. 208

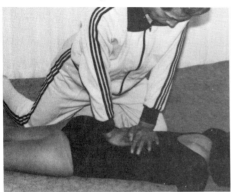

Spinal Adjustment

When the muscles around the spine are relaxed, distortions in the spine can be adjusted naturally through movement. In order to induce such self-adjustment of the spine, the helper performs the same procedure as in the previous Spine Press exercise. Although the exercise is done in basically the same way, the purpose of these same movements differs from before. Both the subject, receiving the pressure, and the helper, giving the pressure, should be able to detect subtle changes in the resiliency of the spine. The helper presses down the spine twice in the same way as in the Spine Press exercise (Fig. 208). After this, the helper begins from the top again with the same hand positioning, but this time he adds a slight bounce after pressing. That is to say, the spine is pressed down for the duration of one breath in the same way, but right after that the helper bounces lightly in place once. The helper does not allow his hands to leave the subject's back, but simply takes some of his weight off suddenly and then quickly presses back down on the same place by bringing his weight over his hands again.

Lumbar Adjustment

The helper places both hands around the back of the subject's waist with the tips of the fingers pointing out to the sides (Fig. 209). The helper's hands are placed right next to the second and third lumbar vertebrae, and he places his weight on his hands for two full breaths and determines which side of the back is harder or more tense. The right side is usually harder, and this is especially marked in people with low back pain. Sometimes both sides of the back are equally hard, but most often there is one side which is harder than the other. When the right side of the waist is harder, the helper stays on the left side of the subject, but if the left side is harder, he moves over to the right side.

Fig. 209

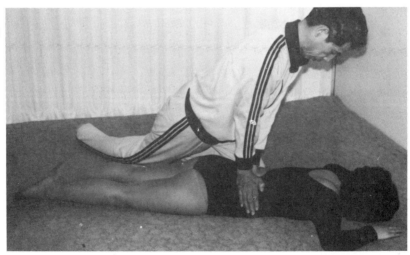

Fig. 210

Fig. 211

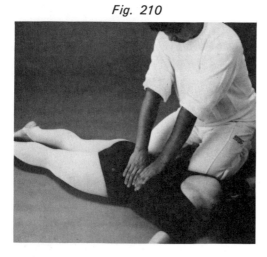

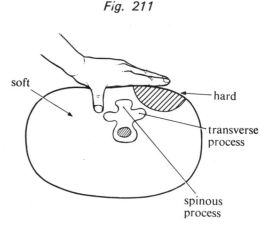

Next the helper places both hands side by side on the lower part of the spine and presses both thumbs in on his side of the spine and supports the other side of the spine with his remaining fingers (Fig. 210). In this way the helper tries to grasp the spine after a fashion by placing his weight over his hands. After holding the spine in this way for the duration of one breath, the helper moves his hands slightly higher up on the lumbar spine and repeats the same procedure. This procedure is also repeated on the lower lumbar spine just below the first position. The side of the spine that feels the hardest to the helper's fingers is usually the place where a distortion exists in the spine. The helper uses his thumbs to press the exact opposite side of the distorted spine right next to the transverse processes of the spine (Fig. 211). The helper must slowly shift his weight forward to lean over the tip of his thumbs. After this Lumbar Adjustment exercise, the helper once more presses both sides of the subject's back with both hands to feel how the exercise has relaxed or evened out the tension in the back muscles.

Leg Press

The helper places his left hand above the sacrum and puts his right hand on the left buttock of the subject and then places his weight over it (Fig. 212). Next he puts pressure on the right buttock with his right hand in the same way to compare the muscle tone and sensitivity on each side. Each side is pressed two or three times to get a good idea of the difference.

After this the helper keeps his left supporting hand in position as he uses his right hand to place weight over the back of the left thigh, from the bottom of the bottock to the back of the knee. Then he applies pressure with his right hand in the same way on the back of the right thigh to compare the two sides (Fig. 213). The above sequence is repeated two or three times.

Next the helper places his left hand on the back of the subject's left thigh, near the top, and uses his right hand to successively grasp the calf muscle of the subject from her knee down to her ankle Then the right calf is grasped in the same manner with the supporting hand also on the right thigh (Fig. 214). . This is repeated two or three times to compare each side.

Fig. 212

Fig. 213

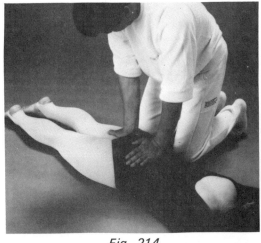

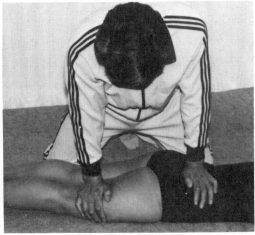

Fig. 214

Fig. 215

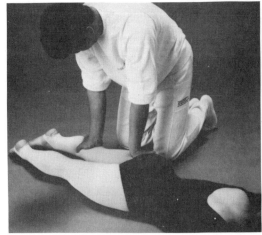

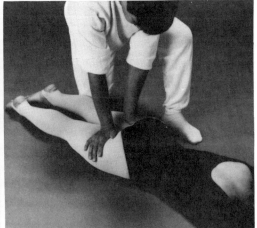

Finally the helper places his hands on both buttocks and presses by using his body weight (Fig. 215). The helper works his way down the legs to press successively until reaching the ankles. The helper's weight must come over both hands evenly. This is true regardless of whether the left hand is used for applying pressure or for giving support. When pressing the limb with the one hand, there is a tendency to become preoccupied with the active hand and to let up on the pressure from the supporting hand. This is not the best way to provide pressure. The best results are obtained when the helper's weight comes over both hands evenly.

All during the Leg Press exercise the condition of each limb should be compared from top to bottom to look for tense or painful areas. In almost all cases you will find some imbalance or difference in muscle tone between the two limbs.

Bent Leg Press

When the condition of each leg is compared from the back, most often the right side is more sensitive or tense. If this is the case, the helper starts this exercise on the right leg. If, however, the left leg seems to be more tense, the helper must begin on the left

Fig. 216

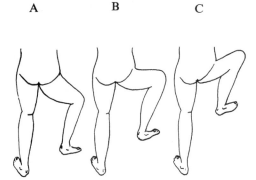

A   B   C

Fig. 217

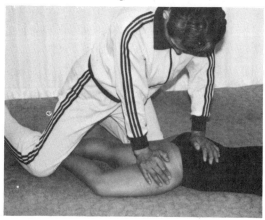

leg. Grasping the subject's ankle, the helper bends her knee and raises this leg up to the subject's side. The extent to which the leg is bent up is divided into three basic leg positions called position A, B, and C for the sake of convenience (Fig. 216). In position B, the thigh is at a right angle to the side of the body.

First the helper bends the subject's leg up to position A and places his left hand on her right hip to press down with his body weight and check the resiliency and tension in her leg from the hip down to the knee (Fig. 217). The same check is made again after moving the leg up to position B, and likewise after bending the leg up into position C. By bending the leg into the above three positions and pressing on it each time, the helper finds the position which causes the buttock to raise off the floor the most. (This is usually the most uncomfortable position for the subject). With the leg of the subject bent this way, the helper checks the top surface of her leg in this position for tension and hard areas.

Next the helper straightens the leg that was checked and bends the other leg into the same three positions. Most often the first leg examined by bending, based on the initial examination during the Leg Press exercise, is harder to bend. It follows that the leg checked last is most often easier to bend, raises the buttock less, press down easier, causes less discomfort.

Fig. 218

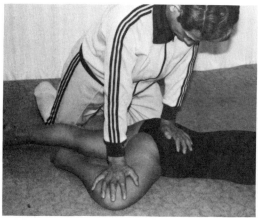

Fig. 219

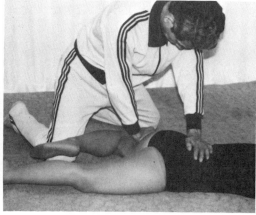

After this the more flexible limb is bent into the three positions. In each position the helper places one hand over the hip for support and the other hand on the thigh to press down successively from below the buttock to above the knee (Fig. 218). The helper places his weight over his hands and then adds a slight bounce. The entire upper half of the leg is pressed two or three times this way in each position. This procedure is done a few extra times with the leg bent up in the same position in which the leg on the other side was most tense and inflexible. After doing this the leg is straightened, and to check for improvement, the other leg is bent up into what was previously the most problematic position (Fig. 219). The subject should be able to bend the leg up with greater ease and the helper should feel less resistance. If the relaxing effect is not so pronounced, it probably means that the helper was preoccupied with his pressing hand and forgot to place his weight evenly and rhythmically over both hands. In this case the helper should repeat the same procedure with greater attention to using his whole body in a balanced way.

Leg Press

The same procedure as the last portion of the Leg Press exercise is repeated, and both hands are used to press down the back of both legs simultaneously. This exercise is performed to feel for changes caused by the previous Bent Leg Press exercise. The helper will usually notice less of a difference in the muscle tone of the right and left legs, and the subject should also feel more symmetry and balance between the right and left legs. After pressing the legs down to the ankles, the helper makes fists with both hands and places them on the arches of the subject's feet. The helper brings his weight over his fists for the duration of two full breaths to complete this sequence of Family Exercises in the face-down position.

Face-up Position

When we stretch out and lie full length on our back, we should be able to relax completely. To assume the face-up position in Family Exercises, the arms should be spread out to the side with the palms facing up and the feet about shoulder width apart. This is exactly the same as Exercise "Z," or the "corpse pose" of yoga, introduced before. Getting in this position may seem easy since all a person has to do is to lie down as if one were dead. Nevertheless, relaxing completely is not nearly as easy as it seems. You may think, "How can just lying down on one's back be so difficult?" However, by assuming this position before and after Imagery or Family Exercises, you will be amazed at the difference you can feel before and after exercising when just relaxing in this position. You will then realize that tension, which you are usually unaware of, is present in many parts of your body. This is why it is important to practice relaxing in this position regularly in order to learn to relax completely. Once you reach that very relaxed state after exercising or being exercised, you should try to let go even more by doing Imagery Breathing. When you learn how to let go totally and truly relax, at times your body will seem as if it were floating several feet off the floor.

Stroking Abdomen

The subject lies on her back to totally relax in the face-up position and the helper kneels to her right. The helper begins Family Exercises in the face-up position by alternately stroking down the center of the subject's abdomen with each hand to draw Ki downward (Fig. 220). This counteracts the general tendency of Ki in our body to rise and become stuck in the pit of our stomach. Next, the helper places his hands right under the rib cage so that the base of his palms are out to each side and the fingers overlap at the pit of the stomach. Applying even and steady pressure, the helper slowly draws his hands down the subject's abdomen without letting up on the pressure. After reaching the lower abdomen, the helper holds his hands in place over the subject's *hara* for one full breath. In stroking down the abdomen the helper, instead of just rubbing down the surface of the abdomen, must use just the right amount of pressure and concentration to draw the energy inside the abdomen downward (Fig. 221). Care must be taken, however, not to press too hard on the subject's abdomen. The abdomen is stroked down in this way two or three times.

Fig. 220

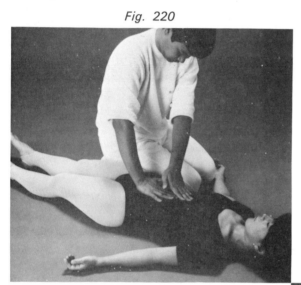

Fig. 221

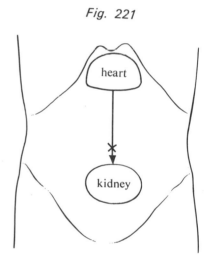

Fig. 222

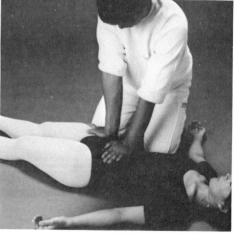

Thigh Press

Next the helper keeps his left hand over the subject's *hara* and uses his right hand to press the area just below the pelvis where the right leg connects to the body. With the intention of guiding the Ki collected in the lower abdomen down to the leg, the helper

Fig. 223

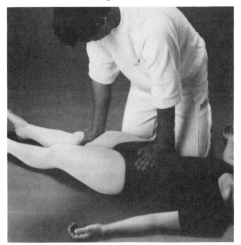

successively applies pressure from the upper thigh down to the knee with his right hand (Figs. 222 and 223). The helper must remember to bring his weight over both hands when pressing. Keeping his left hand over the subject's *hara*, the helper repeats this same procedure again from the topmost part of the thigh. After this the helper applies pressure over the left thigh twice from top to bottom.

Stretching Inside of Leg

The helper keeps his left hand on the subject's *hara* and uses his right hand to bend the left knee out to the side at less than a ninety degree angle. He places his hand over the bent knee and presses down lightly to test for flexibility. The helper changes the angle of the bent knee to find where the leg has the most resistance to being pressed against the floor. Then the helper does the same thing on the opposite leg to compare its flexibility. The leg which felt harder in the previous Thigh Press exercise is most often less flexible in this exercise, and the subject is more likely to experience discomfort in this leg. All the following leg stretch exercises must first be performed on the leg which is more flexible.

Keeping his left hand in place over the subject's *hara*, the helper bends the knee out to the same angle at which the other leg was most tense and inflexible. Then he presses from the top of that thigh down to the knee in five or six steps to stretch the leg in this position (Figs. 224 and 225). The helper must avoid using his strength, but instead he should bring his weight evenly over both hands so that the left hand is fully supporting the stretching action of the right hand. This pressing and stretching on the inside of the thigh is repeated two or three times.

Fig. 224

Fig. 225

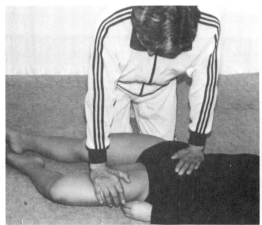 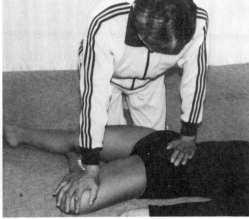

Stretching Outside of Leg

The helper, continuing to support the subject's *hara* with his left hand, uses his right hand to lift the knee which was bent out to the side and brings it inside to place it over the other leg. The outside of the leg therefore comes to face upward. Then the helper presses down on the bent leg successively from below the hip to the knee in five or six steps in order to press and stretch the outside of the leg (Fig. 226). This exercise is done about three times. The flexibility of the leg should increase with each repetition.

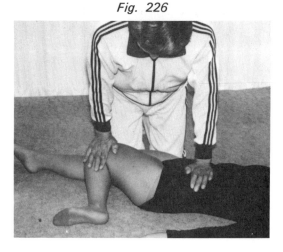

Fig. 226

The resiliency of the leg to downward pressure will vary according to the angle at which the knee is bent. When doing this exercise, it is best to first straighten the bent leg and bend the other leg over the straightened leg to find the least flexible angle for the other leg. Then the legs can be switched back again to bend the first leg in the same angle as the least flexible angle for the other leg to stretch it in the same position. This will serve to relax the other leg and increase its flexibility. It is not very useful to force the leg to stretch in a position in which it is not flexible. The best approach is to first stretch the other leg in the same position. Doing this will cause the leg that was less flexible to automatically relax and the circulation of Ki is improved. In this way, immediate and appreciable improvement in flexibility can be obtained with a minimal amount of pain and strain.

Stretching Back of Leg

The helper bends the more flexible knee of the subject up toward her chest while keeping his left hand on her *hara*. He then leans over the subject and uses the base of his right hand to press down on the back of the thigh from behind the knees to the buttock (Fig. 227). The helper uses his body weight to give steady pressure over the

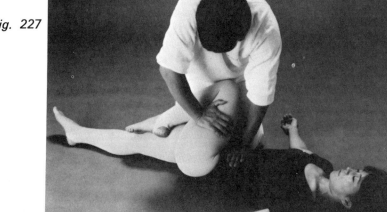

Fig. 227

back of the thigh so that his supporting hand underneath is pressed into the subject's lower abdomen. If the helper finds it difficult to hold the subject's leg steady with just his pressing hand, he can apply pressure on the back of the leg with his knee. To do this he must kneel directly across from the subject's leg that is bent up and raise his knee to pull the subject's leg back toward it (Fig. 228). Rather than pressing with his knee, the helper pulls the subject's leg down toward his raised knee with his left hand on her knee.

Fig. 228

Fig. 229

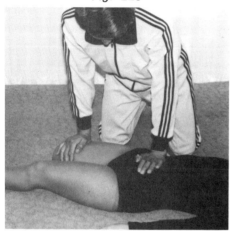

Fig. 230

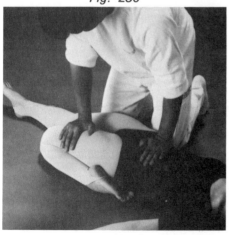

Stretching Front of Leg

The helper, keeping the subject's raised leg bent, grasps her foot in one hand and her knee in the other to bring her leg down with the knee bent so the foot comes back under her buttock. If this stretch is too difficult for the subject, the helper can just bend her leg out to the side so that her foot comes beside the buttock with the toes pointing out. In order to increase the stretch of the leg which has been bent in this manner, the helper places his weight over the subject's leg with one hand on her *hara* and the other hand over her knee. After this, the helper gently presses down the front of the thigh from below the pelvis to the knee (Figs. 229 and 230).

After completing the sequences of stretching the inside, outside, back, and front of the leg two or three times respectively on the more flexible limb, the helper goes to the less flexible limb and quickly repeats the entire sequence once to check how the flexibility has increased.

Preparation for Lumbar Twist

The helper stands at the foot of the subject and lifts her legs up by holding each foot from the outside (Fig. 231). Then he briskly shakes the subject's legs up and down alternately. Next he shakes both legs up and down together so that the movement reaches all the way to the subject's shoulders. After this, the helper places the soles of the subject's feet on each of his knees and holds her legs on the outside as he walks forward in small steps to bend her knees up toward her chest. After bending the subject's knees as far up as they will go, the helper presses down on them to check the flexibility of the waist (Fig. 232). The helper can determine the subject's flexibility by how close her knees get to her chest. The helper uses his weight to press down on the knees gently. Even though there may be initial resistance to the movement, this will gradually diminish with steady pressure. The helper must avoid the use of excessive force and should use his whole body to effect the stretch gently.

Fig. 231

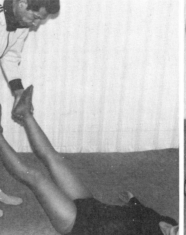

Fig. 232

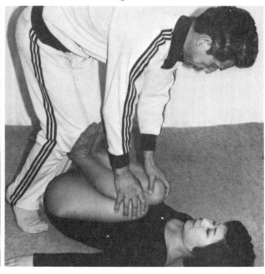

Fig. 233

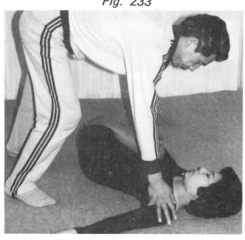

Lumbar Twist

The helper compares the flexibility of each leg by pressing the subject's legs up against her chest. Usually there is some difference in height between the right and left legs even though the difference is sometimes slight. The helper first turns both knees down to the side toward the lower knee (Fig. 233). Then he compares this movement with the same movement in the other direction. Turning the knees down in the direction of the less flexible knee is easier. Turning the knees down the other way, the knees will not reach the floor as easily and the subject will have more difficulty or discomfort. The helper takes turn the legs down to the more difficult side as far as they will go by keeping one hand on the knee on top to turn it down to the other side while pressing down on the front of the subject's shoulder on the same side. The helper uses his body weight to keep the shoulder on the floor and gently presses the knees down in the

Fig. 234   *Fig. 235*

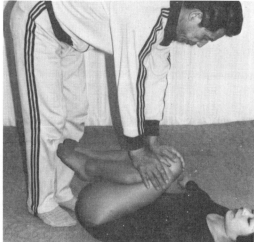

other direction so there is no excessive strain. In this way both the helper and subject can see the extent of movement on the more difficult side.

After this, the helper moves the subject's knees back up and then down in the other direction, switching his hand placement in the meantime to turn her legs down in the other direction (Fig. 234). This twist will be easier than the first twist, and the knees will reach closer to the floor. The helper presses down on the subject's knee and shoulder three or four times on this side using his weight. This serves to increase the flexibility of the waist on that side. Then the helper switches his hand placement once more to raise and then turn the legs down in the direction which was less flexible. There should be noticeable improvement in flexibility this time. The helper brings both legs back above the subject once again to press the knees toward the subject's chest (Fig. 235). The flexibility should increase in this movement also.

Ankle Exercise

The helper straightens both the subject's legs and kneels at the feet of the subject. He then places one knee against one of the subject's feet and holds the other foot in both hands. (As a rule, the foot of the more flexible leg is exercised first.) Then the helper pulls and stretches one foot while pushing against the sole of the other foot

Fig. 236

with one knee. Holding the heel in his left hand and the toes in his right hand, the helper works the ankle joint by bending the foot forward and backward, inside and out, and by rotating it in both directions (Fig. 236). After exercising one foot, the helper sets the foot down and puts his knee against the sole, and picks up the other foot to repeat the same exercise on the other side.

Shoulder Adjustment

The helper begins by observing the subject's shoulders closely to see if they are flush against the floor and whether they are even. It is usual for there to be at least a slight difference between the shoulders. The helper kneels to the right of the subject and presses down on both shoulders using his weight. One side should feel more rigid and offer more resistance to the pressure.

The helper then moves over to the side of the subject where the shoulder is more relaxed or free of tension. (This is usually the left side so the explanations which follow are for exercising the left arm.) The helper kneels on the left side of the subject and grasps the top of her left shoulder with his left hand to provide support and uses his right hand to grasp and press successively from the top of her arm down to her wrist (Fig. 237).

Fig. 237	*Fig. 238*

Next the helper takes the subject's wrist in his right hand and bends her elbow so her forearm is vertical to the floor. Then he lifts the elbow off the floor and moves her arm up next to her head and pushes her forearm down to the floor so that her palm faces up (Fig. 238). He then slides the arm back down to the original position and lifts the forearm up to vertical once more. He again lifts the forearm and elbow up after that to repeat the same movement and rotate the shoulder about three times.

After this the helper turns the subject's forearm down from the vertical position so that it points down to her toes. Keeping the upper arm at a right angle to the subject's body, the helper bends the wrist up toward her armpit (Fig. 239). This should cause both the elbow and shoulder to move up toward the subject's head. After reaching

Fig. 239

the limit of movement, the helper raises the forearm back into the original vertical position with the elbow bent. This movement is repeated about three times.

It is important that steady pressure be applied on the shoulder with the left hand while doing the Shoulder Adjustment exercise. The same sequence of grasping and pressing down the arm and special arm movements is performed on the other arm. The movements should be a little easier to perform on the other arm.

After completing the Shoulder Adjustment on both sides, press the shoulders against the floor to compare the difference between the right and left sides. The difference should have diminished considerably and both shoulders should be much more relaxed.

Neck Adjustment

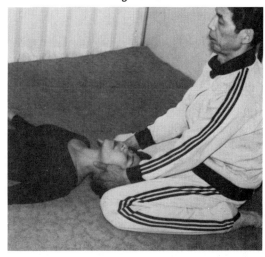
Fig. 240

The helper sits at the head of the subject, facing the direction of her toes. He places both hands under the subject's head to lift up and press the neck on both sides of the cervical vertebrae from the bottom up. The helper takes note of the places along the vertebrae which are specially tense or sensitive and compares the right and left sides of the same vertebra for tension or hard areas. It can be seen how it is more difficult to turn the neck in the opposite direction or move in a way which stretches the tense or sensitive area. After getting an idea of which side has the most tension, the helper holds the back of the neck below the skull and stretches the neck (Fig. 240). Instead of pulling with just his arms, the helper leans back and uses his weight.

After this the helper places his fingers on the back of the subject's neck (especially where there is tension or tenderness) and supports the back of her head with the palms of his hands and his thumbs. Next, he turns the neck in the more difficult direction to see how far it turns, and then he turns it to the easier side repeatedly up to three times (Figs. 241 and 242).

The main point of this exercise is to turn the neck as far as it will go to the easier side and then to turn it just a little past its limit. One must be very careful, however, because the use of too much force can be injurious. After this the neck is turned to the more difficult side. The range of motion should increase noticeably. Follow this

Fig. 241

Fig. 242

Fig. 243

Fig. 244

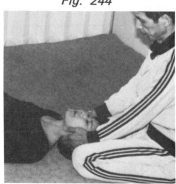

by bending the neck sideways down toward both shoulders by applying the very same principle (Fig. 243). The head is bent down repeatedly to the easier side and a little extra bend is added at the limit.

This Neck Adjustment exercise is concluded by holding the subject's head under the back of the skull and gently pulling and extending her neck once more (Fig. 244).

Two-Arm Stretch

The helper squats down at the head of the subject and grasps both wrists and pulls them over his knees (Fig. 245). Then he leans back in this position to stretch the subject's arms (Fig. 246).

Next the helper stands up while keeping hold of the subject's wrists and stretches her arms again by leaning back slightly in the standing position (Fig. 247). Then he circles the subject's arms out to either side by alternately moving her hands down by her head and bringing them back up over her head. The helper circles the arms in

Fig. 245

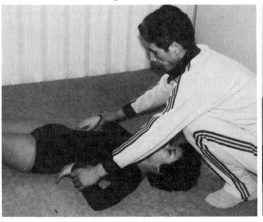

Fig. 246

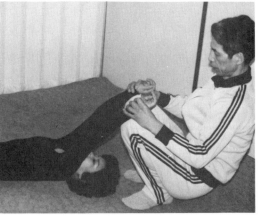

Fig. 247

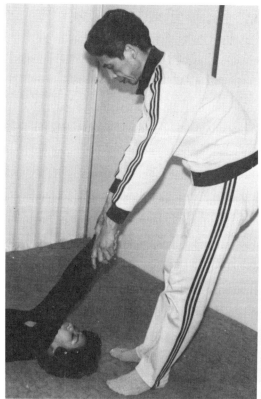

such a way as to open up the subject's chest with each rotation. This rotation of both arms is repeated about three times in a row. The helper ends the arm rotations by pressing the subject's arms down to the floor just next to her shoulders (Fig. 248).

Fig. 248

Next the helper stands up over the subject's head and pulls both arms upward to lift her shoulders slightly off the floor. Then the helper alternately pulls up on one arm while letting the other arm down a little to cause a shaking movement from side to side. This is done about four times back and forth.

Finally, the helper stretches the subject's arms up over her head so that the stretch reaches all the way down to her feet. After holding this stretch for one breath, the helper continues pulling on both arms as he walks over to the subject's right side (Fig. 249). He ends this exercise by placing the arms on the floor, palms down, just next to the subject.

Fig. 249

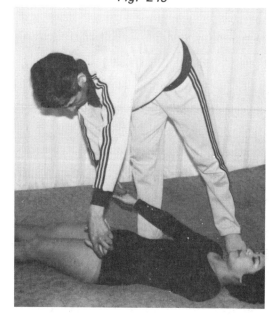

Waist Lift

The helper kneels next to the subject, facing her head, and puts both hands around her waist so that his fingers reach her back. Then he lifts up gently on either side of her spine with his fingers to apply pressure with the weight of the subject on his hands. He begins by pressing the subject's back on both sides of the seventh thoracic vertebra and works downward in several steps to finish next to the third lumbar vertebra.

Fig. 250

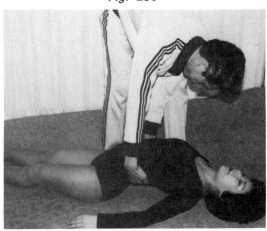

After pressing along the side of the spine, the helper reaches farther around the subject's waist to interlace his fingers and get a firm hold across her lower back. Keeping his elbows as close together as he can, the helper slowly stands up. Lifting up the subject this way will arch her back and raise the back up, but the buttocks will stay on the floor (Fig. 250). Before standing and lifting, the helper gets in a half squat position to perform the lift by straightening his legs. This method of lifting conforms with the rule that all heavy objects must be lifted with one's legs, not one's arms and back. If the helper keeps the top half of his body relaxed and slowly lifts the subject from his waist with the straightening of his legs, he will be able to lift the subject more easily. After lifting and holding the subject's back in an arched position for the duration of two breaths, the helper gently lets her back down to the floor.

After finishing the last exercise, the helper sits next to the subject and gently places both his hands over her lower abdomen, one hand over the other at right angles to each other. The helper closes his eyes to harmonize his own breathing with the subject's breathing and the subject relaxes completely to do exercise "Z" once more as in the beginning. A sequence of Family Exercises should always be concluded by the helper and subject doing Imagery Breathing together as one.

Chapter 13

Balancing Ki According to Types

Working with Ki

A great variety of exercise systems have been developed up to now and each method seems to emphasize different aspects of exercise and advocates its own special approach to movement. More recently there has been a shift in popularity from exercises for developing muscular strength and physical performance toward exercises for adjusting one's physical balance and enhancing one's appearance and health. Interest is growing about the question of what appropriate exercise really means. To this day there is no real agreement on a definition of exercise and which exercises are best for one's health. Through my long years of study and practice of Oriental medicine I am convinced that the meridians represent a network of essential life energy, or Ki, which relates to all life processes and serves as a unifying principle for all activity including exercise. It stands to reason that exercise is intimately related to the circulation of Ki since movement is an innate function of all animal life. Therefore all theories and approaches to exercise can be understood in terms of the dynamics of Ki or the function of meridians. Furthermore, I have discovered that through exercising it is possible to gain a deeper insight into the true significance of meridians.

The posture of standing upright on two limbs can be regarded as the foundation of all human activity and behavior. A prominent Japanese anthropologist, Dr. Kinji Imanishi* stated that "It was really inevitable that man came to stand upright." Man is able to support the comparatively heavy weight of his head only because standing and sitting upright is his basic posture. Also our options in terms of physical movement were increased by assuming an upright posture and having the spine serve as a vertical beam supporting all organs. Professor Michizo Noguchi suggests that man opened up new possibilities for development by standing upright and freeing his hands for other uses. He also made a paradoxical point that "We can make light and nimble movements just because our bodies are weighted down by gravity." It may be said that all life on earth is lived in relation or reaction to the pull of gravity. This perspective on one basic condition of life sheds light on the words of my respected predecessor: "There is no life where there is not also the burden of death." To stand upright is to work against gravity, and if this resistance to the pull of gravity is defined as the force of life, it can be said that those who expend the least amount of effort in holding a vertical posture have the greatest potential to direct their life energies toward some other activity.

* Dr. Kinji Imanishi, Professor Emeritus of Kyoto University, is a Japanese anthropologist and primatologist who is distinguished by his research of Japanese monkeys. He has been awarded many honors in Japan including the Order of Cultural Merits.

The six essential functions, or orientations of life-force, are represented by six characteristic postures, each of which relates to a Yin-Yang pair of meridians. The less effort expended in each type of basic life activity represented by these postures, the more one has possibilities to expand and enhance each of these aspects of life activity. This is why learning to relax both mentally and physically is a prerequisite for finding fulfillment in life. All the meridian exercises in this book are designed to work out the stress and tension which keep us from relaxing fully. Since the six Basic Exercises cover all the essential life functions, each in conjunction with one of the six Yin-Yang meridian pairs, one might consider them sufficient to balance the workings of Ki. Nevertheless, since we human beings are so highly developed as life forms, there is a chance that our essential life functions do not automatically strike a balance and work as a whole. Imbalances in our mind and body can keep the natural workings of Ki from balancing all the essential functions.

The reason the system of Six Zang (Yin organs) and Six Fu (Yang organs) was conceived in Chinese medicine along with the twelve meridians was to provide a more specific "meridian treatment" for fine tuning the workings of Ki. There are only six essential life functions, but each of the Yin-Yang components represented by one meridian represents a different aspect of an essential life function. Singling out one aspect of a basic life function enables us to modify and facilitate the working of Ki in a more specific and effective manner. Although the meridians are different aspects of essential life functions, it must be remembered that they are closely interrelated. The Ki (functions) of all the meridians blend together to work as one. This means that all meridians are interconnected and the activity of one affects the activity of all others.

For this reason, even when one who is inexperienced attempts to improve the balance of Ki in the body, as long as he is working with Ki and not adversely affecting some structural component, a positive outcome can be expected. Therefore diagnosing a patient incorrectly is not such a big concern in Oriental medicine. This is quite different from Western medicine, where a mistaken diagnosis and the wrong treatment can have serious consequences. The treatment in Oriental medicine is not nearly as drastic and full of risk as that in Western medicine. In the Orient all manner of diseases have traditionally been cured by a minimum of intervention, whether using herbs, needles, or manipulation. Thus the primary aim of a meridian treatment is to effect an adjustment in the energetic balance.

Developing an Awareness of Types

All forms of life possess two opposite characteristics: that of having a common functional framework and that of having totally unique and unmatched features. A therapist in Oriental medicine has to be sensitive to subtle changes and indications in each patient since the common traits in imbalances of essential life functions (meridian imbalances) have to be ascertained for effective treatments. It is not such a simple matter to accurately distinguish which meridian is most out of balance since there are always several possibilities.

Working with just the six Basic Exercises to determine which meridian is most excessive or deficient is difficult because the condition of the Yin-Yang counterpart can mask the imbalance of the meridian. However, the amount of ease or difficulty in doing a Basic Exercise can serve as a general indicator of a Kyo or Jitsu condition in one of the meridians of the pair. Judging the Kyo or Jitsu condition of a particular meridian is easier when doing one of the Type Exercises, but still you must pay close attention while doing them to detect subtle differences. To get a more accurate picture of imbalances, you also have to note the differences between movements to the right and left. In order to feel subtle differences, it is very important that you pay as much attention as you can while doing Imagery Exercises.

The basic phenomena of life and its various functions take place largely in the relative sphere of subjective perception. And this is something that can only be experienced by the individuals directly involved. Furthermore, it is almost impossible to detect meridian imbalances with exercises which emphasize only external form and measurable phenomena. Once you gain some experience and develop a sense for what meridian imbalances or types mean, you will begin to notice subtle differences in the movements of others which they themselves may not be aware of. Developing your subjective perception to a point where you can sense differences which usually go unnoticed is the key to using exercises for balancing Ki. The effect of the very same exercise or movement often varies according to who teaches it especially because the experience and awareness of the teacher is a big factor.

In Imagery Exercises ease in movement and difficulty in movement are respectively designated as Kyo and Jitsu. The Jitsu movement is usually more obvious because it causes more pain or discomfort and points out inflexible parts. The Jitsu meridian (overactive life function) is one which is most obviously distorted by the accumulation of too much Ki. The root cause of the imbalance (Kyo) and its obvious manifestation (Jitsu) are always found in two different functions among the six essential life functions. This is because the cause and effect of a distortion never appear in the same place at once. When one meridian is Kyo, the meridian which is Jitsu is always among the ten other meridians that are not associated with the same life function. In other words, the meridians which are in a Yin-Yang relationship cannot be the most Kyo and the most Jitsu meridians at the same time. This means that there are one hundred and twenty possible Kyo-Jitsu combinations, or meridian imbalances, which are meridian types determined by the most Kyo and most Jitsu meridians in the body.

When all the essential life functions are totally balanced, Ki circulates freely inside the body. In this case, viewed from outside, the body appears to be at rest. On the other hand, when there is visible activity or motion, it indicates that Ki is being directed in some way. In life, activity originates from some aspect in which Ki is lacking. Thus all activity has its origin in a Kyo condition which in turn creates a corresponding Jitsu condition. When the state of activity naturally returns to a state of balance or rest, this is called a dynamic equilibrium, which is also a special characteristic of life. When the imbalance of Ki (Kyo and Jitsu) produced by activity cannot be returned to the balanced state of rest for some reason, this is manifested first as discomfort, then as distortion and dysfunction, and finally as a disease. No matter how great an imbalance is, it almost always contains the power to return one to a balanced state. Therefore if one can only recognize the type of imbalance and provide a little impetus to that potential of recovery, the body is able to return to a healthy state on its own. This is called natural or innate healing power, and this is close to dynamic equilibrium as one of the special characteristics of life.

The best way to provide impetus toward recovery is to make Ki move toward the Kyo meridian which is lacking in Ki. By moving Ki to alleviate the Ki deficiency and improving the Kyo condition, the circulation of Ki throughout the body becomes smooth and balanced by itself. Therefore the main point is to find the Kyo aspect. The Jitsu aspect is easy to detect even when just looking at one part of the body, but the Kyo aspect is hard to make out unless the entire body is viewed as a whole. When something is clearly present, just verifying it in several ways is enough evidence that it is indeed there. However, when you have to verify that something is missing, you have to look everywhere and check all possibilities to cover every angle. This analogy applies to finding the Kyo aspect.

The phenomenon of Jitsu, on the other hand, affects only certain parts of the body and draws our attention to the condition of these areas. Conditions such as imbalances, physical symptoms, and difficulty in movement are usually very obvious. These conditions can serve as hints for determining the person's type or meridian imbalance. In other words, the Jitsu aspect can be used as a clue in searching for the underlying cause, which is the Kyo aspect. The importance of dealing with the Kyo meridian first is emphasized repeatedly in classics of Chinese medicine. In order to move Ki and restore the balance, one must first learn how to detect the Kyo aspect or meridian.

Since it is so hard to pinpoint the Kyo aspect, how do you know when you have found it? You can be sure a certain aspect is Kyo because giving this aspect attention (Ki) has a positive effect on the Jitsu condition. The reason a difficult movement can become easier by moving in the opposite direction is because the easier movement directs Ki to the Kyo aspect. When moving to the right and left and one direction is Jitsu (more difficult), the other direction is always Kyo (easier). In terms of the six Basic Exercises, if there is one which is particularly difficult (Jitsu), one of the remaining five can always be done quite easily (Kyo). When speaking in terms of the twelve meridians, as soon as the most Jitsu meridian is found, you can be sure that one of the other meridians (except the meridian in a Yin-Yang relationship) is Kyo. The Kyo meridian can be verified by checking to see if treatment of the Kyo meridian serves to correct the Jitsu condition.

The Meaning of Emptiness

The reason meditation is such an important part of yoga as well as Zen Buddhism is that it has the purpose of getting people to experience the universal emptiness, which is the most powerful force behind life. Lao Tsu, the great sage of Taoist philosophy, stated: "Everything which exists begins from nothing and issues from emptiness." The basic teaching in Taoism is that one must realize the importance of emptiness or nonbeing and aspire to nonaction, which means to let nature take its course. There is no way that we can realize the profound significance of such philosophical and enigmatic truths just upon hearing it. One of the best things about Imagery Exercises is that you are able, through your experience of the meridians, to get an idea of what emptiness might mean and get a feeling for the profound truths contained in this Oriental philosophy.

Some people may regard this philosophy of nonaction as just an ideology of passivity in which a person either does nothing or is faltering and hesitant to act, but this is a mistaken view. The real intent behind this philosophy is to have people realize that in emptiness lies the power which controls everything. Medicine in this day and age would have the public believe that if not for the active role of physicians, our life would be in jeopardy and even the survival of mankind itself would be threatened. Be that as it may, the power which is doing all the healing is the natural healing force in everyone. Diseases can be best cured in most cases by leaving nature alone to do her work. This is often misinterpreted to mean that all diseases can be cured just by leaving patients alone. What is really meant by allowing nature to do the healing is to encourage the Ki of the patient, which is preoccupied both mentally and physically with the disease, to circulate freely and naturally once more. This is why it is so important to fathom the emptiness which is the cause of all disease.

The purpose of treating meridians lies in working with the Kyo (emptiness) to relieve the preoccupation with the Jitsu (excess). I have tried to explain what Kyo actually is, but as Lao Tsu has said, "The way which can be told is not the everlasting way." Therefore the characteristics of Kyo which I have outlined, far from covering every aspect, are only a small part of what Kyo can be. Nevertheless, since I have already listed various manifestations of Kyo along with the function of the meridians in Chapter 4, you should have some idea of how Kyo can appear as physical signs. The symptoms which are manifested as the Jitsu aspect are simple to identify and are quite tangible from both the objective and subjective standpoint. In the case of Kyo, the functions controlled by the meridian involved decline and symptoms resembling those of a Jitsu condition can appear. However, even though the symptoms may be similar to a Jitsu condition, they are not as obvious because the primary role of the Kyo aspect is one of remaining in the background as the cause of the disorder or physical problem.

In order to help you identify the Kyo meridian, I will list the tendencies and conditions most often seen in the case of Kyo for each of the twelve meridians. Nevertheless, you should not become too preoccupied with these definitions of Kyo conditions. After all, the primary features of the Kyo aspect are to be concealed and hard to pinpoint and running the whole show from behind the scenes. These descriptions are no more than a fleeting glimpse of what lies at the root. The whole truth lies in getting a real sense for the presence of the Kyo aspect and uncovering its secrets on your own.

Those things in life which stand out and draw one's attention and are consequently easy to become preoccupied with rarely have the essential power which motivates things. The real essence of life can only be found in what lies hidden under the surface. This is that mysterious power which is present in all aspects of life, but is hard to pin down. Yet this power constantly gives us hints and glimpses of itself to make us aware of its presence. Through the practice of Imagery Exercises, we can come to experience this ineffable power which animates us all. I am sure that you will reach a new awareness through Zen Imagery Exercises that this emptiness is something which permeates every aspect of life, for surely it holds the key to the mystery of life and gives life its meaning.

Lung Meridian Kyo

CAUSE:	One becomes isolated and closed off so that exchange of Ki with the environment is hindered.
MENTAL ASPECT:	worry which causes one's chest to feel blocked, an overanxious and hypersensitive emotional state, getting concerned after taking on too much work, becoming too anxious over fine details and being unable to relax and breath deeply, a lack of spirit and motivation, exhaustion and lethargy
PHYSICAL ASPECT:	hunched shoulders, shallow breathing, difficulty in breathing, discomfort in lying on back, susceptibility to colds and coughing especially after the upper body has been exposed to wind or cold, feverishness with pain between the shoulder blades, tendency for the eyes to water, pale complexion, dry skin, lack of stamina, extreme fatigue

Jitsu Symptoms of Other Meridians with Lung Meridian Kyo

Stomach:	tendency toward prolonged colds, coughing, and fatigue in legs, constriction in chest, lack of energy
Spleen:	worrying causing heaviness in chest, shallow breathing, and food stagnation in upper digestive tract
Heart:	emotional collapse, continuous tension leading to a feeling of growing oppression in chest
Small Intestine:	fatigue of hands and arms leading to shoulder stiffness, diarrhea as a result of a cold, respiratory disease, poor digestion and absorption of nutrients
Bladder:	loss of sleep due to coughing, chilling of upper body, fatigue due to hypertension, mental and physical overwork
Kidney:	difficulty in breathing, coughing and phlegm causing tightness in chest, prolonged exposure to wind
Heart Constrictor:	dizziness due to hypertension, mental and physical overwork
Triple Heater:	feeling of heaviness in the head with congestion of blood, tendency to catch colds
Gallbladder:	lack of vigor due to shoulder stiffness and fatigue
Liver:	loss of stamina due to overwork, thick phlegm

Large Intestine Meridian Kyo

CAUSE:	One is lacking in initiative and openness.
MENTAL ASPECT:	problems with personal relationships and lack of friends that can be trusted, inability to adequately express oneself to others, loss of motivation after a disappointment, depending on others instead of taking initiative
PHYSICAL ASPECT:	prone to nasal congestion and dry coughs, hypersensitivity in upper respiratory tract which causes coughing, tendency to exercise very little, not breathing deeply, tendency toward diarrhea especially when eating hard-to-digest food, chilling of lower abdomen and extremities, lack of strength, pain in arms and hand (especially in line with the thumb), pale complexion

Jitsu Symptoms of Other Meridians with Large Intestine Meridian Kyo

Stomach:	chilling during sleep, heaviness in stomach from chilling, too little exercise for the amount of food consumed, diarrhea, empyema
Spleen:	dryness and stickiness in mouth, frozen shoulders, shallow sleep

Heart:	impatient yet unable to act, low back pain, mental fatigue, sudden shock making one unable to stand
Small Intestine:	hardening of the arteries causing the legs to be anemic, hypersensitive skin, poor digestion, elbow pain
Bladder:	listlessness from continuous tension, nervous diarrhea, chilling of legs
Kidney:	constipation due to lack of exercise, fatigue of kidneys due to poor excretion, diarrhea due to nervous causes
Heart Constrictor:	chilling of extremities with hotness of the head, tendency to have palpitations
Triple Heater:	prolonged colds, swelling of gums, inability to open mouth widely
Gallbladder:	eyestrain from overuse of hands, low back pain resulting from chilling, overeating and indigestion
Liver:	tendency to be constipated, jerky finger movements, eczema, hemorrhoids, allergic rhinitis

Stomach Meridian Kyo

CAUSE:	One is unable to accept things as they are, and has difficulty in adapting to a new environment.
MENTAL ASPECT:	tendency to brood over things and indulge in vain regrets, appetite influenced by the type of food or one's mood, eating when mind is preoccupied with something else, irregular eating habits and great variation in quantity consumed, desire to lie down right after a meal, always worrying about the condition of the stomach, facial skin lacking in tone, blank facial expression
PHYSICAL ASPECT:	stomach problems or loss of appetite associated with worry, chilling of abdominal area, tightness in shoulders, tension and pain in the middle of the back, excessive yawning, tendency to have thick and heavy legs, inflexibility in wrist and ankle joints, pain in joints, tendency toward nasal congestion and slight coughs, chilling down the front of the body and feeling cold in knees, lack of body fat, lack of stomach acids leading to anemia, weak and sagging stomach, lack of strength in abdominal muscles causing the stomach area to appear depressed

Jitsu Symptoms of Other Meridians with Stomach Meridian Kyo

Lung:	lack of appetite or poor appetite due to coughing, inability to inhale deeply
Large Intestine:	excessive intake of cold drinks, poor appetite and complete enervation
Heart:	restlessness and tendency to eat too fast, feeling of obstruction in solar plexus
Small Intestine:	fatigue in legs and low back, shoulder stiffness and poor appetite
Bladder:	gastritis or diarrhea due to nervous causes, irritability and poor disposition
Kidney:	bitter taste and stickiness in mouth, nausea after overeating
Heart Constrictor:	poor digestion and tendency toward palpitations, feeling of heaviness in stomach after eating
Triple Heater:	gastritis due to overeating, stomach pains caused by chilling
Gallbladder:	general feeling of fatigue and lassitude, shoulder stiffness, indigestion and distension of stomach
Liver:	excessive eating and drinking, food poisoning, gastritis as a side effect of medication

Spleen Meridian Kyo

CAUSE:	One does not chew and digest things sufficiently. One lacks the perseverance to thoroughly assimilate things.
MENTAL ASPECT:	tendency to worry about something all by oneself, obsession with details and excessive worry, restlessness and anxiety, inclination to interfere with the work of others, inability to "blow off steam" and tendency to hold things inside, overuse of the mind and underuse of the body, tendency to be forgetful, difficulty in bringing things to an end, overeating or constantly nibbling, eating too quickly and never feeling full, always sleepy
PHYSICAL ASPECT:	poor salivation and tendency for mouth to become sticky, bitter taste in the mouth, excessive thirst, preference for a lot of liquids with a meal, preference for foods with high liquid content, lack of digestive juices causing anemia, poor discrimination of tastes, dark brown facial coloration, lack of exercise, tendency for front of legs to become cold, hard knot around navel, excessive belching and flatulence, unhealthy color in gums, tension down the whole back, plump physique with excess body fat, roughness in skin of hands and feet, cracks in the heel

Jitsu Symptoms of Other Meridians with Spleen Meridian Kyo

Lung:	poor sense of smell with nasal congestion, effusiveness
Large Intestine:	pain in arms, constipation due to poor digestion, sensation of heaviness in legs after being chilled, thinking too much
Heart:	feeling of constraint associated with overwork, tightness in throat, impatience, shoulder stiffness
Small Intestine:	low back pain from overstrain in childbirth, voracious appetite, pain in the heels
Bladder:	restlessness, overeating, swelling of knees, nasal congestion
Kidney:	diabetes, overeating and preference for sweet foods, thinking too much
Heart Constrictor:	rounded back, great anxiety with no chance for release
Triple Heater:	lack of stomach acids leading to anemia, sleep disturbed by obsessive thinking
Gallbladder:	difficulty in getting to sleep and restless sleep, tendency to brood over things and overeat, indecisiveness, arthritis in knee
Liver:	tendency to be single-minded, excessive intake of sugar, excessive alcohol consumption

Heart Meridian Kyo

CAUSE:	One feels unstable in one's center, which causes inappropriate responses to one's surroundings.
MENTAL ASPECT:	emotional exhaustion after some crisis, excessive stress, longstanding anxiety or nervous tension, tendency to be oversensitive and neurotic, anxiety and worrying which affect appetite, restlessness and inability to calm down, forgetfulness, tendency to be paranoid, jittery, easily startled or very timid, tension in the tongue which causes stuttering, poor concentration
PHYSICAL ASPECT:	feeling of tension or constriction in solar plexus, rounded back caused by weakness of muscles in abdomen, tendency toward palpitations, strong tension in the abdominal wall and a feeling of oppression in the solar plexus when pressed, nervous stomach, thick tongue coating, feeling as if something is caught in the

throat, rigidity in hands, sweaty palms, tendency to tire easily, soreness and redness in corner of eyes

Jitsu Syptoms of Other Meridians with Heart Meridian Kyo

Lung:	feeling of blockage in solar plexus or constriction in chest, nasal congestion
Large Intestine:	low spirits, feeling of legs dragging after a big disappointment
Stomach:	feeling of heaviness in stomach, loss of appetite due to shock, restless sleep
Spleen:	timidity and hesitancy, irregular appeitite, lack of exercise
Bladder:	fatigue caused by constant tension, feeling of something caught in throat
Kidney:	fatigue after a big disappointment, prolonged anxiety, loss of motivation
Heart Constrictor:	backache associated with excessive concern, cold sweat on the face
Triple Heater:	head feeling unclear (hazy), heaviness over the whole body
Gallbladder:	strained nerves after concentrating too hard, hotness of the head and feeling irritable
Liver:	feeling of tension and discomfort in upper half of the body, eye irritation

Small Intestine Meridian Kyo

CAUSE:	One lacks the confidence to assert oneself, and has a tendency to be shy and retiring.
MENTAL ASPECT:	becoming too involved with details, great patience, holding in feelings, suppressing deep sorrow, wearing out one's nerves concentrating too hard, excessive anxiety and worry, a strong desire not to be outdone, tendency to be introverted, awkwardness in manner, psychological trauma
PHYSICAL ASPECT:	poor intestinal function which causes one to be thin, loose or flabby flesh, poor absorption of nutrients causing anemia and lack of energy, constipation or diarrhea caused by poor digestion, chilling of legs and waist along with hotness of face, weakness in lower half of body causing a feeling of heaviness from the waist down, fatigue and soreness in lower back leading to heaviness in legs, blood stagnation, appendicitis or problems stemming from appendix operation, susceptibility to food poisoning, stiffness and tension in back of neck, shoulder stiffness with migraine headaches, ringing in ears, loss of hearing, dysmenorrhea and gynecological problems

Jitsu Symptoms of Other Meridians with Small Intestine Meridian Kyo

Lung:	mental fatigue along with heaviness in the hips and legs, loss of spirit
Large Intestine:	gynecological problems accompanied with chilling of hips and legs, congestion in lower abdomen caused by shock
Stomach:	irregular appetite and eating too many sweets, dysfunction of ovaries, shoulder stiffness
Spleen:	digestive problems caused by excessive worry, chilling of back, excessive gas
Bladder:	overworking, state of shock, autotoxemia
Kidney:	lingering fatigue after childbirth, low back pain, subject to great stress
Heart Constrictor:	general fatigue, tendency toward palpitations, stiffness in back or low back pain
Triple Heater:	whiplash injury, lack of exercise, ringing in ears, Ménière's disease, overexertion

Gallbladder:	lack of stamina, eyestrain, arthritis
Liver:	duodenal ulcer, dark spots on skin, intermittent claudication*

Bladder Meridian Kyo

CAUSE:	The whole body is out of balance, and although one feels the need to do something, one has no stamina to act.
MENTAL ASPECT:	fatigue after extended period of stress, fretting over little things, easily startled, tendency to overreact, anxiety and fear which causes one to break out in a cold sweat, anxiety and restlessness, mental instability, neurotic tendency, complaints of general malice
PHYSICAL ASPECT:	nasal congestion, discomfort in the base of nose, heaviness in the head, pain down the back, palpitations, profuse sweating, dizziness, distension of stomach, sciatica or low back pain, hypersensitivity to cold, chilling in the lower abdomen and the legs, pain and heaviness in legs, difficulty in bending backward, ticklishness, dysfunctions in the uterus or bladder, frequent urination or sparse urination, dribbling urination, poor urinary excretion causing body to swell slightly

Jitsu Symptoms of Other Meridians with Bladder Meridian Kyo

Lung:	inability to express one's thoughts, sighing, tension in the thumbs, bronchitis
Large Intestine:	feeling of distension in lower abdomen associated with nervous tension, sciatica
Stomach:	weak stomach due to nervousness, chilling of extremities, heaviness in stomach
Spleen:	poor appetite from thinking too much, poor digestion due to chilling, neurosis
Heart:	insomnia from shock or excessive stress, nervousness and irritability leading to poor absorption of nutrients
Small Intestine:	impatience, being overworked, fatigue after shock, weak function of intestines
Heart Constrictor:	hotness in hands and soles due to circulatory imbalance, pain down the back and hips, eyestrain, tendency for eyes to water
Triple Heater:	chilling causing distension of the lower abdomen, general swelling, uterine discharge, dysfunction of autonomic nervous system
Gallbladder:	costal neuralgia, constant worrying and oversensitivity, eyestrain
Liver:	extreme fatigue, fever, hemorrhoids, cramps in the Achilles tendon

Kidney Meridian Kyo

CAUSE:	One has a tendency of overdoing things and to reach a state of total exhaustion by working too hard.
MENTAL ASPECT:	unabating anxiety or sense of emptiness, lack of perseverance and motivation, easily startled and fearful of the slightest thing, lack of composure, restlessness, continual stress at home or work from which there is no escape, loss of determination and drive

* Intermittent claudication is a form of limping which is caused by hardening of the arteries in the legs. There is no pain or discomfort when the limbs are at rest, but after walking is begun, the pain intensifies until walking becomes impossible.

PHYSICAL ASPECT:	dark complexion lacking luster, puffy skin lacking in resiliency, chilling sensation extending from the lower abdomen and hips down the legs, frequent urination or sparse urination, overwork and loss of sleep for extended period, body heavy with fatigue as if weighted down, bad breath, hormonal deficiency, excessive sexual activity, loss of sexual drive and impotence, weak and brittle bones, tendency to trip and fall, tension and hardness in waist area, tightness in rectus abdominis muscle*

Jitsu Symptoms of Other Meridians with Kidney Meridian Kyo

Lung:	pulmonary emphysema, copious phlegm, chilling of upper half of body
Large Intestine:	stiffness and tension in the legs from chilling, leg cramps as a result of back strain
Stomach:	hotness of head, oversensitivity to cold, hyperacidity, gastritis due to overwork, overeating
Spleen:	dry mouth from poor salivation, low back pain, cracks in the heels
Heart:	insomnia despite physical fatigue, headaches
Small Intestine:	fatigue after childbirth or stagnation of blood in lower abdomen
Heart Constrictor:	high or low blood pressure, angina pectoris, swelling of arms and legs, overwork
Triple Heater:	tonsillitis, hotness of head, oversensitivity to cold, allergic constitution, susceptibility to infections
Gallbladder:	difficulty in getting to sleep, restless sleep, swelling of face and extremities, nausea
Liver:	drug abuse, insect bites, liver disorders

Heart Constrictor Meridian Kyo

CAUSE:	The circulatory function declines and an excessive burden is placed on the heart because of poor posture or working in one position too long.
MENTAL: ASPECT: .	great impatience without any ability to act, total exhaustion causing one to be in a daze, restless sleep and excessive dreaming, anxiety caused by breathing difficulties, being repeatedly startled by small things, great shock which almost seems to cause a heart attack
PHYSICAL ASPECT:	tendency for the throat to swell, feeling of obstruction in chest which makes it hard to inhale, chest pains, heart problems, palpitations, shortness of breath, tendency to tire easily and inability to exercise vigorously, abnormal and fluctuating blood pressure, swelling and chilling of extremities, tendency toward gastric and duodenal ulcers, heartburn, tenderness on the sternum and pectoral muscles

Jitsu Symptoms of Other Meridians with Heart Constrictor Meridian Kyo

Lung:	cardiac asthma, numbness in the toes, heaviness in the shoulders, back, and chest
Large Intestine:	hotness of head and cold legs, great tension from the neck down to the shoulders, chilling during sleep
Stomach:	poor digestion due to overwork, high blood pressure
Spleen:	exhaustion after too much mental work, gastroptosis

* The rectus abdominis muscle is the vertical band of muscle which extends down the center of the abdomen from the ribs to the pubic bone.

Heart:	fatigue coming from restlessness, ringing in the ears, hotness of head and palpitations
Small Intestine:	fatigue due to anxiety, cerebral infarction, palpitations
Bladder:	high blood pressure due to stress, pyloric ulcer, labored breathing
Kidney:	overwork and straining one's nerves, tension over the shoulders, heaviness in the chest
Gallbladder:	Basedow's disease, hardness of forearms, heartburn, pain in the back and shoulders
Liver:	dizziness upon standing, feeling tired all over

Triple Heater Meridian Kyo

CAUSE:	One is overprotected at home and cast out into the world unprepared. One tends to be poorly adapted, overly cautious, tense, and awkward, and does not have enough opportunity to get release from nervous tension.
MENTAL ASPECT:	tendency to carry a mental burden or to be overanxious, excessive worrying over trivial matters in dealing with others, tendency for thinking to be disorganized due to fatigue, a feeling of being in a daze
PHYSICAL ASPECT:	hypersensitive skin, and weakness in mucous membrane and lymphatic system, tendency toward allergic reactions in the tonsils, nose, and throat, frequent colds which take a long time to go away, headaches, ringing in the ears, and dizziness, eyestrain, hotness of head, excessive discomfort with changes in temperature and humidity, feeling of constriction in chest, tension in abdominal walls, extreme ticklishness, inflammation of peritoneum causing abdominal cramps and pain, misalignment of cervical vertebrae, and tension in neck, numbness from the neck down to the back of the arms

Jitsu Symptoms of Other Meridians with Triple Heater Meridian Kyo

Lung:	chest pains with a cold, pleurisy
Large Intestine:	common cold, dizziness, fatigue in arms and lower half of body
Stomach:	acute gastritis, lack of exercise, feeling tired after overeating
Spleen:	feeling ill after eating, heaviness in head from excessive anxiety
Heart:	hotness of head and chilling of extremities, feeling of general lassitude, fatigue or strain felt in the back of the eyes
Small Intestine:	whiplash injury, appendicitis, ringing in the ears, shoulder tension from lack of exercise
Bladder:	allergic constitution, numbness down arms and legs, frequent urination
Kidney:	lack of sleep or restless sleep, prone to nosebleed, blurred vision
Gallbladder:	tendency for protracted colds, bitter taste in mouth, nausea, eyestrain
Liver:	hypersensitivity of peritoneum and abdominal wall causing frequent diarrhea, tendency to be ticklish, rhinitis

Gallbladder Meridian Kyo

| CAUSE: | One is indecisive about where to focus one's energy when undertaking something and tends to vacillate about which direction to go. One has lost vigor after great disappointment. |

MENTAL ASPECT:	fatigue after continued emotional excitement, fatigue after being pressed to make a decision, prolonged stress, fatigue from having to deal with many details, emotional exhaustion after a big disappointment, tendency to be nervous and jittery, frayed nerves, loss of will-power, low motivation because of fatigue
PHYSICAL ASPECT:	uneven distribution of nutrients in the body, symptoms of fatigue in specific areas especially the eyes, fatigue from overuse of eyes, mucus from eyes and blurred vision, deteriorating vision, headache due to eyestrain, insufficient bile and poor digestion of fats leading to constipation, diarrhea, or discolored stools, anemic tendency and sallow complexion, tendency to gain weight easily even when cutting down on fat, dislike of fatty foods, preference for foods with mild flavor, hyperacidity, rigidity and pain in joints

Jitsu Symptoms of Other Meridians with Gallbladder Meridian Kyo

Lung:	pulling pain in thumbs, stiffness in pectoral muscles, phlegm
Large Intestine:	poor elimination and fecal stasis, tendency to tire easily, bloodshot eyes
Stomach:	insufficient chewing, lack of sleep, blurred vision, car sickness
Spleen:	poor secretion of digestive enzymes, tendency to get skin rashes, stomatitis
Heart:	nervous strain, difficulty in getting to sleep, dizziness
Small Intestine:	efforts beyond one's capacity, weak intestinal function, tendency to tire easily, allergic condition
Bladder:	overwork, duodenal ulcer, spasm in bile duct, jaundice
Kidney:	coughing with phlegm, stiffness in back and shoulders, eyestrain
Heart Constrictor:	obesity, Basedow's disease, palpitations, tendency to fret and worry
Triple Heater:	susceptibility to colds, distension of abdomen, bitter taste in mouth, restless sleep, nausea, phlegm

Liver Meridian Kyo

CAUSE:	A loss of stamina and endurance so that even if one is motivated there is insufficient energy to persist. The reserve of nutrients in the body is diminished and the detoxification function declines.
MENTAL ASPECT:	lack of perseverance and tendency to become bored, impatient and irritabie, tendency for nerves to be on end, short temperedness and sudden explosive release of emotions, easily irritated by noise, worrying unneccesarily
PHYSICAL ASPECT:	weak joints, shaky feeling in joints when making vigorous movements, total exhaustion, tendency to have dizzy spells or to trip and fall, hardness in Achilles tendon, things appear yellowish, tendency toward food poisoning with nausea and vomiting, inability to gain weight, low fever lasting a long time, high fever of unknown causes, stiffness and rigidity in muscles which cause movements to become awkward, loss of sexual drive and impotence

Jitsu Symptoms of Other Meridians with Liver Meridian Kyo

Lung:	tendency to be constipated, stiffness in back and shoulders, asthma
Large Intestine:	tendency to be constipated, hotness of the head, pent-up energy, tired and heavy legs
Stomach:	liver disorders, loss of appetite, lack of motivation to work

Spleen:	dark complexion lacking luster, fatigue and heaviness over whole body, loss of sexual drive
Heart:	a state of total exhaustion after emotional excitement
Small Intestine:	symptoms of duodenal ulcer, intermittent claudication, facial blemishes
Bladder:	difficulty in urination, nervous strain, impotence, symptoms of poisoning
Kidney:	excessive alcohol consumption, loss of drive due to overexertion, prostatic hypertrophy
Heart Constrictor:	restlessness and inability to relax, nervousness in personal relationships, strong palpitations
Triple Heater:	rhinitis, stomatitis, hypersensitive peritoneum, ticklishness, tendency to get diarrhea after being chilled

Chapter 14

Working with Specific Physical Problems

Treat the Basic Cause

Among the diversity of methods used today for improving one's state of health, one feature that almost all of the methods have in common is that of placing an emphasis on how to deal with current physical problems or symptoms. This takes after the basic approach in Western medicine, that of analyzing quantifiable findings to determine the "cause" of the disease and yet administering treatments largely for relief from symptoms. One of the characteristics of diseases in human beings is that by the time the cause of a symptom can be verified objectively, the real cause is obscured. Attempting to predict the progress of someone's disease based only on what is apparent at the time is ignoring the individual's personal history up to that point. Somewhere in the overall picture, our present condition always contains something of the past which gave rise to it.

Symptoms only appear as outcomes of distortions or imbalances in our whole being. No disease ever appears all of a sudden from nowhere for no cause. Disease is an inevitable result of imbalances in an individual's life originating from the past. The disease is, in fact, a product of a force which is working to cure it. Therefore only by viewing the sick person as a whole can be identified the mental and physical imbalances which really gave rise to the problem. It is a misdirected approach that attempts to deal only with the apparent symptoms of a disease.

Likewise, it is a mistake to assume that just because two people have similar symptoms their disease can be categorized as the same and that their disease can be treated in the same way. In Oriental medicine the emphasis has traditionally been placed on the Yin factor (Kyo) which lies behind the more obvious Yang factor (Jitsu). Even when the apparent Yang factor (Jitsu symptom) is identical for two people, its significance is completely different when it is viewed from an overall perspective to consider the Yin factor (cause) which gave rise to the problem.

As an illustration of this point, suppose three people received a score of 80 percent on a test. If only the present situation were to be taken into account, these three people may be regarded as being at the same level. If, however, these identical scores were to be viewed from a larger perspective, we might learn that one person usually gets 100 percent, the second person usually gets 60, and the third person usually gets 80. The meaning of the same score of 80 percent becomes decidedly different in such a case. Accordingly, the way in which we treat the same score of 80 should be different for each person. Sometimes it may seem easier and more practical to consider only the latest test result because it represents an objective assessment everyone can understand. Nevertheless, even though it is more difficult to judge how hard a person is working, whether he is being lazy or trying to the best of his ability, it is best for the person to view his performance as a whole. The total picture about why a person performed the way he did is often hard to see and one must look deeper for hidden factors. Only by going through this process, however, can the real reason for the person's score be understood. And only then can the score be best used to help the person.

The diagnostic approach in Oriental medicine can be compared to contemplating the meaning of many paintings on an individual basis. This is completely different from the treatment of symptoms which is like classifying pictures systematically by the subject matter. Even when the central figure in two pictures are identical, the significance and impact of the same figure varies considerably by the background of the picture. If we classify pictures only by the main subject, the all important setting or background of the picture eludes us. It is therefore necessary to apply our own intuition in judging the meaning of each picture by looking at the background as well as the subject. In this process our own subjective viewpoint becomes a big factor, but subjective perception is all important if we wish to gain anything of value from the experience.

So in order to really understand and appreciate a given situation we have to be able to see what lies under surface appearances. Behind everything that is seen there always lie crucial factors which are unseen. This means that, in order to see these, we must direct our attention away from the obvious aspects to view the situation as a whole. The Jitsu aspect, or the obvious problem, is naturally clearly evident because it stands out by drawing attention away from other parts to itself. In terms of the Kyo and Jitsu condition of meridians, the obvious problem or symptom is most often manifested in the Jitsu meridian. The Kyo or deficient meridian is always one of the other meridians not in a Yin-Yang pair with the Jitsu. There may be several Kyo meridians among the ten possibilities, but one particularly Kyo meridian is causing the Jitsu to manifest as a problem. The meridian which is most Kyo is also the deepest and most difficult to locate. This is why the situation must be examined as a whole to identify the meridian which is most Kyo. You will know when you have found the greatest Kyo (the basic cause) because working on it affects the Jitsu aspect positively and begins to resolve the problem.

Working on the Kyo aspect has a remarkable effect in relieving the Jitsu problem. When only the Jitsu aspect is considered, one may become doubtful about being able to resolve the problem or symptom because it appears so great. However, the problem seems insurmountable only because one's Ki, or attention, has become absorbed by that one aspect. Once the Ki which is preoccupied is redirected, the symptoms which seemed to present such a difficult problem begin to go away. Working with the Kyo aspect (the emptiness or the basic cause) automatically resolves the problem. Since emptiness has no form, it is able to reabsorb the Jitsu manifestation back into nothingness. A fundamental rule in the Yin-Yang principle is that Yin sustains Yang. All that has happened when symptoms go away is that the Yin (Kyo) and Yang (Jitsu) have balanced each other out.

This profound concept must not remain just a theory. It is meaningless unless we put it into practice. Therefore when you do Imagery Exercises, first find the exercise which is the hardest to do (Jitsu) and then look for another one which is the easiest

(Kyo). If doing the easiest exercise causes an improvement in the performance of the most difficult one, or relieves a Jitsu symptom, it is effectively reinforcing the Ki in the Kyo meridian. Keep practicing various Imagery Exercises and work toward a practical understanding of what lies at the root of your problems. When the exercise is not effective or the effects are not clear, keep looking for the deepest Kyo, which is elusive by nature. Work on developing your intuitive ability to identify the Kyo aspect which is the cause.

Overcoming emotional or physical problems is naturally most important to the individual who has such a problem. Also there is really very little others can do to help until the person with the problem earnestly decides to work on it. The process of seeking the Kyo aspect, or the basic cause, is a very personal and subjective endeavor. It follows that the person with the problem should be the first one to seek out the underlying cause and find a solution which works for him. Individual differences have always been important in Oriental medicine and an attempt is made to get a total picture of patients, down to details of their everyday life. This approach enables a practitioner to identify the basic cause and select the best treatment for each individual. In much the same way Imagery Exercises enables you to find the exercises most suited to yourself. Your own feelings and sensations experienced in moving your body become your guide. Just as no two things in life are ever exactly the same the very same exercise is experienced in a different way by every individual. All persons move according to their own balance and inner rhythm, so naturally even the performance of the same set of movements will differ from person to person. This being the case, we must each work to heighten our own awareness of our bodies and seek the basic cause or emptiness which is the key to our life. In this way we can bring about a more profound and lasting change in our whole being.

Disorders of Musculoskeletal System

Neck and Shoulder Tension (Stiff Shoulders)
Most people do not consider stiff shoulders as being a real physical problem so they rarely give it serious attention. In Japan physicians just appease patients with such complaints by giving them tranquilizers, vitamin injections in the shoulder, or traction on the neck. Even in the case of acupuncture and shiatsu practitioners, many of them mostly concentrate on treating the neck and shoulder area. Some people contend that all such treatments are unnecessary as long as one gets sufficient exercise. Whatever the case, the real cause of the neck and shoulder tension is seldom considered when dealing with the problem.

The causes of neck and shoulder tension are many. There are jobs which cause shoulder tension, and sometimes just unpleasant conversation alone can cause your shoulders to become stiff. Some people seem to carry the weight of life's burdens around on their shoulders. Other people get what is called "frozen shoulders" from age or overuse of the arms. All cases of shoulder stiffness cannot be treated in the same way because the root cause varies so much. All the meridians on the shoulders travel up the neck as well as down the arms, waist, and legs. Using Imagery Exercises to adjust imbalances in these meridians, which cover the length of the body, has a special effect in relieving shoulder tension.

Shoulder stiffness often appears as Jitsu of the Gallbladder Meridian when it is mostly on the right side, or as Jitsu of the Stomach Meridian when it is on the left side. Otherwise, cases of Jitsu of the Small Intestine Meridian or Bladder Meridian are also common. In terms of Kyo meridians, shoulder stiffness is often caused by Kyo of the Large Intestine, Small Intestine, Heart, Triple Heater, or Heart Constrictor Meridian. In all cases it is important to identify the meridians involved in the neck and shoulder tension. The Basic and Complementary Exercises are effective ways to balance the meridians along the whole body. Also, doing Exercise "M" and "N" right after doing the appropriate Type Exercises is most effective in relieving the symptom of stiffness in the neck and shoulders.

Cervico-brachialgia

In the past cervico-brachialgia, a condition of intense pain from the neck down to the arm, was often seen in people over fifty and was associated with "frozen shoulders." More recently the number of younger people with this condition has increased, especially in relation to occupations such as key punching, typing, and drafting. In Japan many people receive acupuncture or shiatsu for such conditions. Recently one Japanese physician stated that exercise was far more effective than such treatments. Be that as it may people with this condition tend to become preoccupied with the symptom of pain from the neck down to the arms and forget to consider the rest of their body. Not too seldom the symptoms on one side of the body go away just to recur on the other side later. The best approach for treating cervico-brachialgia is to work on the Kyo meridian.

Therefore if you are lacking exercise or tend to get chilled, work on the Large Intestine Meridian. In cases accompanied with indigestion, work on the Spleen Meridian. If there is a dental problem, the Stomach and Small Intestine Meridians should be treated. In cases of shock or mental strain, work on the Heart Meridian, and otherwise, if you have overworked or have remained in one position for too long, work on the Heart Constrictor Meridian. In most cases of cervico-brachialgia, there is a slight displacement in the shoulder joint which is pulled in the direction of the Kyo meridian. The pain usually appears on the other side along the Jitsu meridian. Treating just the side which has the symptom only gives temporary relief at best. You must avoid forcing movements on the painful side. Instead you should exercise the side which is free of symptoms. Work on relieving tension in the Kyo meridian by stretching as far as you can in the easy direction and releasing Ki while exhaling.

Tenosynovitis (Inflammation of Tendon Sheath)

Tenosynovitis usually occurs in the wrist and fingers, especially the thumb, and causes difficulty in movement. Sometimes it causes the condition of "trigger finger,"* and usually moving the hand causes pain. Most treatments for tenosynovitis concentrate on the affected part. In serious cases, an operation is performed. The cause of this condition is usually distortions in the joints of the wrist, elbow, shoulder, and neck. On occasion it is even caused by the misalignment of thoracic vertebrae. This is the

---

* A trigger finger is one which is affected by a momentary spasmodic arrest in movement during flexing or bending which is followed by a snapping into place. Trigger finger is caused by inflammation of the tendon sheath or the formation of a nodule in the tendon.

reason Imagery Exercises which balance the meridians through the whole body can be considered as being most effective. Tenosynovitis is most often the result of misuse or overuse of the fingers coupled with Kyo of the Lung, Large Intestine, Spleen, Stomach, Heart, Small Intestine, Heart Constrictor, or Triple Heater Meridian. It is important to perform the exercises most suited to balancing the affected meridians in each individual.

Inflammation of Knee Joint

The majority of knee problems which do not involve injury are caused by Kyo of the Spleen Meridian. The tendencies of eating in a hurry, not chewing food well, and thinking too much are associated with Kyo of the Spleen Meridian. Other tendencies of people with Kyo of the Spleen Meridian include lack of exercise and sitting and talking for extended periods. The Jitsu meridian which appears along with Kyo of the Spleen Meridian varies according to the symptoms. When a person finds it impossible to get into the Seiza position, the Gallbladder Meridian is Jitsu. When the Bladder Meridian is Jitsu, there is pain upon sitting down or standing up. If the Triple Heater Meridian is Jitsu, water tends to collect in the knees. In the case of Jitsu of the Small Intestine Meridian, the pain radiates from the hips down to the knees.

In all cases, a person should not force movement in the painful knee. However, neither should one stop moving the knee because it is painful. It is also important to use the bad knee wherever this is possible without pain. One can assist the knee by using one's arms to make most of the weight come over the good knee. Those Imagery Exercises which do not place a burden on the knees are most suitable in this case. There is no need to force any movement that increases the pain in the knees. Often the reason the knee is in such a poor condition in the first place is that a person's ankle and hip joints are very rigid. Therefore you should concentrate on exercising these joints. Rotating the ankles with your hand while sitting cross-legged is good. The leg stretching exercises in Family Exercises are also very effective. Having your ankles exercised will make movement in the other joints easier.

Low Back Pain

There seems to be a greater tendency toward low back pain in Western style environments, where people sit in chairs and wear shoes all day. The incidence of low back pain is on the increase in Japan as it is becoming more westernized. This could also be related to the use of cars and other convenient forms of transportation from a young age and not developing sufficient strength in the legs and pelvis. Since the knee is seldom bent fully in Western environments, the muscles from the knees up to the hips which are the foundation for the upper half of the body are more susceptible to fatigue.

Commonly low back pain is caused by Kyo of the Heart or Small Intestine Meridian. The Basic Exercise "C" and the Complementary Exercise "U" can be done even when the low back pain is severe. The Family Exercises of stretching the inside of legs in the face-up position and pressing and adjusting the lumbar region and legs in the face-down position are good for low back pain. When the pain has eased somewhat, you can also attempt the "lumbar twist." In the Family Exercises the leg stretching exercises on the back and inside of the leg are good for Kyo of the Kidney, Heart Constrictor and Large Intestine Meridians. Therefore stretch and press along these meridians while taking care not to cause pain. Remember to always begin working on the side with the least discomfort and pain. When exercising alone, always begin with the easy movement first.

Imagery Exercises include many movements which exercise the lower half of the body and it is essential to concentrate on the *hara* as you do them. Practicing Imagery Breathing and centering your Ki in your *hara* on a regular basis is important for the prevention of low back pain. Acute cases of severe back pain, sometimes referred to as a "slipped disk," mostly occur when a person makes an uncoordinated movement with the arms or the legs without being centered in the *hara*. You should bear this in mind when practicing these exercises.

Arthritis

Rheumatoid arthritis is very difficult to cure once it reaches the chronic stage. If the joints are not moved because of the pain, the deformation of the joints progresses faster and recovery becomes impossible. Arthritis, similar to low back pain, is caused mostly by Kyo of the Heart or Small Intestine Meridian. The symptoms of pain in the joints appear with Jitsu of the Gallbladder Meridian. The key point in working with arthritis is to exercise the joints which are not affected so as to improve circulation and thereby purify the blood and nourish the tissues. It is most important to keep up hope and persevere without giving up. The whole body tenses up when the emphasis is put on exercising the affected joints. The best approach is to do those Imagery Exercises in which the whole body can be relaxed. Do all these exercises by moving in the easier direction first.

Disorders of Digestive System

Indigestion

Many people these days have indigestion from unhealthy living habits such as overworking and staying up late, as well as from immoderation in eating and drinking. Even when an attempt is made to salvage the situation by taking medication for indigestion, it is inevitable that keeping up an unhealthy lifestyle will eventually lead to serious gastrointestinal disorders. All medication does is to suppress the symptoms temporarily, for it is unable to improve the digestive function as such. The habitual use of medication such as antacids can even be harmful to your health. The element of stress—the foremost cause of disease in this modern age—has a tremendous impact on digestion.

In the condition of Stomach Kyo-Small Intestine Jitsu, the function of the intestines have been impaired by stress or overwork. In cases like this, rather than taking medication, doing exercises to stimulate the digestive function is far more beneficial. In the case of Spleen Kyo-Small Intestine Jitsu, poor absorption in the intestines can cause an unnatural craving for food. Such an abnormal appetite very often precedes stomach problems so one must be careful. In the case of Small Intestine Kyo-Stomach Jitsu, often a person has become overanxious and the intestinal function is weakened. The best thing in this case is to relax and recover from fatigue. The light and restful variety of Imagery Exercises such as the Reclining Exercises are ideal for this.

Indigestion is caused by lack of exercise in conditions such as Triple Heater Kyo-

Small Intestine Jitsu, Large Intestine Kyo-Small Intestine Jitsu, and Stomach Kyo-Large Intestine Jitsu. In these cases exercise, especially of the legs, is a necessity. When the condition is Stomach Kyo-Bladder Jitsu, indigestion is usually due to nervous causes. In the case of Stomach Kyo-Kidney Jitsu, drinking too much alcohol, lack of sleep, or overwork are usually the cause. The combination and emphasis of exercises for indigestion varies according to each condition. It is important to look for the causes in terms of imbalances in the meridians and to exercise according to your individual needs.

Constipation

The tendency to become constipated can be considered as an inevitable result of the modern diet, consisting mainly of easily digested processed foods low in fiber content, coupled with lack of exercise. Eating soft and easily digested foods also leads to the habit of gulping down a meal. Laxatives are used far too much in the Western countries and this tendency is also growing in Japan. While the amount of physical labor at work is usually minimal, overworking our mental faculty is very common. Just getting a little exercise on the weekend is obviously not enough to rectify this constant imbalance between the use of our mind and our body. The best solution to this problem is to incorporate an exercise regimen into our daily routine and to do those Imagery Exercises which deal with the basic cause (imbalance) of our condition.

Constipation is usually due to insufficient chewing in the case of Spleen Kyo-Large Intestine Jitsu. In the case of Large Intestine Kyo-Gallbladder Jitsu, it is caused by a lack of bile excretion. Similarly, Large Intestine Kyo-Triple Heater Jitsu is associated with constipation from nervous causes or being chilled. Large Intestine Kyo-Small Intestine Jitsu is associated with indigestion as well as constipation. In the case of Small Intestine Kyo-Large Intestine Jitsu, constipation is connected to the psychological factor or being unable to vent one's feelings.

Hemorrhoids

Cases of constipation are often compounded by the congestion of blood around the anus which causes hemorrhoids. Those exercises which improve bowel movements are often helpful in cases of hemorrhoids. Treating the Large Intestine Meridian often helps bring hemorrhoids under control.

When the Bladder Meridian is Kyo, being chilled or lack of exercise are likely to be the cause. Otherwise hemorrhoids are related to stress in this modern society and could be caused by anxiety associated with Kyo of the Heart Meridian or thinking too much, which is assoicated with Kyo of the Spleen Meridian. If the latter is the case, the Basic Exercise "B" and the Work Exercise "O" can be done from time to time to counteract the tendency to overwork the brain.

Disorders of Circulatory System

Hypertension

Some people become overly concerned when informed that their blood pressure is slightly high. There are even those who take drugs to lower their blood pressure without a real need to do so. They fear greater complications and worry about the results every time their blood pressure is taken. It is unlikely that people with this kind of temperament will ever be cured of their hypertension. In many cases such neurotic tendencies are best treated by psychotherapy. Although it is true that strokes and other complications occur more frequently in people with hypertension, in reality less than 10 percent of those with hypertension suffer strokes. Hypertension is often seen in those who do not get enough exercise. Cardiovascular exercise such as light jogging is therefore a good idea. Before jogging, however, it is best to do some Imagery Exercises to relax and balance the whole body.

Those Imagery Exercises which stimulate the Heart Constrictor and Triple Heater Meridians are the most beneficial for people with poor peripheral circulation and scarce perspiration. In their case just enough exercise to work up a light sweat on a daily basis is recommended. Even in just a weeks time, the improvement should be substantial. Lack of sleep (Kidney Jitsu) and nervous tension (Bladder Jitsu) are also associated with hypertension. Doing Exercise "M" to reduce tension around the neck and shoulders is often enough to remove various symptoms associated with hypertension. Further, exercising all the other joints in the body such as the ankles, waist, and wrists will stimulate the main points of constriction in circulation and will thus enable the heart to function more smoothly and reduce blood pressure.

Angina Pectoris

In the past the greatest killer among the deadly diseases in Japan was strokes. More recently, however, the mortality rate for heart diseases has become very high, just as in the Western countries. It sometimes happens that jogging, taken up for the sake of exercise, becomes the direct cause of death. When living a life with relatively little physical activity, it is not advisable to place a sudden load on the heart. Even normally beneficial exercises can be dangerous when overdone without adequate preparation.

If you wish to have a stronger heart, you should not think only in terms of strengthening the central cardiovascular system. Cardiac pain is a signal that the function of the circulatory system over the whole body has weakened. Therefore you must find out what the underlying causes are to treat these first. In angina pectoris there is a sudden feeling of heavy pressure and pain in the heart area. Along with this "heart attack" one often experiences the fear of death. However, angina pectoris is usually just a spasm in the coronary arteries, and it rarely leads to death. The causes of angina pectoris quite often lie in emotional trauma or mental and physical overwork. Angina pectoris occurs repeatedly when there is a displacement in the vertebrae, and therefore it is important to adjust the alignment of the spine. When people complain of labored breathing and a feeling of constriction in their chest, they frequently have displaced vertebrae in areas associated either with the Heart (fourth, fifth, and sixth thoracic vertebrae), Heart Constrictor (seventh, eighth, and ninth thoracic vertebrae) or Small Intestine Meridian (first and second lumbar vertebrae). Adjusting the alignment of the spine by Family Exercises is a very effective way to correct this problem. By having the spinal adjustment exercises performed on a regular basis and performing other Imagery Exercises which stretch the spine, one can prevent the onset of more severe heart attacks.

Hypotension

Traditionally in the Orient difficulty in getting up in the morning and the head feeling hazy in the afternoon, a typical problem among women, was called "morning malady." This condition was most often seen in ladies of the court, and it was probably an anemic condition resulting from their overly sheltered life in the court. In this modern age low blood pressure often becomes a problem in women who worry about their figure and diet too much or otherwise in office workers who do not take good care of themselves. Hypotension also stems from poor digestive function. People with this condition must work particularly on correcting the Kyo of either the Stomach or the Triple Heater Meridian with Imagery Exercises. The Reclining Exercises which improve both the figure and the digestive function are also highly recommended.

Disorders of Respiratory System

The Common Cold

There is a saying in the Far East that "the common cold is the source of all diseases." This was probably said because, when the body loses its balance and vitality, it issues its first warning in the form of a cold, and if we only heed this warning and take care of our body, all manner of complications can be prevented. It may also have been said because the onset of many serious diseases exhibit many of the same symptoms as a cold. Whatever the case, it is unwise to try and rid oneself of just the symptoms by taking cold medicine. The use of medication to supress the symptoms of a cold can even be called the first step toward polluting the body with drugs.

The condition of Triple Heater Kyo-Large Intestine Jitsu is very common at the onset of a cold. In this case the symptoms begin along the course of the Large Intestine Meridian in the nose and throat. Also the back and shoulders can become quite tense. Sometimes there is also a feeling of being chilled from the lower abdomen down to the legs. This means that the function of peripheral circulation in the skin and mucous membranes of the Triple Heater Meridian has declined so that a person has become unable to adjust to external temperatures. The importance of keeping the Triple Heater Meridian in balance is understandable since loss of sleep, anxiety, and mental instability (Jitsu of Kidney or Bladder Meridians along with Kyo of Triple Heater Meridian) can lead to a cold. Even drug companies emphasize the importance of keeping warm and getting adequate rest.

The old-fashioned remedy of sweating a cold out is also quite effective in the early stages of a cold. When a full sequence of Imagery Exercises is done in a warm room, this is often enough to induce sweating. One must do those exercises which are more strenuous in order for exercising to be most effective. Nevertheless, you have to expend a lot more energy before working up a sweat with other types of exercise such as jogging. This is because the movements in most other types of exercises mainly work the muscles. Imagery Exercises focus on working with Ki and this stimulates the parasympathetic nervous system responsible for adjusting the internal environment in relation to the external environment. This serves to improve peripheral circulation and open up the pores and facilitate perspiration. Good peripheral circulation is basic to health, and exercise which helps this is also most effective in curing colds. It may even be said that any method effective against a cold is effective against "all manner of diseases."

When a cold lingers for a while to affect the bronchial tubes, the condition of Large Intestine Kyo-Triple Heater Jitsu is the most common. When the inflammation in the respiratory tract gets worse, this condition often changes to Lung Kyo-Triple Heater Jitsu. In cases where a cold becomes protracted, the Large Intestine or Triple Heater Meridian becomes Kyo and the Kidney or Bladder Meridian becomes Jitsu. The various symptoms of a cold can be alleviated by exercising according to your own meridian type to work with the cold in each stage. Colds, more than anything else, require deep and thorough rest. Instead of just getting some rest, however, you should exercise a little at appropriate intervals to help your body adjust itself; this way you will get over the cold faster.

Coughing

Coughing which often accompanies a cold can be a real nuisance, but trying to suppress a cough can make things even worse. Inflammation of the mucous lining of the bronchial tubes is typically a condition of Triple Heater Jitsu. Since the Large Intestine or Bladder Meridian is often Kyo in this case, the Ki of the Kyo meridian must be reinforced. Sometimes people get a slight cough which does not go away. This is usually caused by Kyo of the Stomach Meridian rather than by a cold as such. When there is enlargement of the tonsils, Jitsu of either the Large Intestine or the Triple Heater Meridian should be considered as a possibility along with Kyo of the Kidney or Small Intestine Meridian. When there is an excessive amount of phlegm the Gallbladder Meridian is usually Jitsu. In all cases, however, the Kyo meridian needs to be worked on first.

Sinus Problems

People with sinus problems, in addition to having to breathe through their mouth due to chronic nasal congestion, often feel a heavy sensation in their head. This leads to hazy memory, a sense of dreariness, and a loss of motivation in work or study. Treatments by an ear, nose, and throat specialist are only effective for a short time and often an operation is required to solve the basic problem. Making a decision to have such an operation, however, is a difficult matter because the problem commonly recurs even after an operation. Even a specialist has trouble in curing this condition in which pus collects in the sinuses to cause a decline in the sense of smell as well as a susceptibility to sore throats because of always breathing through the mouth. This can be viewed as an opportunity to improve the condition of the whole body through the practice of Imagery Exercises. By the time the sinus problem has been relieved, a person will most likely to find that his whole outlook on life has changed.

Among people with sinus problems the most common condition is Large Intestine Kyo-Stomach Jitsu. People like this tend to overeat despite poor stomach function and also they lack exercise, especially of the legs. Those who have sinus problems from an allergic consitution usually belong to the Large Intestine Kyo-Liver Jitsu type, and a poor diet with excessive intake of meat and eggs is often the problem. Another type prone to sinus problems is Spleen Kyo-Bladder Jitsu, and people of this type are nervous and anxious and have the habit of nibbling on food constantly. The common factor in most sinus problems is a lack of well-rounded exercise for the whole body. A vicious circle is created by not exercising because of difficulty in breathing. By practicing Imagery Breathing where one inhales slowly and exhales completely through the mouth, one can more easily get well-rounded exercise for the whole body.

Asthma

Asthma is a condition characterized by labored breathing and wheezing. In the case of cardiac asthma, the cause is lack of oxygen from poor circulation. In bronchial asthma the cause is an allergic condition or hypersensitivity in the bronchial lining. When sporadic attacks of asthma occur, an asthmatic prefers to sit up rather than to lie down because breathing is easier when sitting up. A fit of coughing and hacking usually follows a period of wheezing and labored breathing, and thick phlegm is expectorated. After this the attack subsides and the asthmatic feels fine again. Since an asthmatic can lead a normal life, except for occasional attacks of asthma, most medical treatments consist of attempts to stop such attacks. However such relief is usually temporary and the attacks often recur despite medical treatment. Further, the toxicity of the drugs present an additional problem. The root cause of asthma lies in a diet which tends to make a person's blood acidic, or in other cases, an extremely stressful environment. This is why Imagery Exercises, which stretch and relax the whole body, can be quite effective.

The most common pattern in asthma is Lung Kyo-Bladder Jitsu. In this case there is often a distortion between the first and third thoracic vertebrae. So this also needs to be corrected. In cases where there is a great deal of phlegm, a Gallbladder Kyo-Triple Heater Jitsu condition is likely. Those with an acidotic constitution are frequently a Gallbladder Kyo-Kidney Jitsu type. Attacks of asthma in this type are associated with mental tension or overworking. Asthmatics who eat an unbalanced diet are generally Small Intestine Kyo-Gallbladder Jitsu types. In all cases, the best remedy is to do the appropriate Imagery Exercises on a regular basis between attacks. Imagery Exercises are beneficial for people with asthma even at times when other types of exercise, which consume too much energy, are not recommended.

Disorders of Nervous System

Neuralgia

Neuralgia is an attack of acute pain which radiates along the course of one or more nerves, and it can be distinguished from rheumatism or arthritis because it occurs whether one moves or not. Since soaking in a hotspring and improving the circulation reduces the pain, it is traditional in Japan for patients with neuralgia to take a vacation at some hotspring resort. The effectiveness of this remedy is deeply related to how people become relaxed and refreshed in this way. Neuralgia often occurs in those with a great deal of nervous tension whose nerves tend to be constantly on end. The cause is usually overwork, chilling, or catching a cold. People who get neuralgia tend to live in fear of pain, and they hold a lot of tension in their body as a defensive reaction. There are other ways to improve circulation besides going to hotsprings. Exercising your whole body in a relaxed manner is very effective. Doing Imagery Exercises serves to soften up the body which has become hardened by stress and tension.

Sciatica is a type of neuralgia which affects the hips and back of the legs, and it is often caused by a slipped disk. In this case most often the Small Intestine Meridian is Kyo and the Bladder Meridian is Jitsu. When sciatica is caused by distortion in the hip joint, Kidney Kyo-Large Intestine Jitsu is the most common type. The leg with the pain is Jitsu since it displays the symptom, and the one without pain is Kyo. The emphasis of treatment must be placed on reinforcing the Ki on the Kyo side. Also Basic Exercise "C" is often useful in correcting distortions in the lumbar vertebrae.

The pain in intercostal neuralgia generally appears along the Gallbladder and Triple Heater Meridians (the Jitsu meridians). In this case the thoracic vertebrae tend to be out of alignment. Such distortions are most often caused by anxiety (Heart Kyo), overwork (Heart Constrictor Kyo), or being chilled (Bladder Kyo). Trigeminal neuralgia is often associated with Spleen Kyo when there is great concern (Gallbladder Jitsu) or when there are dental problems (Large Intestine Jitsu). Occipital neuralgia also tends to come from overwork and exposure to cold (Gallbladder Kyo-Bladder Jitsu). Whatever the case may be, these conditions can be best remedied by practicing those Imagery Exercises suited to each type.

Paralysis

There are basically two kinds of paralysis—that caused by disturbances in the central nervous system, such as in the case of a stroke or polio, and that involving just a few peripheral nerves and the muscles under their control. In the olden days there was no way to treat cases of paralysis except to massage the affected part, but in recent years physical therapy has developed and the treatment of paralysis has advanced to a remarkable degree. The attempt to restore enervation in the paralyzed part by repeated exercise, however, is time-consuming and ineffective in many cases. Rather than working just on the paralyzed part, the holistic approach of Imagery Exercise is more effective. The paralyzed person can concentrate on exercises which can be done easily, and in this process he can also work on relaxing and releasing Ki in the affected part.

Generally the Triple Heater Meridian is involved in cases of paralysis. Facial paralysis which comes from exposure to cold is often Stomach Kyo-Triple Heater Jitsu. Paralysis resulting from whiplash injury can be Triple Heater Kyo-Small Intestine Jitsu. Otherwise paralysis in the arm due to displacement of cervical vertebrae is likely to be Triple Heater Kyo-Gallbladder Jitsu. Whatever the case, paralysis is very hard to cure as long as Ki remains blocked up and stagnates in one part. By exercising the body on the better side, the opposite side is also stimulated. The best idea is to work on restoring the overall balance and this should facilitate the recovery of the affected part.

Insomnia

It is normal to accumulate many imbalances both mental and physical during our waking hours. A balance can be restored by appropriate amounts of exercise and rest. Insomnia results when the mind becomes overactive and a person becomes preoccupied with a certain problem, whether it is physical or mental. It is fruitless to carry such problems on our mind when there is nothing that can be done about it. Likewise, worrying about loss of sleep is pointless because it never helps a person to sleep.

Generally speaking, people with insomnia have excessive tension (Jitsu) in the

Kidney and Bladder Meridians. People who have worked their minds too hard and cannot calm down are usually Bladder Kyo-Spleen Jitsu. Those who dream excessively and have difficulty in getting deep sleep are often Stomach Kyo-Bladder Jitsu. Heart Kyo-Bladder Jitsu is common for those who have difficulty in getting to sleep. When anxiety is the main cause of insomnia, Heart Kyo-Kidney Jitsu is likely. Otherwise, where excessive thinking is a problem, the Stomach or the Spleen Meridian is out of balance. Heart Kyo-Stomach Jitsu is often seen when an upset or unsettled stomach makes it hard to sleep. Also Spleen Kyo-Gallbladder Jitsu is commonly seen in those who have difficulty in getting to and staying asleep.

In all cases the best thing to do is to relax. This can best be accomplished through slow moving exercise with deep breathing. The Reclining Exercises are ideal for this purpose because it allows you to relax gradually in stages. Imagery Breathing alone, if done over and over in a slow and relaxed manner, is enough to bring on deep sleep for some people.

Metabolic and Hormonal Disorders

Diabetes
Diabetes is a disease in which there are high levels of sugar in the blood and urine. Diabetes is characterized by great thirst, increase of urine, and excessive intake of food, especially sweets. Other symptoms are general lassitude, loss of sexual drive, itching, neuralgia, and numbness in the extremities. Also, it can eventually lead to loss of weight, deterioration in vision and other serious complications due to a general lowering of resistance. In many cases people are told they have diabetes as soon as sugar is detected in their blood. Yet the administration of insulin and the sudden restriction on the intake of sugar and starches often ends up sapping their vitality.

Sugar often appears in the urine with Spleen Kyo, and this type of person tends to be overweight, crave sweet or rich foods, and eat too much, and in other cases such people fail to get enough exercise and worry too much. Diabetes is generally associated with Spleen Kyo, and unless people of this type correct their living habits and practice moderation, this problem can become a real threat to their life. Kidney or Bladder Jitsu often appear with Spleen Kyo in those with nervous tension and acidosis. Liver or Gallbladder Jitsu along with Spleen Kyo is often related to a rich diet and excessive caloric intake. Lack of exercise is usually the problem for those with Jitsu of the Triple Heater, Small Intestine, or Large Intestine Meridian. Suitable exercises must be selected in each case for the best results.

Gout
Gout is marked by excessive quantities of uric acid in the blood and deposits of uric acid crystals in the joints. Gout was once known as the "emperor's disease" because it was common among the royalty who ate a rich diet. In more modern times this disease began to increase among the wealthier people of the West. Gout also became more common in Japan after World War II with the westernization of the diet. Gout is most often seen among middle-aged men. In the middle of the night a person all of a sudden experiences severe pain in the joints of the big toe. This is a difficult condition to treat because the pain goes away by itself in about a week, but no sooner

than one thinks it is gone, it recurs. The joint where the big toe connects to the foot swells up and turns red and purple. This also occurs quite frequently in the ankle and Achilles tendon. Typically this is a Spleen Kyo-Liver Jitsu condition, but also Jitsu of the Kidney or Bladder Meridian is common. People with gout should remedy their lack of exercise by doing the Imagery Exercises suited to their individual type. Along with this they have to correct their diet and eating habits in order to restore an overall balance in their body.

Basedow's Disease

This is a case of hyperthyroidism, which occurs most often in young women, in which hyperactivity of the thyroid gland causes palpitations, bulging eyes, and a large swelling in the throat. In addition to these main symptoms there is often trembling in the fingertips and eyelids, nervous excitement, insomnia, and loss of weight. These symptoms resemble the emotional reactions of surprise and fear, and it may be called the physical expression of emotional insecurity. People with this disease tend to be somber and serious types with a defensive attitude in life who constantly carry a great deal of tension. This disease is also related to distortions in the cervical and thoracic vertebrae. Distortions in the cervical vertebrae are generally caused by imbalances in the Gallbladder, Triple Heater, or Small Intestine Meridian. Distortions in the thoracic vertebrae occur at the level of the Heart and Heart Constrictor Meridians (from the fourth to ninth thoracic vertebrae). The typical meridian type associated with this disease is Heart Constrictor Kyo-Gallbladder Jitsu. The opposite condition of Gallbladder Kyo-Heart Constrictor Jitsu is also common, in which a person is inclined to brood over things. Otherwise, the forearm being tense and stiff is often associated with Jitsu of the Kidney, Bladder, or Triple Heater Meridian.

People with Basedow's disease should consider including seaweed in their diet since it is high in iodine, which is a mineral indispensable for the normal functioning of the thyroids. When people have hyperthyroidism, they tend to move around as little as possible to avoid the occurrence of palpitations. Lack of physical activity, however, just leads to more worrying and only increases anxiety. Imagery Exercises are especially good in cases like this because they do not place a burden on the heart and they serve to balance the whole body. It is important that people practice Imagery Exercises by taking into account their individual meridian type.

Excretory and Reproductive Disorders

Kidney Diseases

Problems with urination, swelling, pain in the lower back, and poor complexion are typical symptoms indicating a kidney problem. Kidney disorders are classified into many types in Western medicine but no one drug is particularly effective, and kidney disorders are difficult to cure. Usually a patient is advised to cut down on the intake of salt and to rest and recuperate. When kidney dysfunction reaches a certain order of magnitude, people have to undergo hemodialysis two or three times a week to purify their blood by artificial means. Once people begin hemodialysis they are bound for life to stay on such treatment (although people with serious kidney disorders do not live so long).

In Oriental medicine the concept of the kidney includes the adrenals. In addition to maintaining the balance of fluids in the body, the kidneys are seen as regulating the overall energy level of the body. The kidneys are also associated with a person's reaction to fatigue and stress. Kidney problems are not as difficult to cure as people may be led to believe. Kidney disorders in terms of the meridians are most often a Jitsu or Kyo condition of the Kidney Meridian. Kidney Kyo-Triple Heater Jitsu types often have an allergic constitution and poor excretory function. In cases of Kidney Kyo-Gallbladder Jitsu, the hands and feet swell up in the morning and there is often nausea. The opposite condition, Gallbladder Kyo-Kidney Jitsu, indicates that one's eyes have been overworked. Liver Kyo-Kidney Jitsu is typical in people with chronic nephritis. Lung Kyo-Kidney Jitsu is related to a lack of oxygen from shallow breathing. Large Intestine Kyo-Kidney Jitsu is associated with fatigue, lack of exercise, and poor elimination. Heart Kyo-Kidney Jitsu is typical of kidney problems related to anxiety and stress.

In the acute stages of kidney disease, rest and reduction of salt intake is important for lightening the load on the kidneys. Sticking to this approach for an extended period, however, will cause a decline in vitality. Also staying in bed for long periods has a way of causing stress to build up, and this can be detrimental to kidney function. Getting some exercise and working up a little sweat reduces the burden on the kidneys and improves the condition of the blood. Of course, if one becomes over-enthusiastic and exercises vigorously and expends a great deal of energy, this can have a negative effect. Doing the appropriate Imagery Exercises to balance the overall condition of the body will serve best to improve the function of the kidneys.

Cystitis

The main symptoms of cystitis are frequent urination, the urine becoming turbid, and strong pain during and after urination. In addition to this, there is often pain and discomfort in the lower abdomen, as well as insomnia, which can lead to a whole array of nervous disorders. The cause of cystitis is generally regarded as being bacterial infection, but the more fundamental problem is the poor condition of the mucous lining of the excretory organs which allow such an infection to occur. It is best to first treat the existing cause of cystitis, such as chilling of extremities, menstrual problems, stagnation of blood in the lower abdomen, and the habit of holding off going to the toilet.

In cases of cystitis Triple Heater Kyo-Bladder Jitsu is common. And especially among the women of this type there is often chilling or blood stagnation in the lower abdomen. The opposite condition of Bladder Kyo-Triple Heater Jitsu is common when inflammation of the bladder is severe. There are also many cases where the Large Intestine or Small Intestine Meridian is Jitsu. Whatever the condition, the Imagery Exercises appropriate to each type must be practiced to alleviate the condition of chilling or blood stagnation in the lower abdomen.

Dysmenorrhea

The condition of dysmenorrhea includes not only menstrual irregularity and inconsistency in the amount of menstrual flow, but also menstrual cramps and various discomfort experienced in relation to the menstrual period. In some cases there are menstrual problems which even the women themselves are unaware of. This is because the mechanisms controlling the menstrual cycle are very delicate and subject to subtle influences. In the majority of cases there are various complaints which accompany dysmenorrhea, such as aversion to cold, headaches, and emotional instability. Such problems often stem from the stagnation of blood in the lower abdomen. Therefore the Small Intestine Meridian, related to circulation in the lower abdomen and ovarian function, is usually involved.

Otherwise dysmenorrhea is caused by imbalances in the following meridians: the Spleen, which is associated with frustration; the Heart, which controls hypothalamic and pituitary function; the Bladder, which is related to the uterus and the autonomic nervous system; the Kidney, which controls the function of the adrenals and sexual organs; the Heart Constrictor, which is involved with distortions in the pelvis and the sacrum; the Triple Heater, which is related to mucous membranes and the inner lining of the uterus.

Some typical meridian imbalances seen in dysmenorrhea are as follows: Small Intestine Kyo-Stomach Jitsu, where there is poor ovarian function and great tension in the neck and shoulders; Spleen Kyo-Small Intestine Jitsu, where there is loss of stamina after childbirth; Kidney Kyo-Small Intestine Jitsu, where there is stagnation of blood after a difficult labor; Heart Kyo-Bladder Jitsu, where there are functional problems in the uterus and discharge. Whatever the case may be, the exercises according to the individual meridian type is the best way to balance the function of the meridians, and this in turn will relieve the many symptoms of dysmenorrhea.

Chilling and Aversion to Cold

Over half of the female patients in Japan seem to be averse to cold or experience chilling below their waist. Most people do not even realize that this condition is abnormal, and many of those who know this just consider it as an inborn physical trait and make no attempt to correct it. People should realize that being "cold blooded" is a sign of poor health and that this condition can be corrected.

Chilling or aversion to cold is most prevalent among women since it is often related to hormonal imbalances and dysfunctions in the female reproductive system. Those women who can go through a winter without thick wool socks or long underwear are typically healthy and free of gynecological problems. Viewed from a psychological perspective, women who have deep love for a man are more likely to have a good hormonal balance, and their warmth is emotional as well as physical. Of course, lack of love for one's husband does not necessarily mean that a woman is a cold person or is averse to cold. This is merely the tendency I have observed among my patients. The main point here is that psychological factors greatly influence people's health.

In women dysfunctions of the reproductive organs, especially of the ovaries, is related to chilling and aversion to cold. Complaints of general malaise like strong tension in the neck and shoulders, tendency for hotness of the face, and never feeling quite up to par are often related to ovarian dysfunctions and stagnation of blood in the lower abdomen which are caused by imbalances in the Small Intestine Meridian. In women the Small Intestine Meridian goes through the ovaries and also relates to circulation in the lower abdomen and pelvis. Typically women of the Small Intestine Kyo-Large Intestine Jitsu type have chilling below the waist area associated with gynecological problems. The Small Intestine Kyo-Spleen Jitsu type often experience chilling down the back to the hips.

Imbalances in the Large Intestine Meridian can also cause aversion to cold, especially when there is constipation. People of the Large Intestine Kyo-Gallbladder Jitsu type have dull low back pain in connection with chilling. Those of the Large Intestine Kyo-Heart Constrictor Jitsu type often experience hotness in the face and general chilling. Those with the opposite condition of Heart Constrictor Kyo-Large Intestine Jitsu experience hotness in the face with chilling mostly in the feet.

An imbalance in the Spleen or Stomach Meridian can also cause aversion to cold in those with gastroptosis* or low blood pressure. People of the Spleen Kyo-Large Intestine Jitsu type usually lack exercise and their lower limbs tend to feel chilled and heavy. Those of the Stomach Kyo-Large Intestine Jitsu type tend to drink too much cold liquid.

Imbalance in the Kidney and Bladder Meridian is another cause of aversion to cold. People of the Kidney Kyo-Stomach Jitsu type experience general chilling and hotness of the face. Those of the Bladder Kyo-Stomach Jitsu type tend to become chilled and feel fatigue in their arms.

Sometimes women with poor functioning of the Triple Heater Meridian, which is related to water metabolism, have swelling in the lower limbs which can lead to chilling. Those of the Triple Heater Kyo-Bladder Jitsu type are averse to cold and tend to have hypersensitive skin. Otherwise Triple Heater Kyo-Heart Jitsu is associated with hotness of the head and chilling from blood stagnation.

Prostatic Hypertrophy

Prostatic hypertrophy is a condition seen in older men, and with this condition the enlargement of the prostate gland compresses the urethra to cause problems in urination. Although operations can be performed to alleviate this condition, it is difficult to cure and operations are not always effective. However, there is no need to give up hope just because it is a disease which comes with age. Starting a regular exercise program can effectively reverse the aging process. Liver Kyo-Kidney Jitsu is the usual condition associated with prostatic hypertrophy, but the opposite condition of Kidney Kyo-Liver Jitsu is also common. The latter type seems to be easier to cure. There are also cases of Kidney Kyo-Large Intestine Jitsu which are caused primarily by lack of exercise. Since exercise serves to prevent prostatic hypertrophy, Imagery Exercises according to individual types is the best way to obtain lasting relief.

Impotence

Impotence usually results from a combination of various factors, such as hormonal imbalances, dysfunction of the autonomic nervous system, and mental and physical exhaustion. Not being able to have a normal sex life often becomes a psychological burden, which only compounds the problem. Impotence corresponds to frigidity in women. In both cases a vicious cycle is created between a decline in self-esteem and loss of intimate contact.

Men of the Liver Kyo-Bladder Jitsu type are unable to get or maintain an erection. Those of the Spleen Kyo-Bladder Jitsu type, similar to those with diabetes, experience a general decline in sexual drive. In the case of Kyo of the Heart or Small Intestine

---

* In gastroptosis the stomach is displaced downward in the abdominal cavity far below its normal position. People with gastroptosis generally have weak visceral function and are prone to digestive problems.

Meridian, stress or emotional problems are usually the cause. Kyo of the Lung or Large Intestine Meridian means that the problem is related to lack of exercise. Practicing Imagery Exercises is the best solution in all cases because it has a rejuvenating effect. The Family Exercises provide an ideal way to reestablish a nonsexual but intimate contact with your partner.

Disorders of the Skin and Sense Organs

Dermatitis (Urticaria)

Dermatitis is general inflammation of the skin, better known as a rash. Often the skin itches unbearably, but scratching only makes the rash spread more. The size of the rash or inflammation generally varies from a tiny spot to an area the size of one's hand. The shape of the rash is irregular and its location may vary, but sometimes there is a correlation between similar meridian types. Generally such skin conditions clear up in a few days or weeks, but they tend to recur, and sometimes they become a chronic problem which lasts for years.

The causes of dermatitis are as varied as its manifestations, but commonly diet, drugs, exposure to cold, or skin irritants, as well as psychological factors are involved. Sometimes the skin condition clears up just by modifying the diet to include fresh fruits and vegetables. Skin conditions related to various psychological factors, however, are much more stubborn and difficult to cure. Therefore it becomes important to work out personal problems and frustrations in addition to increasing the intake of fluids and getting regularity in bowel movements. The most important thing in all cases is to improve the detoxifying function of the liver and the eliminating function of the large intestine.

Dermatitis may be attributed to a variety of meridian imbalances, but the Large Intestine, Heart, Small Intestine, Bladder, Kidney, Gallbladder and Liver Meridians are the main ones involved. In cases of Kidney Kyo-Liver Jitsu an itching skin rash develops due to a decline in the detoxifying function of the liver. With Triple Heater Kyo-Kidney Jitsu, skin rashes develop as a result of allergies and hypersensitivity. Gallbladder Kyo-Small Intestine Jitsu is associated with indigestion. Heart Kyo-Gallbladder Jitsu is usually a case of skin hypersensitivity related to psychological factors. The appropriate Imagery Exercises can be beneficial in all these cases because they serve to improve the overall physical condition of a person which is closely reflected in the skin.

Eczema and Athlete's Foot

Eczema and athlete's foot tend to appear in specific areas of the body that are often on the path of the meridians which are imbalanced. Such skin problems often involve the Triple Heater Meridian, which functions as the first line of defense in the skin and mucous membranes. Eczema is also related to imbalances in the Large Intestine Meridian, which is associated with the condition of the skin as well as elimination. Sometimes autointoxication caused by poor functioning of the Small Intestine or anxiety and frustration related to imbalances in the Heart Meridian are contributing factors. Otherwise the Liver and Gallbladder Meridians are involved when there is a decline in the detoxifying function. The Kidney and Bladder Meridians become involved when there is nervous tension or inadequate purification of blood.

In the case of Large Intestine Kyo-Small Intestine Jitsu, poor elimination causes autointoxication, or gradual poisoning by the build-up of toxins occurring within the body. With Large Intestine Kyo-Liver Jitsu, constipation becomes the cause of eczema. People of the Spleen Kyo-Liver Jitsu type get eczema by eating too many sweets. Triple Heater Kyo-Bladder Jitsu types often get eczema or athlete's foot as a result of allergies.

In this way a variety of meridians can be involved even in a simple skin problem like eczema. It is best to adopt a holistic approach even for such minor problems. Corns and calluses also appear in relation to imbalanced meridians. Thus applying the perspective of meridians to take the whole picture into account is by far the best way to take care of even minor symptoms.

Rough Skin and Blemishes

Current advertising practices seem to deceive women into thinking that their beauty problems can be taken care of just by applying the right kind of makeup. Skin problems such as roughness and blemishes cannot be solved merely by applying creams and lotions. Roughness and blemishes in the facial skin of women are usually a result of dysfunction in the visceral organs, and external skin care is just a superficial and temporary solution. Complete and lasting results can only be obtained by improving the dysfunction of the organs which is the basic cause of the skin problem.

Blemishes which appear in women after pregnancy are often related to the stagnation of blood. In younger women, blemishes are mostly related to the poor condition of their blood caused by a decline in the detoxifying function of the liver. The typical condition in the former case is Kidney Kyo-Small Intestine Jitsu, and in the latter case it is Liver Kyo-Small Intestine Jitsu. Also fatigue can affect skin condition as with Triple Heater Kyo-Small Intestine Jitsu, in which lack of sleep causes the skin to become rough. Otherwise the skin in people of the Gallbladder Kyo-Spleen Jitsu type tends to break out easily. Also abnormalities in the hormonal system are reflected by the condition of the skin, particularly in women. Staying in good physical condition is by far the best way to keep your skin clear and healthy.

Eyestrain and Myopia

Eye problems such as eyestrain and myopia, which often begin from childhood are products of this modern age. Actually such eye problems go much deeper than just the eyes. It is worth noting that oxygen consumption for a given weight of tissue is the greatest in the eyes. This rate of consumption is almost three times that in the liver or brain. When the overall amount of oxygen in the body begins to decrease, the body reduces the supply of oxygen to those parts not absolutely essential for survival, including the eyes, in order to keep the more vital organs supplied. This is a problem today especially because our chances to breathe deeply and draw in an ample amount of oxygen have decreased.

In terms of the meridian imbalances, Kyo of the Gallbladder or Triple Heater Meridian is the most common. In cases of Gallbladder Kyo-Large Intestine Jitsu, poor vision is often related to hotness of the head. In cases of Gallbladder Kyo-Stomach Jitsu, blurred vision becomes a problem. In cases of Gallbladder Jitsu-

Spleen Kyo, there is a tendency to overwork the eyes. In cases of Gallbladder Kyo-Bladder Jitsu, eyestrain is associated with excessive tension in the body. There is a decline in visual acuity in cases of Gallbladder Kyo-Kidney Jitsu. Eyestrain is the result of poor circulation to the eyes, especially in cases of Gallbladder Kyo-Triple Heater Jitsu. In the opposite condition of Triple Heater Kyo-Gallbladder Jitsu, there is often pain in the back of the eyes. In cases of Triple Heater Kyo-Heart Jitsu also, eyestrain is felt more in the back of the eyes. Otherwise, in cases of Heart Kyo-Liver Jitsu, one often sees spots or flashes of light.

One of the main factors today which aggravates poor eyesight is the consumption of highly processed foods containing excessive sugar. These foods are full of calories but empty of life sustaining vitamins and minerals. The availability of vitamins and minerals in our body greatly influences our ability to metabolize oxygen. Imagery Exercises suited to each type is the most effective approach, but your vision can be improved progressively just by practicing the Basic Exercises regularly.

Hearing Problems

In Oriental medicine all the sense organs or "openings" in the face correspond to specific Yin organs. The eyes relate to the liver, the tongue to the heart, the mouth to the spleen, the nose to the lungs, and the ears to the kidneys. A problem in any one of these openings is associated with the corresponding organ. Thus even for a localized problem like one of the ear, imbalances in the organs and meridians are always considered. Recently reports from China about curing otitis media and deafness with acupuncture have received great attention, but the remarkable effectiveness of this acupuncture, rather than being a result of using newly discovered acupuncture points, is more a result of the holistic approach of Oriental medicine which seeks to correct constitutional energy imbalances.

Although hearing problems including tinnitis, or ringing in the ears, are regarded as being an inevitable part of aging by some, there is no need to be pessimistic about a recovery just because one is advanced in age. Improving the overall balance of energy in meridians greatly improves the chances of recovery. In Oriental medicine deafness is usually regarded as being a case of a deficient Kidney Meridian. Since energy in the Kidney Meridian tends to become increasingly depleted with age, it stands to reason that older people are more prone to hearing problems. In addition to the Kidney Meridian, the Triple Heater, Small Intestine, and Gallbladder Meridians are most often associated with hearing problems. The typical type of imbalance seen in tinnitis is Small Intestine Kyo-Kidney Jitsu. The type common in otitis media is Triple Heater Kyo-Kidney Jitsu. Ménière's disease, where dizziness and nausea accompany hearing problems, is sometimes seen in Triple Heater Kyo-Small Intestine Jitsu types.

Many people get hearing problems as a result of distortions in their cervical vertebrae. Therefore doing the Family Exercises for adjusting the cervical and thoracic vertebrae usually yield good results. Doing Imagery Exercises appropriate to ones type is, of course, the best way to bring progressive improvement. You can be sure of positive results with this simple method since the regular practice of Imagery Exercises has brought recovery from many seemingly incurable conditions.

Afterword

I am very grateful and pleased that my late husband's last book on meridian exercises has been translated into English so that people in other countries can read and appreciate his work. I would be most gratified if this revolutionary approach to exercise contributes to the health and well-being of people not only in Japan but all over the world. I am sincerely grateful to the translator Stephen Brown and Dr. Yoshinaru Fujioka, who has been a dedicated supporter of this exercise system. Also I would like to express my heartfelt gratitude to Mr. Iwao Yoshizaki, the President of Japan Publications, Inc. I feel it is most appropriate as an afterword to conclude this book with some of the words of my husband to his students in his last lectures.

I felt strongly after working with these exercises which I had no experience with before that there was some special purpose in my having been given this work. When confronted with the task of creating an exercise system I boldly decided that the concepts of Kyo and Jitsu in Zen Shiatsu had to be applied. As I worked on developing forms for various exercises and studied other methods such as Sotai, I realized that what I discovered also had to be applied to shiatsu.

The problem in learning exercises like yoga is that everyone tries to conform to the outward shape which is given as an example. Many people try things beyond their ability and hurt themselves. The outward shape is not nearly as effective in conveying the essence of an exercise as the overall form is. The formalities of the tea ceremonies are learned by observing form. The way to prepare and serve tea must be mastered as a continuous flowing sequence. This is identical to learning shiatsu. When learning to work with the meridians in shiatsu one should not observe the outward shape. What is required is mastery of a certain form. When I teach shiatsu, I say, "Don't look at the outward appearance of my techniques. Watch my overall form." This is exactly the way in which Imagery Exercises should be learned. You must not become preoccupied with the outward shape in these exercises. Watch the process which is flowing motion that shapes the overall form. You should detect the flow of Ki in this process. The flow is what is most important. Looking for the flow of Ki leads us to an awareness of the meridians.

The primary aim of Shinsen-Jyutsu (ancient Chinese methods for physical and spiritual development), which I have been practicing, is to facilitate the flow of Ki. This is a practice for preserving the essence of life, which is vital energy. To preserve the essence of life means to seek repletion or an abundance of energy. Repletion which leads to fixation is not the ideal state of repletion. One must liberate or find outward expression for the life within. In other words, rather than becoming fixed or caught up on something, one's life energy is allowed to move about freely. Since life energy is always moving in a certain direction in a cyclic fashion, it eventually covers every aspect by its continual movement. The meridians can be understood as this free play of life energy.

The aim of shiatsu is just the same as in Shinsen-Jyutsu. I used to think that the liberation of energy was something unique to shiatsu, but now I have realized that there are other ways. Freeing energy is the purpose of shiatsu as well as Do-In. I had to do Do-In exercises to reach a more complete understanding of the meridians. Do-In and Anma (traditional massage) are fundamental to the practice of Shinsen-Jyutsu. My shiatsu practice has now become one and the same as Shinsen-Jyutsu. The aim is to follow the direction of life energy and to thereby cover every aspect. This is what the meridians are all about and it is the basis for Imagery Exercises.

Today I am taking a whole new look at shiatsu because of having done these exercises. When I was teaching foreign students, I came across a good way to explain my approach. In shiatsu we are usually trying to *do* something. Actually when giving shiatsu we should be impartial and free of preconceptions. It is not necessarily bad to become tense or preoccupied with something. In order to live we must all become (obsessed) like demons in a sense. But we must not remain fixed in this state. We have to relax and let go. When there is tension which remains, the solution is not to *do* something. Even if we know that we need to relax and soften up, our conscious mind is unable to do this. The point is not to *do*, but to *undo*. We must stop trying to control or manipulate with our mind. What is necessary is to relax and let the energy guide us to return the patients to their original state of wholeness. This is how we can *undo*. As long as we are trying to *do* something, the patient is aware of this and there will be resistance on some level.

This means that, in doing shiatsu, we have to leave everything up to our weight and use as little of our strength as possible. Take our brain, for example, it does not make any effort to support itself. It has control but allows all its weight to be supported by the body. Letting weight settle naturally is a fundamental principle of Zen Shiatsu. With the cooperation of your partner or patient, you should assume a position which requires the least effort to maintain. The most effective pressure in shiatsu is that applied by the natural use of your body weight.

In order to use our body most effectively in shiatsu, it is necessary to train our body through certain exercises. These must be a kind of exercise which teaches us how to relax with movement. The important thing to be learned is what posture enables us to move with the least effort. Also we must learn the mental attitude which enables us to use the minimum strength and maintain a posture with our weight naturally settled. Normally, as soon as we decide to begin some movement, our energy momentarily collects in our *hara*. If our energy, or Ki, went to our chest or the tips of our feet, we would become off balance and unable to properly begin the movement.

In practicing Imagery Exercises we learn to breathe out through our mouth as we make a stretching movement. Breathing out slowly releases Ki and relaxes the body so that tense areas can be moved with greater ease. We must remember, however, that even when breathing out, we have to work slowly without undue force because sudden or forceful movements create the very tension we are trying to eliminate.

In working with these exercises I made the important discovery that the order of the meridians, beginning with the Lung and Large Intestine and ending with the Gallbladder and Liver, was the order of the development of life. No one has ever explained why the meridians are in the sequence they are. A relationship to the Three Yin-Three Yang principle is implied in the naming of the meridians, but no clear explanation is given on how this relates to the order of the meridians. But when I created the meridian exercises and started practicing them, I realized that there was a special meaning in doing the exercises in the order of the meridians. There is something innately right about beginning with the Lung and Large Intestine and ending with the Gallbladder and Liver. This is because it is the developmental order of all animal life which applies to every aspect of our lives. It was stunning to realize that the order of the meridians was the basic order of all life.

In doing the Basic Exercises we are following the flow of energy along its natural course. Even in breathing we follow this basic order. We take in Ki from the environment and convert this into a usable form and collect this into our *hara*, where it is further transformed to reach every part of the body. This energy is then converted into movement as we exhale and release Ki. In this way one complete breath contains each of the aspects of the meridians. In another sense, our breathing is only complete after all the aspects of the twelve meridians are represented. That is to say, all of the basic functions of life represented by six Yin-Yang pairs of meridians must be fully integrated in one breath.

I experienced the sequence of meridians in myself. From the Lung and Large Intestine, the Ki went to the Stomach and Spleen and then to the Heart and Small Intestine, and then entered the *hara* (center point) with the Bladder and Kidney. The Ki in my *hara* then circulated throughout my whole body by way of the Heart Constrictor and Triple Heater and was finally released by the Gallbladder and Liver. In this way, it became abundantly clear that these meridian exercises were identical to Do-In exercises, which are specially for facilitating the circulation of meridians and guiding the flow of energy through the meridians. Do-In is nothing more than exercises emphasizing movement of energy along the meridians. Do-In is exercise done by oneself to improve one's own energy circulation. Anma, which was known as Ankyo in ancient times, is massage and manipulation done by someone else to improve energy circulation. These are the two practices which are the main components of Shinsen-Jyutsu as taught in the Chinese classics.

My working with these exercises has made my system of meridian shiatsu complete. It was, after all, impossible to make shiatsu complete in and of itself. After I began to learn about Shinsen-Jyutsu, it became clear to me that it was up to me to systematize Do-In and make it more understandable to people today. When I created the first set of meridian exercises in 1975, there was no need to give them names or symbols. As I began making more meridian exercises, however, I decided to assign the first letters of the alphabet to the Basic Exercises. It occurred to me later that each of these letters might resemble the form in each of the meridian exercises. I went on to assign a letter of the alphabet for each one of the meridian exercises. Naturally I created the exercises first and then found a letter to match each one, since the main point is to experience the meridians.

After creating the whole system of Imagery Exercises, I myself was amazed that all 52 letters of the alphabet could be applied so neatly to these exercises. Most importantly, these exercises cover all the meridians individually and as pairs. I have no reason to be proud of this accomplishment. Though I did work at creating this system, I feel that this is something I received from God. That is also why I have complete confidence in this system. Promoting Imagery Exercises is now my new mission. I am certain of its value for beginners since I personally experienced the slow process of teaching an inflexible body like my own to become more soft and supple. I worked on Imagery Exercises with the awareness that this was my special task and that my own experience would be helpful to others.

The thing that must be avoided in doing Imagery Exercises is to do them with your conscious mind. Also it is wrong to think of the anatomy such as certain muscles and joints when doing these exercises. The more an emphasis is given to specific parts of the body, the farther the exercise becomes removed from the essence of life. In living things all movement occurs as a whole and is guided by the flow of Ki which is unconscious. All that has to be done when a certain movement is difficult is to release the Ki which is blocked. These are the basic rules of Imagery Exercises which I arrived at through my own practice.

The main difference between these exercises and other forms of exercise is the application of the meridians, or the energy circulation system that sustains our life by the six basic functions. The point is to follow through the full sequence of this energy circulation. Doing a complete sequence of meridian exercises allows us to experience the wholeness of life. We are always living as one whole, but we must become aware of this. Wholeness in living is our most important goal.

KEIKO MASUNAGA

References

Bertherat, Therese, and Carol Bernstein. *The Body Has Its Reasons: Anti-Exercise and Self-Awareness*. New York, New York: Avon Books, 1976.

Chang, Edward C. *Knocking at the Gate of Life, and Other Healing Exercises from China*. Emmaus, Pennsylvania: Rodale Press, 1985.

Eisenberg, David, M.D. *Encounters with Qi*. New York, New York: W. W. Norton & Company, 1985.

Gach, Michael Reed, with Carolyn Marco. *Acu-Yoga: Self Help Techniques to Relieve Tension*. Tokyo & New York: Japan Publications, Inc., 1981.

Hashimoto, Keizo, M.D. *Sotai: Natural Exercise*. Translated by Herman Aihara, Oroville, California: Macrobiotic Foundation, 1981.

Hashimoto, Keizo, M.D., with Yoshiaki Kawakami. *Sôtai: Balance and Health through Natural Movement*. Tokyo & New York: Japan Publications, Inc., 1983.

Kaibara, Ekiken. *Yojokun: Japanese Secret of Good Health*. Tokyo, Japan: Tokuma Shoten Publishing Company, 1974.

Kushi, Michio. *The Book of Dō-In: Natural Health Massage for Spiritual Development*. Tokyo & New York: Japan Publications, Inc., 1979.

Kushi, Michio, and Olivia Oredson. *Macrobiotic Palm Healing: Energy at Your Finger-Tips*. Tokyo & New York: Japan Publications, Inc., 1987.

Larre, Claude, and Jean Schatz, M.D. and Elizabeth Rochat de la Vallee. *Survey of Traditional Chinese Medicine*. Translated by Stang, S. Elizabeth. Columbia, Maryland: Traditional Acupuncture Foundation, 1986.

Lao Tsu. *Tao De Ching*. Translated by Gia-gu Feng and Jane English. New York, New York: Vintage Books, 1972.

Lee, Hor Ming, and Gregory Whincup. *Chinese Massage Therapy: A Handbook of Therapeutic Massage*. Boulder, Colorado: Shambhala, 1983.

Liu, Da. *Taoist Health Exercise Book*. New York, New York: Quick Fox, 1974.

Lu, Gwei-djen, and Joseph Needham. *Celestial Lancets: A History and Rationale of Acupuncture and Moxa*. Cambridge, England: Cambridge University Press, 1980.

Manaka, Yoshio, M.D., and Ian A. Urquhart. *The Layman's Guide to Acupuncture*. New York, New York: Weatherhill, 1972.

Masunaga, Shizuto, with Wataru Ohashi and the Shiatsu Education Center of America. *Zen Shiatsu: How to Harmonize Yin and Yang for Better Health*. Tokyo & New York: Japan Publications, Inc., 1977.

Motoyama, Hiroshi, with Rande Brown. *Science and the Evolution of Consciousness: Chakras, Ki, and Psi*. Brookline, Massachusetts: Autumn Press, 1978.

Nakamura, Takashi. *Oriental Breathing Therapy*. Tokyo & New York: Japan Publications, Inc., 1981.

Namikoshi, Tokujiro. *Shiatsu: Japanese Finger-Pressure Therapy*. Tokyo & New York: Japan Publications, Inc., 1972.

Namikoshi, Toru. *The Complete Book of Shiatsu Therapy*. Tokyo & New York: Japan Publications, Inc., 1981.

———. *Shiatsu+Stretching*. Tokyo & New York: Japan Publications, Inc., 1985.

———. *Shiatsu Therapy: Theory and Practice*. Tokyo & New York: Japan Publications, Inc., 1974.

Ohashi, Wataru. *Do-it-yourself Shiatsu: How to Perform the Ancient Japanese Art of "Acupuncture without Needles."* New York, New York: Dutton, 1976.

Omura, Yoshiaki. *Acupuncture Medicine: Its Historical and Clinical Background.* Tokyo & New York: Japan Publications, Inc., 1982.

Reed, William. *Ki: A Practical Guide for Westerners.* Tokyo & New York: Japan Publications, Inc., 1986.

Sergel, David. *Macrobiotic Shiatsu.* Tokyo & New York: Japan Publications, Inc., 1987.

Serizawa, Katsusuke, M.D. *Effective Tsubo Therapy: Simple and Natural Relief without Drugs.* Tokyo & New York: Japan Publications, Inc., 1984.

———. *Massage: The Oriental Method.* Tokyo & New York: Japan Publications, Inc., 1972.

———. *Tsubo: Vital Points for Oriental Therapy.* Tokyo & New York: Japan Publications, Inc., 1976.

Shealy, C. Norman, M.D. *90 Days to Self-Health.* New York, New York: Dial Press, 1977.

Solveborn, Sven-A, M.D. *The Book about Stretching.* Tokyo & New York: Japan Publications, Inc., 1985.

Takahashi, Masaru, and Stephen Brown. *Qigong for Health: Chinese Traditional Exercise for Cure and Prevention.* Tokyo & New York: Japan Publications, Inc., 1986.

The Tao Teh-King: Sayings of Lao Tsu. Translated by C. Spurgeon Medhurst. Wheaton, Illinois: Quest Books, 1972.

Taylor, Louise, and Betty Bryant. *Acupressure Yoga and You.* Tokyo & New York: Japan Publications, Inc., 1984.

Teeguarden, Iona Marsaa. *Acupressure Way of Health: Jin Shin Do®.* Tokyo & New York: Japan Publications, Inc., 1978.

Tohei, Koichi. *Book of Ki: Co-ordinating Mind and Body in Daily Life.* Tokyo & New York: Japan Publications, Inc., 1979.

Tulku, Tarthang. *Gesture of Balance: A Guide to Awareness, Self-Healing and Meditation.* Dharma Publishing, 1977.

Watson, Burton. *Chuang Tzu: Basic Writings.* New York, New York: Columbia University Press, 1964.

Yamamoto, Shizuko. *Barefoot Shiatsu.* Tokyo & New York: Japan Publications, Inc., 1979.

The Yellow Emperor's Classic of Internal Medicine. Translated by Ilza Veith, Berkeley, California: University of California Press, 1949.

Zhou, Dahong, M.D. The Chinese Exercise Book: *From ancient & modern China—Exercises for Well-being and Treatment of Illness.* Point Roberts, Washington: Hartley and Marks, 1984.

List of Exercises

Index